THE SACRED HARP

by

B. F. White and E. J. King

(facsimile of the third edition, 1859)

Including as a historical introduction

THE STORY OF THE SACRED HARP

by GEORGE PULLEN JACKSON

BROADMAN PRESS
NASHVILLE, TENNESSEE

An unabridged republication of an
1860 imprint of the third edition
of 1859. This facsimile has been
made from an original copy in the
personal library of William J. Reynolds.

Library of Congress Catalog Card Number: 68-18032
Printed in the United States of America
2.5AT6713

PREFACE

Baptists in the South during the early nineteenth century were experiencing rapid growth. The singing school movement was spreading from New England southward during this time and the sound of "fasola" singing rang from Baptist meetinghouses and from Baptist homes. These Baptists were sturdy dependable people who lived in a rural society. Some were operators of large plantations, but for the most part they were of the pioneer stock who were able to provide for their families little more than the basic essentials of life. They found great joy in expressing their Christian faith in song in their church meetings and when they gathered for "social" singing.

These early Christian groups in singing the metrical hymns and psalms of Watts and the texts of indigenous songs used many tunes of unknown origin. These tunes existed in the oral tradition long before they appeared in published tunebooks. When the Southern tunebooks were first published, they included many of these tunes, and George Pullen Jackson was the first to designate many of them as "Old Baptist tunes." Dr. Jackson was a member of the faculty of Vanderbilt University, and was a recognized authority in the field of Southern folk tunes.

Those musicians of the South who compiled tunebooks during the first half of the nineteenth century were God-fearing, Christian men. The tunebooks were compiled for the use of Christian people of staunch faith and goodwill. While the tunebooks did not indicate a particular denominational slant, the compilers were recognized churchmen and they were identified with their local congregations and denominations without apology.

Ananias Davisson of Virginia, compiler of *The Kentucky Harmony*, 1815, was a Presbyterian elder. Joseph Funk of Virginia, compiler of *Choral-Music* 1816, and *Genuine Church Music*, 1832, was a Mennonite. James P. Carrell of Virginia, compiler of *Songs of Zion*, 1820, and *Virginia Harmony*, 1831, was a Methodist preacher. William Hauser of Georgia, compiler of *Hesperian Harp*, 1848, was a Methodist preacher.

William Walker of South Carolina, compiler of the *Southern Harmony*, 1835; B. F. White of Georgia, compiler of *Sacred Harp*, 1844; and John G. McCurry, Georgia, compiler of the *Social Harp*, 1855, were all Baptists. A number of these sacred folk tunes from Sacred Harp tradition are sung by Baptists today. Those tunes which are to be found in *Baptist Hymnal*, published by Convention Press (Baptist Sunday School Board, Nashville, Tennessee) are:

BELLEVUE (page 72) now called FOUNDATION—How firm a foundation
NEW BRITAIN (page 45) now called AMAZING GRACE—Amazing grace! how sweet the sound

PISGAH (page 58)—When I can read my title clear

HOLY MANNA (page 59)—Brethren, we have met to worship

PROMISED LAND (page 128)—On Jordan's stormy banks I stand

RESTORATION (page 265) now called ARISE—Come, ye sinners, poor and needy

GREENFIELDS (page 161) now called CONTRAST—How tedious and tasteless the hours

In addition to these, two other tunes are to be found in both the *Sacred Harp* and *Baptist Hymnal*. These are not Southern tunes, but are from the earlier collections of New England compilers:

CORONATION (page 63)—All hail the power of Jesus' name

LENOX (page 40)—Blow ye the trumpet, blow

Because of the historical significance of the Sacred Harp among Baptists of the South for more than a century, the Historical Commission of the Southern Baptist Convention recommended that Broadman Press publish a facsimile edition. The Historical Commission seriously desired in this way to preserve this facet of Baptist heritage and bring to the attention of Baptists the musical contribution of this tradition to present-day practice.

This has been further prompted by the new surge of interest on the part of many musicians in obtaining copies of collections of hymns and tunebooks used by Baptists in the eighteenth and nineteenth centuries. This interest has likewise been expressed by music historians and curators of Baptist historical collections.

The decision to use the third edition of *The Sacred Harp* for the facsimile edition was predicated on the belief that this 1859 edition contains the main body of literature of this tradition. In later editions, changes were made in the contents. Beginning in 1911, alto parts were added to most of the original three-part tunes. This change may have been more satisfying to twentieth-century singers, but the sound and character of these folk tunes were altered. The first edition of *The Sacred Harp* contained 262 pages. The second edition added an appendix of 104 pages. To these 366 pages, the third edition added another appendix of 66 pages, enlarging the collection by 1859 to 432 pages. This facsimile of the third edition preserves all of the collection of the early tunes.

Appreciation is expressed to David Howell Jones, director of Vanderbilt University Press, and to the family of Dr. Jackson for permission to reprint in this edition of *The Sacred Harp* Dr. Jackson's story—the historical account of the Sacred Harp movement.

It is sincerely hoped that this book may be the means of extending the musical influence of early Baptists of America as well as of creating a genuine appreciation for the musical heritage of Baptists. This facsimile edition is certain to preserve the history of the Sacred Harp movement as well as perpetuate the third edition of *The Sacred Harp*. This type of music is used today by some churches, musical groups, and "singing schools" where the "fasola" method of tune singing is continued much as it was one hundred and fifty years ago. This edition will help keep alive this musical heritage.

DAVIS C. WOOLLEY
Historical Commission
Southern Baptist Convention

THE STORY OF THE SACRED HARP 1844-1944

GEORGE PULLEN JACKSON

OLD BAPTIST MUSIC

Aside from the Holy Bible, the book found oftenest in the homes of rural southern people is without doubt the big oblong volume of song called *The Sacred Harp*. It is not a church hymnal, though its contents are religious songs. Most of those who use it and know it well, if asked what sort of music it was, would answer: "Well, I reckon it's just Old Baptist song." Not a bad answer, this, despite the probability that the book was never used in Old or Primitive Baptist church services. But ask such people why it is called Old Baptist music, if the Baptists made it themselves or if they adopted it from elsewhere, and when, and where, and how, and why—and their answers, if any, would probably be vague and various.

This material, written in 1944 for the centennial of the first edition of *The Sacred Harp*, was published by Vanderbilt University Press, Copyright 1944, Vanderbilt University. It is reprinted here by permission.

This little book is intended to give answers to such questions. For the hoary *Sacred Harp* is now (1944) just a hundred years old, and it is therefore quite appropriate that those concerned with the remarkable volume should give some thought to its past.

The search for the beginnings of the types of song embodied in the *Sacred Harp* takes us back in time to a little before the birth of our United States, into the last years of the American colonies, or about 200 years ago. All Baptists were then Old Baptists. They were also country folk in the main and very much opposed to, and opposed by, those other religious denominations which centered in the few cities and towns along the eastern coast and were linked with the government. But the Baptists were growing fast in those days, perhaps *because* they were "the outs," the religious "leftists." And as they grew in numbers they grew in their antagonism to control either from the government or from any centralized religious (even Baptist) authority.

Freedom! Complete freedom of religion was the Baptist watchword. What wonder then, that in the Revolutionary War for freedom from Britain, the Baptists played an extremely important part. What wonder, then, that after the war was won the Baptists who had suffered so grievously at the hands of the magistracy should be in the vanguard of those who saw to it that the new constitution of the new United States should guarantee them that freedom which they had so long striven for and so long been denied—the freedom to worship God according to the dictates of their conscience.

The new free nation was born. The Baptists found themselves not only free but inspired with unbounded zeal to develop their manner of worship independently, without contamination from the *established* religious orders.

One taint could come, they felt, from their singing the songs of the governmentally linked denominations. The Baptists had not given much thought to group song in earlier times. Some congregations had not sung at all. So while Congregationalists, Presbyterians, Episcopalians, and Roman Catholics had sung psalms (perhaps *because* of this) the Baptists remained quite cold to psalm singing. But song was in the air. They had to sing something. So they decided, quite reasonably, to develop their own body of song. And this is just what they went about doing.

It was while George Washington was still alive that the country Baptists—then the fastest growing and soon to become one of the largest denominations—began to develop what we know now as Old Baptist music. The way they went about it was this: Their preachers collected a lot of hymns which had been written by Baptists or by those others like Isaac Watts, John Cennick, and John Newton, whose religious ideas were much like those of the Baptists. These hymns they published without tunes in books like the *Dover Selection*, *Dossey's Choice*, *Mercer's Cluster*, *The Baptist Harmony* and Lloyd's *Hymns*. For many, many years these tuneless books were all they had and all they needed. Indeed, they didn't use even these as we do our hymnals nowadays, with a book in every seat. Proba-

bly the preacher had a copy. But as for the rank and file, they depended on the preacher to "line out" the hymn and "hist" the tune, a practice which has not yet entirely died out among some groups, notably the Negro Baptists. So from the point of view of the singers, the songs—and certainly their tunes—deserved the name "unwritten music"; and that is what they were called generally.

What was this unwritten music? What tunes did the preachers "tone" and everybody sing without ever having seen such melodies in notation? The *Sacred Harp* with its scores of Old Baptist tunes gives the answer. But it was not the first tunebook of such music. The very first collection of that sort appeared forty years before the *Sacred Harp* was born; and, strange to say, it appeared among the backwoods Baptists of New England. It was Jeremiah Ingalls' *Christian Harmony*, published in Exeter, New Hampshire, in 1805. And still other books, before the *Sacred Harp* and after it, added to our store of that unwritten music, now written, with the result that we have today some 600 different recorded tunes of this type.

We have the tunes. But where did the Old

Baptists get them? For nearly twenty years this question has bothered me. I can answer it now with a degree of certainty: By and large the Old Baptist tunes found in the old books of the *Sacred Harp* sort were and are melodies of England, Scotland, Ireland, and Wales. They are airs which have been sung for hundreds of years in those parts from which most of our forefathers came, and were brought by our forefathers to these shores—unwritten music, but fixed in the memory of those forebears.

But these remembered tunes did not have religious texts. They had been sung usually with worldly words—old love songs or ballads such as "Barbara Allen," "Lord Lovel," "The Bailiff's Daughter," "The Wife of Usher's Well," and "Captain Kidd." And many of the remembered tunes, fiddle or bagpipe melodies for example, had no words at all. To such known and loved tunes as these the Baptists began to sing their equally beloved religious poetry. This was the way Old Baptist music came into being.

It may make the process of "spiritualizing" the older worldly songs clearer if I give an example. Take "Wondrous Love" in the *Sa-*

cred Harp, page 159. Its tune and its stanzaic structure were borrowed from the worldly song about the famous pirate, Captain Kidd. The link between the two songs may be seen clearly if one sings the "Wondrous Love" tune to the following words:

My name was Robert Kidd, when I sailed; when
  I sailed
My name was Robert Kidd, when I sailed;
My name was Robert Kidd, God's laws I did forbid,
So wickedly I did when I sailed, when I sailed,
So wickedly I did when I sailed.

The "Captain Kidd" tune was already a very old and widely sung melody when it was picked up nearly 250 years ago and associated with the tale of the wild pirate who was executed in England in 1701. There were several forms of the melody, all of which had nevertheless a clear family resemblance. The "Wondrous Love" tune is one. Three other forms are "Mercy's Free," page 337; "Saints Bound for Heaven," page 35; and "You Shall See" (Jackson, *Down-East Spirituals,* No. 272).

One by one the sources of the Old Baptist songs in the worldly folk airs have been found. The search for the sources has been made easier by three circumstances: (1) Those who have been interested in recording the worldly folk songs have been many; (2) they began their labors much earlier than I did mine; and (3) they have recorded, in the Old Country and this, a very large number of tunes which I have been able to compare with their close kindred, the religious folk melodies.

So the answer to the questions, what the Old Baptist tunes were and where they came from, is sure. They were not to any extent "composed" tunes, those made by individuals. They were folk tunes, made and made over by ages of singing by the race from which we all have sprung. These tunes with their comparatively recently associated spiritual texts ("Wondrous Love" is probably not more than 125 years old) were sung lustily and without need of book or musical notation.

While religious music of the sort we have been discussing was developed first largely by the Baptists, as we have explained, they couldn't hold it. It was too good, too infectious. By Andrew Jackson's time it had spread also to other denominations. William Caldwell made this clear in the preface to his *Union Harmony* of 110 years ago (Maryville, Tennessee, 1834). He declared there that "Many of the tunes which I have reduced to system and harmonized have been selected from the *unwritten music* (italics mine) in general use in the Methodist Church, others from the Baptist and many more from the Presbyterian taste." And when we examine Caldwell's tunes we find them to be largely the same as those in other country books of the time and in the *Sacred Harp* of ten years later.

As the Old Baptist music spread into other denominations, it spread also into the all-denominational camp meetings. And in that environment it underwent a change which gave the world a new variety of the same music, one which became known as the "chorus song" or the "revival spiritual song," a sort which may be recognized by the much repetition in the texts through refrains and choruses. This type is represented in the *Sacred Harp* by "The Morning Trumpet," page 85, "I Have a Mother in the Promised Land," "I Belong to That Band," "Old Ship of Zion," page 79, "Old-Time Religion," and many others. In this form few of the chorus songs were really Old Baptist; and this simply because that denomination leaned originally toward predestination and thus did not adopt the revival method of growth widely.

The chief practical reason for the development of the repetitive revival spiritual song was simply the combination of a great desire to sing with an equally great scarcity of books to sing from. We all know how more people will sing and sing louder when they are not bothered with a lot of verses which they can't or won't learn. And it was due to just these conditions that "The Old-Time Religion" and hundreds of other textually easy songs sprang from the big revivals which had their beginning in southern Kentucky around 1800 as camp meetings and quickly spread with the revival movement over the land. From these facts it is easy to see also why the Negroes were quick to adopt precisely this simple variety of the white man's songs and to make them their own to such an extent that they have been looked on widely, although erroneously, as of Negro origin—as "Negro spirituals."

I must mention also another kind of music. This kind was neither Old Baptist nor camp-meeting music nor even folk music. I refer to the "fuguing tunes" and their close relatives, the "odes and anthems" which are found in profusion in the *Sacred Harp* as well as all country songbooks in America for a hundred years before the *Sacred Harp* appeared. Where did the fuguing tunes come from? And how did they happen to get into the books of Old Baptist music? To answer the first question properly, we must go back rather far.

As far back as 200 years before the *Sacred Harp*, that is 300 years ago, groups of singers in Europe and the British Isles had their greatest fun in singing a number of tunes at once. They called it "polyphony." Another sort of song-fun, one growing out of polyphony, was to have one voice start a tune and other voices come in one at a time, beginning the same tune a bar or two apart. This was somewhat like the older "round," but as it became stylized the different voices soon came together in good harmonic fashion and ended that way. This song structure became known as the fuguing tune form (from the Latin word meaning appropriately to flee). It became widely popular in Britain and later also in the singing schools of the American colonies and remained so till some time after the Revolutionary War. William Billing's fuguing tunes, many of which are to be found in the *Sacred Harp*, are typical of the compositions of scores of New England musicians which filled the numerous singing school songbooks of the northeast.

Now for an answer to the second question: How did the fuguing tunes happen to get into the southern books of Old Baptist music? This is how it came about: The Old Baptists, as we have seen, had no *written*-musical tradition of their own. So when they went about the establishment of such a tradition, that is, of putting their own songs into notation, nothing was more natural than that they should adopt for its style of presentation the forms already established, the singing-school forms. So the Old Baptist music, never originally much more than a single tune affair, was dressed up in harmonic clothes—three and four parts. And once the Old Baptist singers found themselves and their songs in the singing-school atmosphere, nothing was more natural than that they should take over into their own collections also a selection of the most popular fuguing tunes, odes and anthems.

It was the backwoods Yankee, Jeremiah Ingalls, mentioned above as the first man to publish Old Baptist music, whose *Christian Harmony* contained the first mixture of that music with the singing-school fuguing songs.

It is somewhat hard to understand why this sort of song mixture, soon to be found in one book after another in the middle states and in the south, should have appeared first in New England where the Ingalls book was the first and the last of its kind. The phenomenon is best explained perhaps by the fact that while the movement of combining the two kinds of music was a general one in the American countryside, there were in the northeast strong influences coming from the cities which were antagonistic to *both* sorts and which tended to alienate even the country people from them, while in the other parts of the land, these home-grown varieties of music were received with open-armed friendliness.

HOW THE *SACRED HARP* CAME TO BE AND HOW IT GREW

Benjamin Franklin had been dead but ten years when the wife of a young farmer, Robert White, living near Spartanburg, South Carolina, gave birth to the first of their fourteen children and named him after the great American statesman. Benjamin Franklin White's schooling, three short terms, was quite meager according to today's standards. It was, however, about the average for those times when many boys acquired on their own initiative much of that education which has since been given over to institutions.

An important part of his self-acquired education was in music; for music, in those times, was a matter of singing schools here and there and, other than this, self-instruction. In the singing schools of Ben White's youth they may have been using any one of half a dozen good books of the sort we have just described. He may have learned his first music from Ananias Davisson's *Kentucky Harmony* (1815), Freeman Lewis' *Beauties of Harmony* (Pittsburgh, 1813), Allen D. Carden's *Missouri Harmony* (1820); or he might have known even Ingalls' *Christian Harmony* (1805) from copies which may have wandered southward.

But early in his musical career young White must have realized that he and his fellow Carolinians needed a book better than these, one which would contain also those many songs in their own southeastern "unwritten" tradition. Be that as it may, we find young White associated early with his brother-in-law, William Walker (they had married the Golightly sisters, Ben's wife being Thurza Golightly), in the compiling of just such a song collection. By the year 1835 it was finished and Walker took the manuscript to New Haven, Connecticut, where the book appeared that same year.

Just what happened at this juncture is not certain. But Joe S. James, in his *A Brief History of the Sacred Harp* (Douglasville, Georgia, 1904, p. 29f), tells that Walker, when he got to New Haven, seemed to forget completely that he had a brother-in-law and that the latter had done a goodly part of the work on the new book and that he deserved credit of some sort. But be the facts as they may, the book came out as "*The Southern Harmony and Musical Companion*, by William Walker" and with no mention at all of B. F. White. Mr. James was usually fairly correct in his statements. But he would himself doubtless have admitted that he presented but one side of the case.

This incident, according to James, caused White to pack up his worldly goods, leave friends and kindred in the Spartanburg section, and move with his family to Hamilton, Harris County, Georgia. This was in the late 1830s.

In his new home White soon became a prominent citizen, editor of the official county newspaper, *The Organ*, clerk of the superior court of his county, and a leading teacher of singing schools there and in the country roundabout. And there it was that he commenced at once to make a new collection of songs. Many of these songs he published one at a time in *The Organ*; and the whole collection appeared in 1844 as *The Sacred Harp*, printed in Philadelphia "for the proprietors, B. F. White and Joel King." (See the frontispiece of this booklet.)

Higher up, on the title page of the *Sacred Harp*, the name "E. J. King" appears with White's name as joint author. Were E. J. King and Joel King the same man? James thought they were brothers, an opinion based on what he had been able to learn from the oldest

Sacred Harp singers then living (1904). It is to be regretted that we are unable to tell more of White's associate in creating the notable book.

The *Sacred Harp* was widely used from the start. It was the official songbook of the Southern Musical Convention (organized at Huntersville, Upton County, Georgia, 1845), the Chattahoochee Musical Convention (organized at Macedonia Church, Coweta County, Georgia, 1852), the Tallapoosa Singing Convention (organized in Haralson County, Georgia, in 1867), and of countless other conventions organized during the following decades in the territory including Georgia and stretching westward with the tide of migration as far as Texas and Oklahoma.

Sacred Harp singing has never spread, as a real country institution, farther north than the southern reaches of Tennessee and Missouri. In the Carolinas the *Southern Harmony* and other books seem to have offered stiff competition. The most recently organized convention, one which is at the same time the farthest north, is the Tennessee Sacred Harp Singing Association, organized in 1939 and meeting in Nashville.

Major Benjamin Franklin White (he gained this title in the Georgia militia before the Civil War) died in Atlanta, Georgia, in 1879, and is buried in the Oakland Cemetery in that city beside his wife under a beautiful memorial stone set by kindred and *Sacred Harp* singers. James says that just before he died he sang plainly and distinctly "Behold, the morning sun begins his glorious way," page 391.

Among the offspring of B. F. White who carried on after their father ceased to labor were J. L. White, D. P. White, W. D. White, R. H. White, B. F. ("Frank") White, Jr., Mary Caroline (White) Adair, Nancy Ogburn (White) Byrd, and Mrs. E. H. Clarke. And these were followed in the work by large numbers of White's grandchildren and great-grandchildren, some of whom are still active singers today.

Among those prominently associated with the Whites were James R. Turner (b. 1807), J. P. Rees (b. 1828), H. S. Rees (his twin brother), I. M. Shell (b. 1826), Absalom Ogletree (b. 1819), Edmund Dumas, Leonard P. Breedlove, S. R. Pennick, R. F. M. Mann, E. L. King, E. T. Pounds, R. F. Ball, J. T. Edmonds, and Marion Patrick.

Among the leading singers of still later years, that is, toward the end of the nineteenth and in the early years of the twentieth century, James lists the following: Miles Edwards (b. 1822), J. M. Hamrick (b. 1838), Stephen James (b. 1821), Joe S. James (son of Stephen, author of the *Brief History* and chief editor of the 1911 edition of the *Sacred Harp*), C. H. Newton, J. A. Burdette, J. B. Henslee, Thomas McLendon, Mrs. A. J. McLendon, Mrs. W. C. Smith, W. S. Turner, J. H. Tyson, G. L. McEwen, Jesse M. Moseley, P. H. Chandler, J. E. Gurley, J. W. Dunford, T. B. Newton, S. P. Barnett, James Storey, J. M. Hutcheson, T. S. Andrews, J. M. Denson, and Tom Waller.

Members of the editorial committee which, under the guidance of the chairman, Joe S. James, revised and enlarged the *Sacred Harp* in 1911 were W. H. Bell, M. F. McWhorter, C. H. Newton, Absalom Ogletree, J. E. Eason, B. S. Aiken, J. C. Brown, M. D. Farris, J. G. Moore, J. H. Tyson, A. J. McLendon, T. M. Payne, J. W. Harding, G. B. Holder, S. W. Everett, C. J. Griggs, S. M. Denson, T. J. Denson, J. D. Laminack, G. B. Daniel, T. R. Newton, and J. W. Long. Together they present a cross section of leading singers, composers, and teachers in the *Sacred Harp* held around the turn of the present century.

The 1911 edition of the *Sacred Harp* was its fifth; the preceding ones having been made, after the first edition of 1844, in 1850, 1859, and 1869. With each edition the formerly published part of the book remained practically unchanged. Merely a supplement of additional songs were added. Thus the original 263 pages of the book grew with the successive editions to 366, 429, 477, and 550. The chief change suffered by former editions at the hands of later editors was the removal of a score of older songs from the 1869 issue. Most of these songs, however, were returned to the book in the James edition of fifty years later and placed on their original pages, thus justifying the title of the later revision—*The Original Sacred Harp*.

Those just mentioned seem to have been all the important and straight-line editions during the 1844-1911 period. There was, however, another *Sacred Harp* which I cannot fully explain. It appeared in 1870, just one year after the edition which was sponsored by B. F. White, Dumas, Ogletree, Mann, and Patrick—a committee of "The Southern Musical Convention of the State of Georgia," in 1869. The preface to the 1870 book was signed by B. F. White alone and the book was copyrighted by him and D(avid) P(atillo) White, his son. Aside from the preface, the book is identical with that of the year before.

The 1870 book was reprinted in 1911 (same year as the James edition) and from the original plates but with a new supplement of 73 pages of song. The additional songs were different. They were composed music signed by such well-known nineteenth-century musicians as William B. Bradbury, N. E. Everett, William Havergal, George Kingsley, Thomas Hastings, R. M. McIntosh, George F. Root, G. J. Webb, and Lowell Mason. The book is known as the "J. L. White edition" (after its chief editor) and is still in use in a number of Georgia and Alabama conventions. Sam C. Mann, a grandson of B. F. White, is active in its propagation.

Still another form of the *Sacred Harp*, widely used today in many states, more especially in the southern parts of Alabama and in Mississippi, Louisiana, Arkansas, and Texas, is what is popularly known as "The Cooper edition." It was made in 1902 by W. M. Cooper of Dothan, Alabama, and was a frank attempt at the "correction" and modernization of the old book. It has appealed thus to those who feel that such changes are justified. The revision work was done by a committee the members of which were entirely different from those active a few years later in making the James and the J. L. White editions. The Cooper edition is now owned by Judge B. P. Poyner of Dothan, Alabama.

The latest authentic *Sacred Harp* is the "Denson Revision" of 1936. It was made by a committee consisting of Thomas J. Denson, Seaborn M. Denson, L. P. Odem, L. A. Mc-Graw, H. N. McGraw, T. B. McGraw, O. A. Parris, George H. Parris, George M. Maddox, Otis L. McCoy, Howard Denson, and Paine Denson. These were formed into the Sacred Harp Publishing Company, Inc., of which Howard Denson was president and Paine Denson, secretary; the financial load of this radical revision was lightened materially by the funds which Lonnie P. Odem generously devoted to the cause which he loved—still loves. Thomas and Seaborn Denson (of whom we shall have more to say presently) died while the revision was being made. The chief music-editorial work was shifted thus to the shoulders of Paine Denson.

The new *Sacred Harp* is based squarely on the James edition. But 176 rarely or never used songs of the latter book have been discarded, and 41 have been added. Some little violence was done also to the earlier page-placing of the songs. But the new song sequence has been accepted by singers with but a little initial confusion.

The Denson revisers have, however, not changed the *character* of the old book one whit. All the newly added pieces have that combination of traits which distinguishes *Sacred Harp* music from all other tonal types. According to my count, about three out of four of the newly added pieces are fuguing songs, composed largely by Densons and other living *Sacred Harp* musicians.

Six thousand copies of the Denson Revision have been printed in the last eight years; and most of them have already been sold. It is the book in general use, especially in the Georgia, Alabama, and southern Tennessee region.

If imitation is the sincerest flattery, the *Sacred Harp* folk should be pleased with *The Colored Sacred Harp*. For this book, edited by J. Jackson for the Negro Dale County (Ala.) Musical Institute and the Alabama and Florida Union State Convention, and published in 1934 in Ozark, Alabama, is clearly inspired by the white man's *Sacred Harp* and its song tradition. It has the same oblong shape and dimensions, the same fa-sol-la solmization, four-shape notation and four-part harmonization, and the same sorts of song—Old Baptist, revival spirituals, and fuguing tunes. And despite the fact that each tune is signed by a "composer," I find many of them merely variants of the white *Sacred Harp* melodies. The white singers greet the singers of *The Colored Sacred Harp* and wish them success in their undertaking.

When the *Sacred Harp* was young it had to fight its way as one of a half-dozen songbooks of its sort or similar. William Walker's *Southern Harmony*, which I have mentioned, was its keenest competitor in Georgia and the Carolinas. And this book was followed by Walker's somewhat modernized *Christian Harmony* with its added grist of songs by Lowell Mason and others and with its seven-shape notes. In eastern Tennessee and northern Alabama competition was offered by the *Harp of Columbia*, a good seven-shape book by W. Harvey Swan and Markus Lafayette Swan which came out in Knoxville in 1849. Another excellent Georgia book, one which was however too bulky for wide use, was William Hauser's *Hesperian Harp* (1848). Large numbers of the lively revival songs or camp-meeting spirituals were published in two books: Walker's *Southern and Western Pocket Harmonist* (1848) and John Gordon McCurry's *Social Harp*, Andersonville, Georgia, 1855. It is also quite likely that many copies of the old, frequently reprinted *Missouri Harmony* were still in use in the *Sacred Harp* territory during the 1840s and 1850s.

These competing books have all but disappeared today. The *Southern Harmony* is the songbook of one lone singing in Benton, western Kentucky. A few years ago the Benton singers, with the help of the federal Works Projects Administration, got out one thousand copies of a photographic reproduction of the 1854 edition of the *Southern Harmony*. On the fourth Sunday in May, 1944, they held their sixty-first annual *Southern Harmony* singing convention. The grist of

new books may add years to the life span of their singings; but it shows no signs as yet of bringing new singing groups to life. The other William Walker book, *The Chritian Harmony*, was obtainable up to a few years ago. There are a number of Alabama singing conventions still using it. Its Philadelphia publisher died recently; but a movement is on foot in Alabama, I understand, to have the old book reprinted from the original plates. The plates of Swan's *Harp of Columbia* are now held by The Methodist Publishing House in Nashville; but there has not been enough demand for the book during the past twenty years to warrant a reprinting. So the "Old Harp" singers, largely in eastern Tennessee, must be running short of books. Thus the *Sacred Harp* stands practically alone today in its unique angle of the musical field as a vigorously living book and institution.

SOME HEARERS DON'T LIKE IT. WHY?

I want to speak now of *Sacred Harp* music as it is found on the page and as it resounds from a thousand singing "classes" in as many courthouses, school auditoriums, and country

churches over many southeastern states on most Sundays and many "Saturdays before" throughout the year and the years. And I shall speak of it first chiefly from the casual listener's point of view. Not that the listener's judgment of this music is important. It is not. This is not listener's music. It is *singer's* music. Listeners at singings are comparatively few. By and large they are those sturdy country people who have grown up with this music, know it thoroughly, love it, but for various reasons prefer to listen, and this by hours on end. I shall not discuss the music from *these* listeners' angle. It is the casual, first-time hearer of the music that I have in mind, and I shall try to portray his reaction. For while it is not important it is interesting.

It is quite usual to hear first-time hearers say, after listening to a few pieces: "It all sounds just alike," or "It is all *minor* music," or "I can't hear any *tune* to it."

I shall not discard such criticisms as simply untrue and the result of pure ignorance. There are elements of truth and untruth in them. And I shall try to point out these elements.

Sacred Harp music is four-part music. The four parts have been composed in such a manner that each voice part is equally "eventful" and thus interesting to the singer. This is quite different from present-day usage in choral music where all voices play a role subordinate to the soprano and thus are reduced often to long strings of notes, monotonous in themselves. When the other parts are brought up to an almost equal importance with the melody, as in the *Sacred Harp,* this part is bound to lose a deal of the prominence which the modern ear feels it should have.

Another condition in *Sacred Harp* singing submerges the tune even more deeply. I refer to the practice of each harmonic part (except the bass) being sung by both men and women. This mixture of male and female voices on the same part gives *Sacred Harp* singing one of its distinctive qualities and differentiates it still further from the usual practice according to which the sopranos and altos must be women and the tenors must be men. The casual hearer does not like this quality; does not realize what it is due to. So he casts the music aside with the disdainful remark that "it all sounds just alike," or that he "can't hear any tune to it."

The other criticism so often heard is as to the music's being "all minor." This criticism is just not true. Fully half the songs in the *Sacred Harp* are major (or in the "ionian" mode) and while the rest are in varying degree minor-*sounding* and while many of them are cast in the "natural" minor there are few "harmonic" minor tunes.

I cannot go into a full proof of the above statement here. I shall simply say, by way of suggesting its truth, that a tune, to be surely harmonic minor, must contain the seven tones of that scale, with lowered third and sixth and with the raised seventh in full cadences. The lowered third is often met with. But the sixth is almost always omitted from otherwise minor-sounding tunes (if not from the other harmonic parts). And the seventh is nearly always *sung as a lowered or natural tone,* even though it may not be printed as such.

There is still another type of minor-sounding scale or mode met with here and there in the *Sacred Harp.* It is that scale which has the lowered third and seventh and the *perfect sixth.* This is what was called in olden time the "dorian mode." In its lower tones it sounds minor (due to the lowered third) and in its upper reaches it sounds major (due to its per-

fect sixth). It has been blurred in some instances in the notation because it was confused, by those who first recorded those old unwritten dorian tunes, with what they took to be "minor." But the mode comes out clearly in such beautiful tunes as "Wondrous Love" where the printed *d*-flat is sung regularly as *d*-natural. Other songs where the perfect sixth of the dorian mode is sung though not printed are on pages 38, 74, 126, 142, 183, 211, 300, 302, 392, and 447. As far as I have been able to find, the only tune in the *Sacred Harp* which is not only sung in correct dorian but is printed that way, too, is "Jordan's Shore" whose sixth was corrected, in the 1911 James edition, from the earlier wrong *f*-natural to an *f*-sharp by George B. Daniel.

In speaking of leaving out or neglecting the sixth of the scale in natural-minor tunes, we are reminded of other gaps or omitted tones in these old folk tunes. The natural-minor tunes often omit the second as well as the sixth. And the major tunes often omit the fourth and the seventh. In such instances we have left, as actual tones employed in the tune, a five-tone scale in its different forms—forms which are very old in the music of Europe and America and are found in the music of primitive peoples the world over. Over half of the tunes in the *Sacred Harp* are gapped. They are, that is to say, either five-tone or six-tone melodies. One familiar example out of the hundreds is "Plenary" (p. 162) which all will recognize as the old Scotch folk tune "Auld Lang Syne."

We must remember that the tones of the gapped scales are the *basic* ones historically, and that the two left out are the less important ones in melody and that they have entered our music in comparatively recent times. We must bear in mind also the fact that the fewer-note tunes are appropriate to a fewer-chord harmonic treatment. With these facts in mind we can easily understand the effect of the *Sacred Harp* songs on the understanding and sympathetic listener. They impress such a hearer as strong, manly music. There is no effeminate ear-tickling in the *Sacred Harp* songs. And this manly strength, this austerity even, may be another reason why the *casual* hearer, with ears tuned to modern major musical niceties, mistakes it for music that is "all minor."

There are still other noteworthy features of the *Sacred Harp* which demand a word of comment. Among these are the form of the book, its pages of "rudiments," and its unique notation.

Its oblong shape (7x10 inches) is that of all singing-school manuals of its time and for a hundred years before its time. It was made necessary by the demands of the notation (one voice only on each staff) and by the demands of harmony according to which the four voices were placed one directly above the other.

The twenty pages or so of "Rudiments of Music" at the beginning of the book represent a feature brought to America from England over 200 years ago. These pages also bring to our minds the times long before individual instruction in music was available to the masses and when the "penmanship schools," the "literary schools" and the singing schools were peers. In the singing schools the one book answered the pupils' needs in helping them learn how to sing and in providing them with a collection of song.

To many, the most interesting feature of the *Sacred Harp* is its system of solmization and the shaped notehead which go with it. The *fa sol la mi* notes are Old English. Shakespeare was familiar with them and has mentioned them in a number of his dramas. The system came with Englishmen to America in earliest Colonial times and remained for nearly 200 years as the only system of sol-fa'ing in use in this country, that is, up to a little over 100 years ago when the continental European *do-re-mi* system was imported into our eastern cities and slowly supplanted the Old English custom. Today the *fa-sol-la* has completely died out in Britain; so our use of it in the south and in the *Sacred Harp* represents its sole survival anywhere in the world today.

The shaped note-heads, on the contrary, are an American innovation. Their invention dates from just one year before B. F. White was born. In that year, 1799, two singing-school teachers, William Little and William Smith of upstate New York, decided that a differently shaped head for each of the four notes would make the teaching and learning of singing easier. So they had types made and published a songbook, *The Easy Instructor*, the very first one to use the four-shape notation.

The book became widely popular especially

in the middle states. And while the patent notation was all but completely shunned in the northeast, it spread from one songbook to another in the southern and western regions and quickly became the only musical alphabet which the masses of rural Americans could read.

In those rural regions where the *do-re-mi* system came eventually into use, the shapes kept pace with the change by increasing to seven; this is the standard notation in southern rural songbooks today with the sole exception of the *Sacred Harp*. A clear idea of the popularity of the seven-shape notation now, 145 years after the shapes were first introduced, may be gained from the fact that the great Methodist Publishing House prints year after year more songbooks in shapes than in round notes.

In every *Sacred Harp* singing we hear echoes of oldtime singing-school practice when each song is sung first once through with the notes—the words following. This fidelity to the old tradition is entirely commendable. There are but two sorts of song where the notes seem less in place in conventions: in the singing of long anthems, where the notes seem to tire the singers, to say nothing of the hearers, and in those few very fast pieces like "Union" (p. 116) where the notes, different in each part of course, become a pretty bad jangle of sound. Otherwise, the notes and the shapes are a valuable birthright without which the *Sacred Harp* would not be the *Sacred Harp*.

The casual listener is apt to sum up his opinion of *Sacred Harp* music by calling it simply "old-fogy." Now let's see just what this means. The word "fogy" once meant a steward or caretaker. An "old" fogy was thus a tried and trusted one who took care of such things as were worth preserving. We assert confidently that the *Sacred Harp* songs are those musical goods worth preserving, and that their singers are the tried and trusted caretakers, the "old fogies," of those "old-fogy" goods. "Old-fogy" songs have good company: the language we speak, the clothes we wear, the food we eat, the houses we live in, the laws we obey, the God we worship. The English tongue we speak has changed but little in the past thousand years. Chaucer, one hundred years before Columbus discovered America, talked about "grouching" and "wet-ting ones whistle." The clothes we wear are about the same (aside from fads which come and go and from the fact that we don't make as many of them ourselves) as they have been for many centuries. The food we eat still comes in the main from our old-fogy gardens and fields as it always has; though Mr. Swift and Mr. Armour do help out a little. The houses we live in have some improvements which add to our comfort, but a room, a window, a stair, a door, a chair, and a bed—the essentials—are as old-fogy as the hills. As to the laws we obey—they are as old as the human race. For over two thousand years they have remained basically the same—Roman law, English common law on down to the enactments of our own states. One law builds on the other. The word "law" means something laid down to stay. Something very "old fogy." The oldest and most changeless of all our institutions is our old-time religion, based on a changeless God, a changeless Jesus Christ, and the moral law which Christian people strive to obey. Few would actually call Christianity "old-fogy."

As to old-fogyism in song generally one might remark that people used to really *sing* such music, still do so in *Sacred Harp* circles. As song has been modernized, however, it is sung less and less. It is listened to, at best. And this is probably largely because for some reason it doesn't appeal to the mass of those who would like to sing. Singing is one of man's most wholesome activities. It is far better, one would think, for mankind to sing old-fogy songs than to remain silent, listen to "better" song, and let his God-sent gift of singing lapse into disuse.

I see the viewpoint of the casual hearer of *Sacred Harp* singing. I understand the reasons for his snap judgments as outlined above. Some of the country people themselves are inclined to agree with him. My advice to all such is like that given by "Uncle Tom" Denson at the beginning of one of his singing schools:

"If some of you don't like this music," he told them plainly, "all I've got to say to you is you'd better get out. If you stay here it's going to get a-hold of you and you *can't* get away."

"Uncle Tom" gives strength to my conviction that *Sacred Harp* music must be sung and not heard.

THE SINGERS

The *Sacred Harp* has always rested in pious hands. While it has never been linked officially with any denomination, its singers have always been devoutly and fundamentally religious. All singings are opened and closed with prayer. The traditional dinner-on-the-grounds is always "graced" likewise. When one singer calls another one "brother" or "sister" and the older ones "uncle" or "aunt" it has a real and deep significance. It means that *Sacred Harp* singers feel themselves as belonging to one great family or clan. This feeling is without doubt deepened by the consciousness that they stand alone in their undertaking—keeping the old songs resounding in a world which has either gone over to lighter, more "entertaining," and frivolous types of song or has given up *all* community singing.

The members of this "clan" used to gather, fifty years ago and before, by neighborhoods. With railroads more available, it became possible for those of many neighborhoods to foregather in bigger, more centrally located and longer conventions (up to three days). Gasoline transport has more recently encouraged visits and return visits of singers living long

distances apart. Until the present war restrictions came, it was no uncommon thing, for example, to see a group from Georgia and Alabama at a Texas singing and to see Texas singers returning the visit later. Today this neighborliness is practiced especially among singers of Georgia, Alabama, and Tennessee.

Musical families, I mean groups of blood kinsfolk, have also been towers of strength in keeping the *Sacred Harp* going. I have already spoken of some of them. I could not, within the covers of this little book, mention all such families even if I knew them all, which I don't. It may help readers understand the situation if I merely name those families represented by the Manns of Decatur, Georgia, and other descendants of B. F. White; the Drakes and Cagles of Atlanta; the Aikens and the Bishops of Carroll County, Georgia; the McWhorters of Birmingham; the McGraws in three states; the Kitchens family of Jasper, Alabama; the Odems and their large and active group of related singers in Lawrence County, Tennessee; the Lovvorns of Carrollton, Georgia; the Parris family in Winston County, Alabama; the Laminacks of Cullman County, Alabama; and the Densons who now spread over northern Alabama and other parts of the south. There is hardly a *Sacred Harp* family, moreover, which has not married into one or more of the others.

I wish to single out the Denson family because of its uniform faithfulness, its unusually long-lasting devotion, and its valuable contributions to the *Sacred Harp*—for special mention.

The first edition of the *Sacred Harp* contained the "Christmas Anthem" composed by James Denson of Walton County, Georgia. L. P. Denson, a Methodist minister, brother of James and, we presume, also a good singer, moved to Cleburne County, Alabama, around Civil War times and established that branch of the family which included two sons, Seaborn M. (b. 1854) and Thomas J. (b. 1863). It was just seventy years ago, when the *Sacred Harp* was only thirty years old when its author, B. F. White, was still active, that young Seaborn Denson taught his first singing school from that book. His much younger brother Thomas also began to teach as soon as he was old enough. This activity alone, carried along to the very end of their lives, might well have earned for the two

brothers the title some observers have given them: "deans of the *Sacred Harp.*"

But their life accomplishments were much wider. In addition to the hundreds of singing schools they conducted and the thousands of singers they educated in southern states from Georgia to Texas, they were ever active in composing music of the *Sacred Harp* types. We see signs of this latter activity first in the 1911 edition of the *Sacred Harp* of which Seaborn was musical editor. There we find one piece signed by both brothers, three pieces composed by Thomas, and ten by Seaborn. Thomas caught up with his big brother in the matter of published compositions twenty-five years later. In the 1936 Denson Revision eight more of his songs appeared. They were largely fuguing tunes. He named three of them for prominent *Sacred Harp* friends: "Coston" (the late W. T. Coston of Dallas, Texas), "Ackers" (the family of Tom Denson's second wife), and "Odem" (Lonnie P. Odem, *Sacred Harp* patriarch of St. Joseph, Tennessee). In the 1911 edition there is also one composition by Amanda Denson—Tom's first wife. And 327 songs which had had three-part settings were made into four-part

harmonizations by the addition of alto parts composed by Seaborn. These then were some of the accomplishments of the second generation of *Sacred Harp* Densons.

The third generation has been more numerous, equally gifted and just as devoted to the old songs and their propagation, Seaborn's eight children have all been enthusiastic singers and/or composers. They are Ida (Denson) McCoy, Iva (Denson) Blake, Seaborn I. ("Shell"), James T., S. Whitt, Robert E., Evan E., and William Philpot ("Phil"). Two of Whitt's compositions are in the 1911 edition. Among Tom's eight musical children, Paine (a Birmingham attorney), Howard (in business in Tuscaloosa, Alabama), and Ruth (Denson) Edwards (a teacher in the public schools of Cullman), have been the most outstanding in *Sacred Harp* work. In producing the 1936 revision, Paine was, as we have already stated, the general music editor; and seven of his compositions appear on its pages. Howard's contributions were two songs. Other third-generation Denson contributors to this volume were Maggie (Denson) Cagle, Ruth (Denson) Edwards, and Annie (Denson) Aaron with one composition each. Three other daughters of Tom Denson, all active singers, are Vera (Denson) Nunn, Violet (Denson) Hinton, and Tommie (Denson) Maulden.

(I think it would be proper to call attention here to other notable contributors of songs to this last *Sacred Harp*, people outside the Denson family. Among these were the three McGraw brothers, H. N. [two songs], L. A. [three], and T. B. [four], L. P. Odem, O. A. Parris, A. M. Cagle, O. H. Frederick, John M. Dye, J. B. Wall, Lee Wells, B. E. Cunningham, W. T. Mitchell, W. A. Yates, and Elmer Kitchens.)

The fourth generation of the musical Denson Dynasty is now maturing with a number of excellent singers and composers. Those already treading worthily in the steps of their forebears are three of Seaborn's grandchildren, Owel Denson, Dalila (Denson) Posey, and Otis L. McCoy.

The fifth generation is coming on fast, prolifically and promisingly.

THE TURN OF THE CENTURY

The current year, 1944, is the centennial of the *Sacred Harp*. Its significance is being recognized at every singing convention big and little. Singers are looking backward over the historic years, looking roundabout and trying to assess the present state of their beloved institution, looking forward and wondering about the *Sacred Harp's* destiny during the second hundred years of its life.

In looking backward the singers are gladly paying a tribute of gratitude and honor to B. F. White and his disciples who brought the *Sacred Harp* into being, and to those later venerable men and women who fostered it after White ceased his earthly labors. The descendants of the founder are planning for this summer a big centennial celebration to be held on or near the spot in western Georgia where the *Sacred Harp* was first used in convention. The descendants and friends of the late Seaborn and Thomas Denson are to hold a singing festival lasting the entire week preceding and including the fourth Sunday in September at Double Springs, Winston County, Alabama. The high point in the week's festivities will be the unveiling of a granite memorial on the courthouse square in Double Springs, Alabama, bearing the following inscription:

To the Memory of the Brothers
SEABORN M. DENSON and
THOMAS J. DENSON
(1854-1936)   (1863-1935)
who devoted their lives and gifts to composing and teaching American religious folk music, as embodied in the Sacred Harp, in most of the southern states but notably in Alabama

THIS STONE IS PLACED

in the midst of their field of labor by the loving hands of their families, pupils of their singing schools, and legions of singers and friends in the summer of the year 1944

THE ONE HUNDREDTH
ANNIVERSARY
OF THE SACRED HARP,
while
"Uncle Seab" and "Uncle Tom" sing on—
"Way over in the promised land."

AMERICA DISCOVERS ITS OWN SONGS

The old standbys are dying off. This is the way of the world. But it bereaves the living and fills them with doubts as to the coming years. Will there be other tireless and excellent teachers like "Uncle Seab" and "Uncle Tom" Denson? Will southern family and neighborhood groups keep on singing as of yore? We don't know the answers.

But there is one fact which may comfort lovers of the old-time songs: *The songs themselves will not die.* For musical people over the entire United States are coming to know them as they were never known before, and are coming to a recognition of their beauty. This recognition and the rebirth of interest in the songs have followed the appearance, twelve years ago, of the present author's book, *White Spirituals in the Southern Uplands*, in which the *Sacred Harp* music and singing institution were portrayed.

The new interest in this music has been shown chiefly by leading American composers and choral leaders. Among the new apostles of the old lore are Henry Cowell, Carl Buchman, Ellie Siegmeister, E. J. Gatwood, Don Malin, Melville Smith, John Powell, John Jacob Niles, Harvey Gaul, Hazel Gertrude Kinscella, Annabel Morris Buchanan, Hilton Rufty, and Charles Bryan. All of these have made and published excellent arrangements of *Sacred Harp* melodies in form suitable to modern choral groups. And some of them, like Henry Cowell, have made settings patterned consciously "after the sparse harmonies of the early American folk hymn," patterned, that is to say, after such harmonies as we find in the *Sacred Harp*.

Randall Thompson, director of the Curtis Institute of Music in Philadelphia, has interwoven *Sacred Harp* melodic themes with the music of his cantata, "The Peaceable Kingdom." Van Denman Thompson has done the same in his "Evangel of the New World" as has also Lewis Henry Horton in his "The White Pilgrim." Melodic material from the same source has formed the background of symphonic works by John Powell, Charles Bryan, and Roy Harris, and of an organ fantasia, "Garden Hymn," by Arthur Shepherd. And Virgil Thomson wove several *Sacred Harp* tunes into his screen score for "The River," a government-sponsored picture.

A goodly part of the renascence has centered around the fuguing tunes. Jeremiah Ingalls and his peers, pushed aside for over a hundred years by the Better Music Boys—by everybody, indeed, but the *Sacred Harp* folk —are now coming into their own. Prominent among the revivers of fuguing tunes are Miss Kinscella, Mr. Buchman, Clarence Dickinson, Mrs. Buchanan, and Joesph W. Clokey. Together they have published dozens of the old "fugues" only slightly altered from their eighteenth-century forms.

An indication of the widening popularity of old American song as found in the *Sacred Harp* may be seen in one piece, "The Poor Wayfaring Stranger." It has been variously arranged and published. One choral arrangement of the beautiful melody, made by the present author and the late E. J. Gatwood, has enjoyed a sale of over ten thousand copies. And for years a noted ballad singer who calls himself "the wayfaring stranger" has broadcast a weekly radio program from New York and has used this song as his theme.

When Sacred Harp singers learn of all this enthusiasm for their old-time songs, shown by practically all leading native American men and women of music and extending to all parts of the land, they will, I feel, have reason to be hopeful as to the future of their beloved art.

POSTSCRIPT

In this twenty-third year of the second century of Sacred Harp singing it seems appropriate to give some accounting as to the present state of this activity and bring up to date the story so vividly told by the late George Pullen Jackson. Generally speaking, there is no strong evidence of any weakening of activity or interest in Sacred Harp singing. On the contrary, there is evidence of vibrant and enthusiastic life in this stream of American sacred folk music expression.

Any accurate description of the extensive activities of Sacred Harp singings today is most difficult. Little evidence of these singings appears in local newspapers. Reminders of the time and place of forthcoming singings are communicated by word of mouth to the participants. The general public even in the immediate vicinity is usually unaware that a singing is going on.

Currently there are four versions of the Sacred Harp in use, and a description of present practice seems most appropriate in terms of these four books already referred to by Jackson. The J. L. White edition seems to be the least popular of the four. It is used for no more than fifteen singings each year in and around Atlanta, Georgia.

Singings which use the James edition may be found in South Georgia. A new printing of this book was made in 1965 but there were no changes in the contents.

The Cooper edition is used along the Gulf Coast, from Jacksonville, Florida, to East Texas. This includes the regions of western Florida, southern portions of Alabama, Mississippi, and Louisiana, and in eastern areas of Texas. A new revision of the Cooper edition was published in 1950 and 3,000 copies were printed. This was prepared by a committee of fourteen men with G. L. Beck, president; T. H. Deal, vice-president; and J. W. Bassett, secretary-treasurer. The title page indicates that this is owned and published by the Sacred Harp Book Co., Inc., Troy, Alabama.

The most popular Sacred Harp edition is the Denson revision, and its popularity and use seem to be increasing. There is evidence that it is gradually replacing some of the other editions as its influence spreads. Two revisions of the Denson book have occurred since the 1936 edition mentioned by Jackson, and both of these were published by the Sacred Harp Publishing Company, Inc., Cullman, Alabama.

The 1960 edition was prepared by a music committee composed of A.M. Cagle, H. N. McGraw, T. B. McGraw, J. Elmer Kitchens, Hugh McGraw, and Ruth Denson Edwards. Five thousand copies were printed. By 1965 the stock was nearly exhausted and another printing was planned. However, it was discovered that the printing plates were so badly worn that new plates were necessary before another printing could be done. Because of these circumstances, the Board of Directors of the Sacred Harp Publishing Co., Inc., in February, 1966, requested the same music committee to prepare a new revision. A printing of 5,000 copies was delivered to the publishing company from Kingsport Press in June, 1967. New front matter, including a brief historical sketch by Ruth Denson Edwards, was prepared and a new index was made. Photocopy was prepared for the first 461 pages (including the rudiments) based on the 1936 edition. New music plates were made for pages 462 through 573. Twenty-one tunes no longer used were deleted. Six tunes were restored from the James edition of 1911, and six newly composed tunes were published for the first time. Considering content, appearance, paper, printing, and binding, this is just the finest of the Denson revisions and it is a tribute to those who made this possible.

The continuing interest and vitality among the singers using the Denson revision can be attributed to many individuals whose dedication to the cause of Sacred Harp singing is unswerving. Hugh McGraw, the executive secretary of the Sacred Harp Publishing Com-

pany, Inc., is the respected leader of this group. His unselfish devotion, his cordial and friendly manner, his wise counsel and judgment have won him a coveted place of leadership among those who use the Denson book. From his home in Bremen, Georgia, he drives each weekend to a singing near or far. Through the efforts of Mr. McGraw, two long-play record albums have been released by the Sacred Harp Publishing Co. These albums, featuring the singing of a select group of singers, gives an authentic sound of the traditional style of Sacred Harp singing as practiced today.

One of the unifying factors of the Denson group is the annual publication of the *Directory and Minutes of Sacred Harp Singings* for Alabama, Florida, Georgia, Tennessee, and Mississippi.

The 1966-67 volume was prepared by W. A. Parker, general secretary, 1521 Center Point Road, Birmingham, Alabama 35215. This volume of 223 pages records the number of singings conducted during 1966 and gives the directory of singings scheduled for 1967. This directory indicates that during 1967 there were scheduled:

- 209 one-day singings (usually Sunday)
- 27 two-day singings (Saturday and Sunday)
- 3 three-day singings (Friday, Saturday, and Sunday)
- 46 Friday night singings
- 61 Saturday night singings
- 24 Sunday night singings
- 370 total singings (involving 403 days)

With regard to location, 187 of the one-, two-, and three-day singings were in Alabama; 35 in Georgia, 9 in Tennessee, 7 in Mississippi, and 1 in Florida. All of the 131 night singings (Friday, Saturday, or Sunday) were in Alabama.

There was a singing scheduled for every Sunday of the year in one or more of these five states, according to the 1966-67 minutes and directory. Usually there are several singings in progress simultaneously on the same Sunday. The busiest Sunday of each year is the first Sunday in July, when eight singings are conducted. Three of these are two-day singings, beginning on Saturday before the first Sunday:

—Henagar Convention, Liberty Church, 2 miles north of Henagar, Alabama, on

Hwy. 40, Pisgah to Hammondville.

—Pickens County Convention, Mt. Carmel Church, 5 miles east of Millport, Alabama, on Hwy. 78.

—Lawrence County Singing Convention, Lawrenceburg, Tennessee. West Highland School.

There are five one-day singings:

—Bethlehem Church, 1½ miles southwest of Gallant, Alabama, on Hwy. 35, Ivalee to junction with US 231.

—Cross Roads Primitive Baptist Church, 9 miles north of Tallapoosa, Georgia, just off Hwy. 100.

—Mountain View Church, 1 mile north of Corner Road.

—New Flat Woods Baptist Church, 4 miles south of Nauvoo, Alabama, and east of Hwy. 11, Nauvoo to Carbon Hill, Alabama.

—Valley Grove Church, 9 miles southwest of Cullman, Alabama, and south of old Hwy. 69.

In addition to these eight singings on the first Sunday of July, there are two annual Fourth of July singings which make the first week in July a busy time:

—Liberty Baptist Church, near Helicon, Alabama, and 6 miles south of Hwy. 278, at Stephenson and 1 mile west of Hwy. 77.

—Friendship Church, 12 miles southwest of Haleyville, 2 miles south of Hwy. 195.

An analysis of the 1967 schedule reveals the following information regarding the frequency and location of the singings in the five states each month:

January— 13 one-day singings (12 in Alabama, 1 in Georgia)

February— 8 one-day singings (7 in Alabama, 1 in Georgia)

March— 22 one-day singings (.19 in Alabama, 2 in Mississippi, 1 in Tennessee

April— 23 one-day singings (20 in Alabama, 1 in Georgia, 2 in Tennessee)

May— 17 one-day singings (11 in Alabama, 5 in Georgia, 1 in Tennessee)

June— 27 one-day singings (18 in Alabama, 8 in Georgia, 1 in Mississippi)

3 two-day singings (2 in Alabama, 1 in Georgia)

July— 25 one-day singings (20 in Alabama, 4 in Georgia, 1 in Tennessee)

10 two-day singings (8 in Alabama, 1 in Georgia, 1 in Tennessee)

August— 10 one-day singings (7 in Alabama, 1 in Georgia, 1 in Tennessee, 1 in Mississippi)

8 two-day singings (5 in Alabama, 2 in Georgia, 1 in Tennessee)

3 three-day singings (3 in Alabama)

September— 18 one-day singings (15 in Alabama, 3 in Georgia)

5 two-day singings (5 in Alabama)

October— 21 one-day singings (15 in Alabama, 3 in Georgia, 2 in Mississippi, 1 in Florida)

1 two day singing (1 in Alabama)

November— 20 one-day singings (14 in Alabama, 4 in Georgia, 1 in Mississippi, 1 in Tennessee)

December— 5 one-day singings (5 in Alabama)

One of the traditional events is the Denson Memorial Singing at Addison, Alabama, the second Sunday in October each year. The minutes of the 1966 singing given here are typical of these singings and show the format followed. An opening song, a prayer, and then the organization of the class. The arranging committee is responsible for calling up the leaders. Each leader usually leads two songs of his own selection. FOOTNOTE— The numbers that appear here are the page numbers in the 1960 edition of *The Sacred Harp* (Denson Revision).

The noon meal is a time of cordial fellowship. A sumptuous meal is spread in "dinner on the ground" style as each family contributes the food they brought to the long table. The singing usually begins at 9:00 A.M. and concludes by 4:00 P.M.

Here, then, is the record of one singing, the activities of the day, the leaders who led, and the songs they sang. During the morning and afternoon, 93 different songs were sung by the class, led by 47 leaders. There were approximately 150 people present.

Denson Memorial Singing
Methodist Church—Addison, Alabama
October 9, 1966

The annual Denson Memorial Sacred Harp Singing was held at the Methodist Church and was called to order by R. E. Denson leading song on page 60. The Rev. Lott, pastor of the church, led in prayer and gave a welcome to all who attended. After this the class was led in singing song, page 57, by R. E. Denson. At this time the class was organized for the day by electing or appointing the following officers: President, Lloyd Redding; Vice President, Charles W. McCoy; Secretary, Ruth D. Edwards; Chaplain, L. L. Welborn; Arranging Committee: Dewey McCullar and King Roberts. President Redding led song, page 47b. Leaders and their selections: Walter Chandler, 328, 434; L. L. Welborn, 110, 211; Lindburg Lacy, 481, 431; Otto Allred, 316, 280; J. H. Ballinger, 470, 270; Hattie Roberts, 99, 420; G. S. Doss, 534, 187; Mrs. O. H. Handley, 530, 546; Lloyd Wood, 302, 500; Charlene Wallace, 517, 365; Tommy Frederick, 217, 222.

Recess.

The class was called to order by Vice President, Charles McCoy, leading song on page 36. Other leaders: Lee Wells, 426b, 196; Zera Tolleson, 384, 296; H. N. McGraw, 396, 411; Mae Seymour, 318, 304; Gresham Akin, 85, 216; Mrs. Arlin Webb, 68b, 560.

Recess.

The President, Lloyd Redding, called the class back in session directing song on page 502. These leaders as follows were called: Cleve Nunnelly, 498, 524; Reba Dell Lacy, 455, 383; T. L. White, 382, 371; Carolyn McGraw, 171, 218; Ira James, 77, 424; Ruth D. Edwards, 379, 79.

Dismissed for lunch.

Vice President, Charles McCoy, called the class to order directing song on page 220. These leaders were called: Noah Lacy, 207, 504; Elene Aldridge, 172, 558; T. B. McGraw, 306, 362; Willie Mae Latham, 122, 283; Robert Aldridge, 200, 380; Elsie McCullar, 63, 460; W. J. Reynolds, 159, 155; Myrtie Mae Duboise, 572; Hugh McGraw, 146, 235; Ila V. Glenn, 436, 419; W. D. Baldy, 432, 553; Ann Chalker, 288, 388; Mack Harper, 442, 355; Mrs. Leonard Lacy, 373, 378.

Recess.

Millard McWhorter called the class to order leading songs, pages 358 and 422. The leaders as follows: A. L. Parker, 430, 440; Josie Frazier, 183, 269; Jim Bennett, 126, 214; Ora Lee Fannin, 471, 268; Emma Walker, 300, 392; Maggie Parris, 454. Lloyd Redding closed the singing by leading song on page 69 and the Chaplain, L. L. Welborn, led the closing prayer.

Lloyd Redding President
Charles W. McCoy, Vice President
Ruth D. Edwards, Secretary

To attend such a singing as this can be a rewarding experience, even for a nonsinger. The cordiality of the fellowship and the warm hospitality is befitting Southern tradition. Dinner-on-the-ground is a long table spread with the best culinary efforts of the lady folks. The music which is sung and the manner and style of the singing has not changed appreciably in more than a century. The fuguing tunes of Yankee tunesmiths William Billings and Daniel Read, sung occasionally by college groups today as amusing bits of Americana, may be heard in an unpolished but vibrant version. These fuguing tunes are fondly loved and sung with wholehearted abandon. There may be less art, but there is certainly more heart, as the strength and fervor of the singing reflects the stalwart faith of the singers.

WILLIAM J. REYNOLDS
Church Music Department
Baptist Sunday School Board

INDEX OF FIRST LINES

NEW AND MUCH IMPROVED AND ENLARGED EDITION.

THE

SACRED HARP,

A COLLECTION OF PSALM AND HYMN TUNES, ODES, AND ANTHEMS,

SELECTED FROM THE MOST EMINENT AUTHORS:

TOGETHER WITH NEARLY ONE HUNDRED PIECES NEVER BEFORE PUBLISHED;

SUITED TO MOST METRES, AND WELL ADAPTED TO CHURCHES OF EVERY DENOMINATION, SINGING SCHOOLS, AND PRIVATE SOCIETIES.

WITH PLAIN RULES FOR LEARNERS.

BY B. F. WHITE & E. J. KING.

TO WHICH IS ADDED APPENDIX I.,

CONTAINING A VARIETY OF

STANDARD AND FAVORITE TUNES NOT COMPRISED IN THE BODY OF THE WORK,

COMPILED BY A COMMITTEE APPOINTED BY

"THE SOUTHERN MUSICAL CONVENTION."

ALSO,

APPENDIX II.,

CONTAINING

77 PIECES OF NEW COMPOSITION BY DISTINGUISHED WRITERS NEVER BEFORE PUBLISHED.

PHILADELPHIA:
PUBLISHED BY S. C. COLLINS, N. E. CORNER SIXTH AND MINOR STREETS,
FOR THE PROPRIETORS, WHITE, MASSENGALE & CO., HAMILTON, GA.
1860.

COLLINS, PRINTER

PREFACE TO THE SACRED HARP.

MANY efforts have been made to please the public with a collection of Sacred Music; and none but those who make the effort, know how difficult it is to accomplish this task. The Compiler of this work has spared no labour or pains in trying to accomplish this desirable object, having taught music for the last twenty years, and being necessarily thrown among churches of various denominations, and all the time observing their wants in that of a variety of church music, has in this work endeavoured to supply that deficiency which heretofore existed, by placing all the church music within his reach, in one book. That such a compilation is needed, no person of piety, observation, and taste, will deny. While the churches may be supplied from this work, others have not been forgotten or neglected; a great variety will be found suited to singing-schools, private societies, and family circles; in fact, the Sacred Harp is designed for all classes who sing, or desire to sing. The Compiler has not aimed at greatness or self-aggrandizement, but has desired, in his humble position, to benefit the public in general: and therefore has set out this work in a plain, easy, and familiar style; and having passed the meridian of life, and entirely withdrawn from the business of teaching, is disposed to leave this work as a specimen of his taste, and recommend it to a generous public, praying God that it may answer in full the purposes intended.

B. F. WHITE.

Hamilton, Harris Co., Georgia. April, 1844.

N. B. The Harp is a selection from the most eminent authors now extant; together with nearly one hundred pieces never before published, all of which have been harmonized and arranged under our immediate inspection expressly for this work.

B. F. WHITE & E. J. KING.

3

INTRODUCTION.

A Singing school, to learn and practise Sacred Music, should be a solemn place—a place of prayer: for it is as solemn a business to learn to sing the praises of God as it is to learn the word of God. A singing-school should be of the same character as a Sabbath-school or a Bible class; it is, in part, of the same class of schools, and should be conducted with the same solemnities. We think it as much the duty of those who have the ability, to learn to sing the praises of God as it is to learn his word; and no parents or guardians, therefore, should consider their religious education, nor that of their children, complete, without a knowledge of sacred music; nor think they are at liberty to sit silent in the sanctuary, to sing or not, as they please. The gift of a talent to sing, implies an obligation to improve it, and not to offer unto the Lord the halt and lame, but to cultivate the voice that they may sing to edification, and not to be an annoyance to every one near them. Sacred music, when sung in a proper style, will generally produce a religious effect in a greater or less degree. We have had the pleasure of seeing, at public rehearsals of sacred music, very deep and strong religious impressions made, not only upon the singers, but upon the congregation: and when such words as

> "The Lord is in this place,
> We see his smiling face;
> Trembling we now adore him;
> Humbly we bow before him"—

were sung, it seemed that every one present felt their power, and felt something of the majesty of Jehovah. We have known, moreover, very extensive and general revivals of religion commence, and make their first appearance, in singing-schools. But who ever knew such blessings follow when secular music was practised in the school, or when the object of public rehearsal was display? We think it is time the Christian public were awake to their duty on this subject.

OF MUSIC IN GENERAL.

Music consists of a succession of pleasing sounds, with reference to a peculiar internal sense implanted in us by the Great Author of nature. Considered as a science, it teaches us the just disposition of sounds; and as an art, it enables us to express them with facility and advantage. The tones of music differ from sounds in general, because they vary from each other by fixed intervals, and are measured by certain proportions of time. There is, indeed, in good speaking, a regularity to be observed, which has some resemblance to this art; and to the orator we frequently use the epithet, musical; but the inflections of the voice in speech are more variable, and slide as it were by insensible degrees, and cannot easily be limited to rule; whereas the gradations of musical sounds are exactly ascertained, and are brought to an uniform standard.

Music naturally divides itself into Melody and Harmony. Melody is the agreeable effect which arises from the succession of single sounds. Harmony is the pleasing union of several sounds at the same time. Modulation consists in rightly disposing and connecting either the melody of a single part, or the harmony of various parts. The two primary and essential qualities of musical sounds are, relative acuteness or gravity, and proportionate duration. The first property is their relative acuteness or gravity. Bodies of unequal size, length, or tension, emit sounds differing in this respect, and are said to be grave or acute. Human voices differ in this respect, viz., a man's voice is more grave than a woman's; and when the voice moves from a grave to an acute sound, it is said to ascend. Some musicians term it high or low, sharp or flat, grave or acute: any of those terms imply the necessary distinction.

The next property is time, or proportional continuance; and here, without varying the acuteness or gravity of a tone, a difference of movement alone may constitute an imperfect species of music, such for example is the drum where the tones are only diversified by the celerity with which they succeed each other. The principal distinction, then, of musical sounds, are time and tune; and to the happy combination of these two qualities, is chiefly to be ascribed the pleasing and endless variety of musical art.

4

RUDIMENTS OF MUSIC.

SCALE OF NOTES.

1. *Q.* How many marks of sound, or kinds of notes are there used in music?

A. There are six kinds of notes used in music, which differ in time. They are the semibreve, minim, crotchet, quaver, semiquaver, and demisemiquaver.

The following scale will show, at one view, the *proportion* one note bears to another.

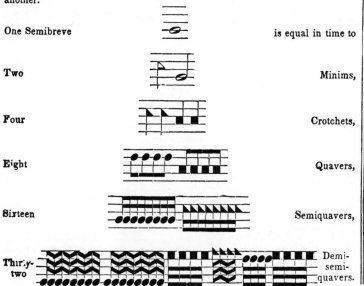

One Semibreve		is equal in time to
Two		Minims,
Four		Crotchets,
Eight		Quavers,
Sixteen		Semiquavers,
Thirty-two		Demi-semi-quavers.

Q. Explain the preceding scale.

A. The semibreve ⊝ is now the longest note used; it is white, without a stem, and is the measure note, and guideth all the others.

The minim is but half the length of a semibreve, and has a stem to it.

The crotchet is but half the length of the minim, and has a black head and straight stem.

The quaver is but half the length of the crotchet, has a black head, and one turn to the stem, sometimes one way, and sometimes another.

The semiquaver is but half the length of the quaver, has also a black head and two turns to the stem, which are likewise various.

The demisemiquaver is half the length of a semiquaver, has a black head, and three turns to its stem, also variously turned.

NOTE.—These notes are sounded sometimes quicker, and sometimes slower, according to the several moods of time. The notes of themselves always bear the same proportion to each other, whatever the mood of time may be.

Q. What are rests.

A. All rests are marks of silence, which signify that you must keep silent so long a time as takes to sound the notes they represent, except the semibreve rest, which is called the measure rest, always filling the measure, let the mood of time be what it may.

5

THE RESTS.

Q. Explain the rests.

A. The semibreve, or measure rest, is a black square underneath the third line.
The minim rest is the same mark above the third line.
The crotchet rest is something like an inverted figure seven.
The quaver rest resembles a right figure of seven.
The semiquaver rest resembles the figure seven with an additional mark to the left.
The demisemiquaver rest is like the last described, with a third mark to the left.
The two bar rest is a strong bar reaching only across the third space.
The four bar rest is a strong bar crossing the second and third space and third line.
The eight bar rest is two strong bars like the last described.

A dot set to the right hand of a rest, adds to it half its length, the same as a pointed note, thus:

2. MOODS OF TIME.

Q How many moods of time are there used in this work?

A. Seven; three of common, two of triple, and two of compound. The original first mood of common time and the third of triple have been dispensed with, they being but little used in the present day.

3. The first mood of common time is known by a figure 2 over a figure 2, having a semibreve for a measure note, or its equivalent in every measure; sung in the time of 3 seconds to the measure, 2 beats with the hand, one down and the other up.

The second mood is known by a figure 4 over a figure 4, having the same measure note; sung in the time of 2½ seconds to the measure, two beats as in the first mood.

The third mood is known by a figure 2 over a figure 4, having a minim for a measure note; sung in the time of 1½ seconds to the measure, and beaten as the other two moods.

4. The first mood of triple time is known by a figure 3 over a figure 2, having a pointed semibreve for a measure note, equal to three minims, &c.; sung in 3 seconds to the measure, three beats with the hand, 2 down and 1 up.

The second mood of triple time is known by a figure 3 over a figure 4, having a pointed minim for a measure note, equal to 3 crotchets, 6 quavers, &c.; sung in two seconds of time to the measure, three beats, 2 down and 1 up.

COMPOUND TIME.

5. The first mood of compound time is known by a figure 6 over a figure 4, having a pointed semibreve for a measure note; sung in the time of 2½ seconds to the measure, two beats with the hand, one down and the other up.

The second mood of compound time is known by a figure 6 over a figure 8, having a pointed minim for a measure note; sung in the time of 1½ seconds to the measure, two beats as in the first mood.

Q. What do the figures over the measure, and the letters d and u under it, in the above examples of time, mean?

A. The figures show how many beats there are in each measure, and the letter d shows when the hand must go down, and the u when up.

Q. What general rule is there for beating time?

A. That the hand fall at the beginning, and rise at the end of each measure, in all moods of time.

OF THE SEVERAL MOODS OF TIME.

6. Q. Why are the first three moods called common time moods?

A. Because they are measured by even numbers, as 2, 4, &c.

Q. Why are the next two called triple moods?

A. Because they are measured by odd numbers, as 3, &c

Q. Why are the remaining two called compound moods?

A. Because they are compounded of common and triple time; of common time as the measure is divided equal; of triple time as each half of the measure is threefold, having three crotchets, three quavers, or their proportion to each beat

OF ACCENT.

MARKS OF ACCENT. +, full accent. !, half accent.

7. Accent is a stress of voice or emphasis on one part of a sentence, strain, or measure, more than another. In the two first moods of common time, the full accent is placed on the first part, and half accent on the third part of each measure. (N.B. Each measure admits of a division into four parts.) In the third mood of common time the measure is generally divided into two parts, and the accent is on the first part; if divided into four parts, it may be accented as the two first moods.

Triple time is divided into three parts to each measure, and the accent is on the first and third parts.

Compound time is divided into six parts, and the accent is on the first and fourth parts. In all cases of accents, the first in the measure is full, and the second, partial. The figures which are used to express the time of the several moods, are to be used single; the under figures are aliquot parts of the semibreve, and the upper figures showing the number of such parts in a measure, to wit: $\frac{2}{2}$ means two minims in a measure; $\frac{4}{4}$ means four crotchets in a measure; $\frac{2}{4}$, two crotchets, &c. In a word, the under figure shows into how many parts the semibreve is divided, and the upper figure shows the number of such parts in a measure; and so of all the movements of time that may be expressed by figures.

OF MUSIC.

8. Q. What is music?

A. Music is a succession of pleasing sounds.

Q. On what is music written?

A. On five parallel lines including the spaces between them, which is called a stave; and these lines and spaces are represented by the first seven letters in the alphabet, A, B, C, D, E, F, and G. These letters also represent the seven sounds that belong to each key-note in music. When eight letters are used, the first is repeated.

Q. How many parts are there used in vocal music?

A. Commonly only four, viz.: Bass, Tenor, Counter, and Treble· and the letters are placed on the staves for the several parts in the following order, commencing at the space below the first line in each stave.

BASS STAVE NATURAL.

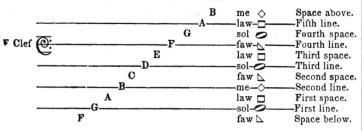

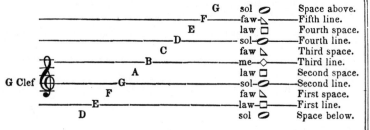

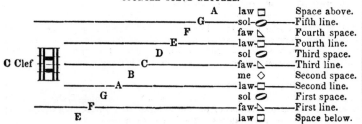

You may observe that the letters are named or called by the names of the four notes used in music. You see in the preceding staves that F is named faw, G sol, A law, B me, C faw, D sol, E law, and F faw again; every eighth letter being the first repeated, which is an octave; for every eighth is an octave.

9. *Q.* How many notes are there used in music; what are their names, and how are they made?

A. All notes of music which represent sounds are called by four names, and each note is known by its shape, viz.: the me is a diamond, faw is triangle, sol is round, and law is square. See the following example.

Q. But in some music books the tunes are written in round notes entirely. How do we know by what names to call the notes in these books?

A. By first finding the *me*, for *me* is the governing and leading note; and when that is found, the notes on the lines and spaces in regular succession are called faw, sol, law, faw, sol, law, (twice;) and those below the *me*, law, sol, faw, law, sol, faw, (twice;) after which *me* will come again. Either way, see the following example.

This is the rule for singing round notes. You must therefore observe that the natural place for the *me* in parts of music is on that line or space represented by B

But if B be flat, ♭, *me* is on ....E

B ♭ and E ♭, it is on ....A

B ♭, E ♭, and A ♭, it is on ....D

B ♭, E ♭, A ♭, and D ♭, it is on ....G

If F be sharp, ♯, *me* is on ....F

F ♯ and C ♯, it is on C

F ♯, C ♯, and G ♯, it is on ....G

F ♯, C ♯, G ♯, and D ♯, it is on ....D

As in the following example, viz.:

ME in its NATURAL ♮ place. Tenor or treble ME.	ME, transposed by flats.				ME, transposed by sharps.			
	B flat, *me* is in E.	B and E flat, *me* is in A.	B, E, and A flat, *me* is in D.	B, E, A, and D flat, *me* is in G.	F sharp, *me* is in F.	F and C sharp, *me* is in C.	F, C, and G sharp, *me* is in G.	F, C, G, D, sharp, *me* is in D.
Counter ME.	ME.	ME.	ME.	ME.	ME.	ME.	ME.	ME.
Bass ME.	ME.	ME.	ME.	ME.	ME.	ME.	ME.	ME.

CHARACTERS USED IN MUSIC.

10. A Stave or staff is five parallel lines, on which notes and other musical characters are written.

Leger line

11. Leger lines are short lines added to the common stave or staff, so as to embrace such notes as may transcend its boundary.

Leger line

12. A Brace is drawn across the first end of a tune, showing that all the parts enclosed are to be sung together; and the order of those parts is as follows: the lowest is Bass; next above, Tenor; and, if but three parts, the third is Treble; but if the Counter is added, the fourth part is **Treble**, and the third, Counter.

13. The G Clef stands on G, second line of the tenor or treble stave, and crosses that line four times. It is always used in tenor and treble, and sometimes in counter.

14. The C Clef stands on C, middle line; is used only in counter.

15. The F Clef is placed on the fourth line of the stave, and belongs to the bass or lower part in music.

16. A single bar is a plain line or mark across the stave, and divides the time into equal parts, according to the mood of time and measure note.

17. A measure note is a note that fills a measure; i.e. from one bar to another, without any other note or rest.

18. A dot or point set to the right hand of a note, adds to that note half its length; and if placed by the first note in the measure, it diminishes from the succeeding part of the measure, by reducing the next note to a smaller denomination. If the point is placed last in the measure, it reduces the preceding note to a smaller denomination. The point never extends its influence out of the measure in which it is placed.

EXAMPLE.

A pointed semibreve is equal to three minims; a pointed minim to three crotchets; and a pointed crotchet to three quavers, &c.

19. A Flat* set immediately preceding or before a note, sinks it half a tone; i.e. causes it to be sung half a tone lower than it would be without the flat.

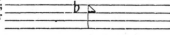

20. A Sharp set before a note, raises it half a tone; i.e. causes it to be sung half a tone higher than it would be without the sharp.

21. A natural restores a note from flat or sharp to its natural sound.

22. A Slur over or under any number of notes, shows that they must be sung to one syllable, gliding softly from one sound to another. The tails of the notes are often joined together, which answers the same purpose as a slur.

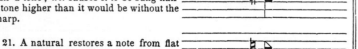

* We recommend singers to omit accidental flats and sharps, unless they understand them properly.

23. A figure 3 over or under three notes, is a mark of diminution, and shows that they must be sung in the time of two of the same kind, without a figure.

24. A Trill shows that the note over which it is placed should be warbled with a soft roll.

25. A Direct shows the place of the succeeding note on the stave.

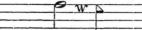

26. A Staccato is seldom used in vocal music. The notes over which it is placed should be sounded distinct and emphatically.

27. Appogiatura, or grace notes, are small extra notes added and set before or after regular notes, to guide the voice more gracefully into the sound of the succeeding note.

28. The Double Bar shows the end of a strain or line of poetry, and sometimes where to repeat.

29. The Hold is without definite bounds; the note over which it is placed is always held longer than its usual sound, and is to be swelled with strength to the centre of the note, then the voice to echo off into soft tone, to the end of the note or sound.

30. A Repeat snows that the tune is to be sung twice from it to the next double bar or close.

31. Figure 1, 2, or double ending, at the end of a strain, or at the end of a tune, shows that the note or notes under 1 are to be sung before you repeat, and those under 2 after omitting those under 1; but if the notes are tied together with a slur, both are sung the second time, as in the second example.

32. A Close shows the end of a tune or anthem.

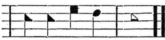

33. A Prisma denotes a repetition of preceding words.

34. Choosing notes are notes set immediately over each other on the same stave, either of which may be sung, but not by the same voice. If two persons are singing the same part, one may sing the upper, and the other the lower notes.

35. A Syncopation is where notes are driven out of their common order, by commencing in one measure and ending in the next, and tied across the bar with a slur, representing the same letter; but if they vary from the same letter, it comes under the denomination of a slur.

In all syncopated notes both notes are sounded, and but one called by name; (that is the first.)

36. A Couplet is where two or more notes are tied together in the same measure, embracing both accents (due to the measure) within its limits, (if there be two;) in this case all the enclosed notes are sounded, and but the first one called, viz.: if they all represent the same letter. But if they vary from the same letter, it breaks the couplet, and is denominated a slur.

Examples of Couplets.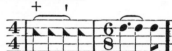

37. *Q.* What is meant by syncope or syncopeed notes?
A. It is when a note is set out of its usual order, requiring the accent to be upon it, as though it were in the usual place of the accent, as in common time, having half the time of the measure in the middle; as a minim between two crotchets, or a crotchet preceding a pointed minim, or a crotchet between two quavers, &c.

OF THE CLIFF OR CLEFTS.

38. This character derived its name from two Latin words, (Clavis signata,) signifying a sealed key, and is set at the beginning of every piece of music, and serves as a key to open the scale of characters, and fully determine their import. If this character is set high on the stave, the music runs low; while, on the contrary, if set low, the music runs high; because the letters of themselves are independent characters, and are thrown above the cliff which stands low on the stave, and below the cliff which is set high on the stave, (for instance :) the F cliff stands on the fourth line of the bass stave, and is a third from the top of that stave; and the G cliff stands on the second line of the tenor and treble stave, and is the third from the bottom of that stave; the alto or counter, occupying the precise centre between the other two; thus we see the bass assigned to the gravest of male voices, and the tenor to the highest of male voices; the treble to the most shrill female voices; the counter to the gravest of female, and boys voices; unless the counter be written on the G or F clef, and if so, take the best and most acute voices of both male and female, and perform it on the octave pitch.

THE GENERAL SCALE, AND RULES FOR PITCHING OR KEYING MUSIC.

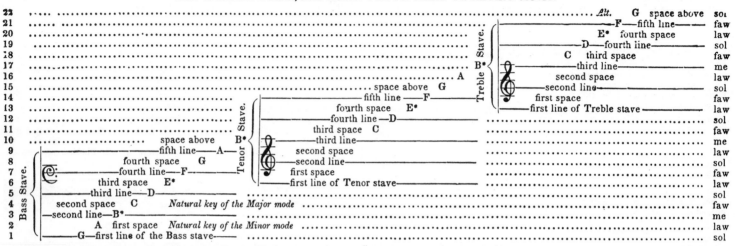

39. The above is a representation of the general scale, showing the connection of the parts, and also what sound of the general scale each letter, line, or space in either of the octaves, represents; for instance: A, the minor key, occupies the 2d, 9th, and 16th sounds of the general scale; C, the natural major key, the 4th, 11th, and 18th. Thus it will appear that every octave being unison, are considered one and the same sound. Although the last in the bass is the key-note, and in case the *me* is not transposed, will either be on the 2d and 4th degrees as above stated, yet with the same propriety we may suppose them on the 9th, 11th, &c. degrees; for when we refer to a pitchpipe for the sound of either of the foregoing keys, if it be properly constructed, it will exactly correspond to the 9th, 11th, &c. degrees of the general scale. Then by descending the octave, we get the sound of the natural key; then by ascending a 3d, 4th, or 5th, as the tune may require, we readily discover whether the piece be properly keyed. If we find, after descending the octave, we can ascend to the highest note in the tenor or treble, and can pronounce them with ease and freedom, the **piece** may be said to be properly keyed; but if, on the contrary, after descend-

ing, we find it difficult to ascend as above, the piece is improperly keyed, and should be set lower.

Note.—This method of proving the keys is infallible to individuals, and will hold good in choirs, when we suppose the teacher or leader capable of judging for the commonality of voices.

The above scale comprises three octaves, or twenty-two sounds.

The F clef, used on the fourth line in the bass, shows that that line is the seventh sound in the general scale.

The G clef, used on the second line in the tenor and treble shows that that line, in the tenor, is the eighth sound in the general scale, and in the treble, (when performed by a female voice,) the fifteenth sound; for if the treble as well as the tenor were performed entirely by men, the general scale would comprise only **fifteen** sounds; hence, the treble stave is raised only an octave above the tenor, in consequence of the female voice being naturally an octave above the male's, and to females the treble is usually assigned. The stars (*) show the natural place of the semitones.

When the C clef 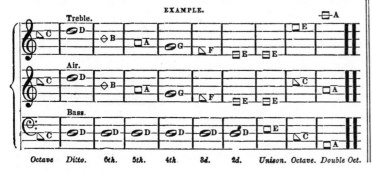 is used, (though it has now become very common to write counter on either the G or F clefs,) the middle line in the counter is in unison with the third space in tenor (C), and a seventh above the middle line in the bass, &c.

Two sounds equally high or equally low, however unequal in their force, are said to be in unison, one with the other. Consequently E, on the lower line of the treble stave, is in unison with E, on the fourth space of the tenor; and E, on the third space in bass, is in unison with E, on the first line of the tenor, and an octave below E, the lower line in the treble. ☞ See the General Scale. From any one letter in the general scale, to another of the same name, the interval is an octave—as from B to B, D to D, &c.

Agreeably to the F and G clefs used in the general scale, a note on any line or space in the bass, is a sixth below a note on a corresponding line or space in the tenor, and a thirteenth below a note in the treble occupying the same line or space, (when the treble is performed by females.) ☞ See the General Scale. Suppose we place a note on D, middle line of the bass, another on B, the middle line of the tenor or treble, the interval will appear as just stated; and to find any other interval, count either ascending or descending, as the case may be.

EXAMPLE.

Treble.
Air.
Bass.

Octave   Ditto.   6th.   5th.   4th.   3d.   2d.   Unison. Octave. Double Oct.

In counting intervals, remember to include both notes or letters, thus: in counting a sixth in the preceding example, D is one, E is two, F is three, G is four, A five, and B six.

In the preceding example, the notes in the treble and air are placed in unison with each other. But assigning the treble to female voices, and the air to male voices, (as is customary,) an octave must be added to the notes in the treble, (as previously observed of a woman's voice being an octave more acute than a man's,) the interval between the bass and treble, in the first measure, would be a fifteenth, or double octave; in the third measure, the note on B, in the treble, a thirteenth above D, in the bass, &c. Observe that an octave and a second make a ninth; an octave and a third make a tenth; an octave and a fourth make an eleventh; an octave and a fifth make a twelfth; an octave and a sixth, a thirteenth; an octave and a seventh, a fourteenth; two octaves a fifteenth, &c., always including both the first and last note.

OF HARMONY AND COMPOSITION.

40. Harmony consists in the proportion of the distance of two, three, or four sounds, performed at the same time, and mingling in a most pleasing manner to the ear.

The notes which produce harmony, when sounded together, are called *concords*, and their intervals, *consonant intervals*. The notes which, when sounded together, produce a disagreeable sound to the ear, are called *discords*, and their intervals, *dissonant intervals*. There are but four concords in music, viz.: *unison, third, fifth,* and *sixth;* (their eighths or octaves are also meant.) The unison is called a perfect chord, and commonly the fifth is so called. If the composer please, however, he may make the fifth imperfect, when composing more than two parts. The third and sixth are called imperfect, their chords being not so full, nor so agreeable to the ear, as the perfect; but in four parts the sixth is often used instead of the fifth; so, in effect, there are but three concords, employed together, in composition.

N.B. The meaning of imperfect signifies that it wants a semitone of its perfections, to what it does when it is perfect: for as the lesser or imperfect third includes but three half tones, the greater or major third includes four, &c. The discords are a *second*, a *fourth*, a *seventh*, and their octaves; though the greater fourth sometimes comes very near to the sound of an imperfect chord, it being the same in ratio as the minor fifth. Indeed, some composers (the writer of these extracts is one of them) seem very partial to the greater fourth, and frequently admit it in composition.

The following is an example of the several concords and discords, and their octaves under them :

	CONCORDS.				DISCORDS.		
Single Chords.	1	3	5	6	2	4	7
Their Octaves.	8	10	12	13	9	11	14
	15	17	19	20	16	18	21
	22	24	26	27	23	25	28

Notwithstanding the 2d, 4th, 7th, &c., are properly discords, yet a skilful composer may use them to some advantage, provided a full chord of all the parts immediately follow; they will then answer a similar purpose to acid, which being tasted previously to sweet, gives the latter a more pleasing flavour. Although the 4th is really a discord, yet it is very often used in composition. The rough sound of the 4th may be so mollified by the sweetness of the 5th and 8th as to harmonize almost as well as any three sounds in nature; and it would be reasonable to suppose that where we have two perfect chords, a discord may be introduced with very little violation to the laws of harmony; but as it is the most difficult part of composition to use a discord in such a manner and place as to show more fully the power and beauty of music, we think composers should only use them sparingly, (as it is much better to have all sweet, than to have too much sour or bitter,) and always let them be followed by a perfect chord.

OF THE DIATONIC SCALE, MAJOR KEY.

41. The diatonic scale is composed of tones and semitones. From the key to the second sound above is a tone; from the second to the third a tone; from the third to the fourth a semitone; from the fourth to the fifth a tone; from the fifth to the sixth a tone; from the sixth to the seventh a tone; and from the seventh to the eighth a semitone; observing that five whole tones and two semitones compose an octave.

OF THE MINOR KEY.

42. The minor key differs from the major because of the semitones occurring between the second and third, and fifth and sixth sounds from the key.

It is unnecessary to treat further on the subject of semitones; for they are natural to the voice, and cannot be avoided by natural performance. It should suffice to know that they do exist, and where they are.

OF DEGREES.

43. A degree is the interval from one letter to another in immediate succession. The first letter in the scale of letters is the foundation for the first degree; the second letter ends that degree, and is the beginning of the second degree; three letters will form two degrees, &c.

OF RELATIVES.

44. Whatever the key may be, whether natural or artificial, the same relatives are produced by the key; the sixth above and the third below are relative minors to the major mode; the sixth below and the third above are relative majors to the minor mode.

45. The reason why one tune is in a sharp key and another in a flat key is, that the third and sixth sounds ascending in the sharp key, are half a tone higher than the same intervals in the flat key; and sharp keyed music is generally applied to poetry that is animating, spirited, and cheerful; while flat keyed music is applied to poetry that is solemn, pensive, and melancholy.

EXAMPLE OF THE KEYS.

46. In the Major key, from faw to law, its third, the interval is two tones, [a Major third;] from faw to law, its sixth, the interval is four tones and a semitone, [a Major sixth;] and from faw to me, its seventh, the interval is five tones and a semitone, [a Major seventh.]

In the Minor key, from law to faw, its third, the interval is one tone and a semitone, [Minor third;] from law to faw, its sixth, the interval is three tones and two semitones, [a Minor sixth;] and from law to sol, its seventh, the interval is four tones and two semitones, [a Minor seventh.]

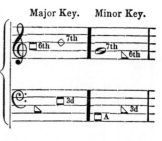

Major Key.   Minor Key.

To prove the utility of removing the key, I will produce an example. Let the tune "Suffield" be written on key note A, (natural flat key,) instead of E, its proper key; and, besides the inconvenience of multiplying leger lines, few voices would be able to perform it, the treble in particular.

SUFFIELD on E, its proper key, from the repeat.

The same on A, the assumed, or natural key A.

47. There are seven sounds bearing distinct names. from their situation and effect in the scale. The key note is called the tonic; the next above, or its second, the supertonic; its third, the mediant; its fourth, the subdominant; its fifth, the dominant; its sixth, the submediant; and its seventh, the leading note

Tonic. Supertonic. Mediant. Subdominant. Dominant. Submediant. L. note.

Q. Why is the key note or tonic numbered one?

A. Because it is the sound most natural to the voice, and determines the principal pitch of every piece of music, and from which all other sounds in composition are reckoned; it is therefore made a station, holding the first and most important position in music. A regular bass always ends with it; hence, in giving the pitch of a piece of music, it should be sounded.

The fifth is the next important sound, and is called a dominant, from its being a perfect fifth, which cannot be varied by natural progression; and produces a sweeter sound than any other, compared with the tonic.

The third is the next important sound, and is called the mediant, from its being midway between the tonic and dominant; this, in some respects, is the most important note or sound in the scale, because it determines the major from the minor mode.

The sixth is the next important sound, and is called the submediant, it being of minor value to the common mediant or third, and is midway between the fourth and eighth sounds. This sound will run as a descending third from the octave, and is an imperfect chord with the tonic.

The fourth is the next in order, and is called a subdominant, it being a descending fifth from the octave, and will run with the eighth, sixth, and second, from the tonic, and is of minor value to the fifth from the tonic.

The second is called the supertonic, from its being next above the tonic, and will only run with the fourth and sixth sounds from the tonic.

The seventh is the leading note, leading all other notes in their order to the key. By this note the system of solmization is made consistent and convenien

OF FLATS AND SHARPS

48. Many inquiries have been made why B is first flatted, and F is first sharped; in answer to this inquiry, B and E are natural sharp sounds, and are first flatted, F and C are natural flat sounds, and are first sharped. In the natural scale of music, the first semitone occurs between B and C, and the next between E and F; and sharps being marks of elevation, F is first sharped for the purpose of elevating the letter F, which was formerly depressed by a semitone between E and F. The letter C is next sharped for the purpose of restoring the letter C on the same general principle; and so on through the scale of seven letters, until every letter takes its proportion of tones and semitones.

When B is flatted, it removes the semitone which existed between B and C, and makes it a whole tone, and places the semitone between E and F. Next, E is flatted for the same general purpose. It will be observed that a sharp, when inserted, operates on the upper part of a semitone degree; but a flat on the lower part of a semitone degree. Furthermore, when a sharp is set, it raises the *me* five letters, and sinks it four, and spaces the octave, as from B to F, which is five letters ascending, and four descending; and when a flat is set, it raises the *me* four letters, and sinks it five, and spaces the octave in like manner, as from B to E. Thus by counting the centre letter twice, as the beginning of each interval, five and four would make but eight.

BY SHARPS.
1. A fifth from B *me*, its natural place, will bring us to............ F
2. A fifth from F *me*, will bring us to.............................. C
3. A fifth from C *me*, will bring us to.............................. G
4. A fifth from G *me*, will bring us to.............................. D
5. A fifth from D *me*, will bring us to.............................. A
6. A fifth from A *me*, will bring us to.............................. E
7. A fifth from E *me*, will bring us back to........................ B

BY FLATS.
1. A fourth from B *me*, will bring us to............................ E
2. A fourth from E *me*, will bring us to............................ A
3. A fourth from A *me*, will bring us to............................ D
4. A fourth from D *me*, will bring us to............................ G
5. A fourth from G *me*, will bring us to............................ C
6. A fourth from C *me*, will bring us to............................ F
7. A fourth from F *me*, will bring us home to...................... B

This accounts for the customary rules of transposition, viz.:

The natural place for *me* is on.. B
If B is ♭, *me* is on... E
If B and E are ♭, *me* is on... A
If B, E, and A are ♭, *me* is on....................................... D
If B, E, A, and D are ♭, *me* is on.................................... G
If B, E, A, D, and G are ♭, *me* is on................................. C
If B, E, A, D, G, and C are ♭, *me* is on.............................. F
If F be ♯, *me* is on.. F
If F and C be ♯, *me* is on C
If F, C and G be ♯, *me* is on... G
If F, C, G, and D be ♯, *me* is on .... D
If F, C, G, D, and A be ♯, *me* is on.................................. A
If F, C, G, D, A, and E be ♯, *me* is on............................... E

A SCALE, SHOWING THE SITUATION OF BOTH KEYS IN EVERY TRANSPOSITION OF THE *ME* BY SHARPS AND FLATS.

A SCALE, SHOWING THE SITUATION OF THE SEMITONES IN EVERY TRANSPOSITION OF THE *ME* BY FLATS AND SHARPS.

OF INTERVALS.

49. There are fourteen intervals in the scale, bearing distinct names, viz: Unison, Minor second, Major second, Minor third, Major third, Perfect fifth, Minor sixth, Major sixth, Minor seventh, Major seventh, Octave.

B

Observe that, by six flats or six sharps, (including the natural place,) the keys occupy every letter in the stave, and by the same number of either character, (including the natural place,) the whole octave is divided into semitones; and it is impossible to use another flat or sharp in transposition, for seven flats or sharps would only put them in their natural places. You may also observe, that one flat, or six sharps, places the semitones precisely in the same situation; and that one sharp, or six flats, has the same effect; and two flats or five sharps, and two sharps or five flats, &c.; and with six flats or one sharp, one of the semitones is in its natural place; *i. e.* between B and C. Also with six sharps or one flat, one of the semitones is in its natural place, *i. e.* between E and F, as the natural places of the semitones are between B and C, and E and F; and we suppose the reason why both of these characters are used in transposition, is to save the trouble and time of making so many of either character; for a person can make one flat much quicker than six sharps, or one sharp quicker than six flats, &c.

As the scale admits of only twelve semitones, so an octave, by counting the first and last note, (which are octaves to each other, and really one and the same sound in effect,) contains thirteen sounds, yet it has but twelve intervals, because the unison cannot properly be called an interval; and the sharp fourth and flat fifth, although necessarily distinguished in harmony, are performed on keyed instruments with the same keys, and make but one interval.

REMOVAL OF THE KEY NOTE.

50. When we remove the key note of the major mode, the arrangement is effected by sharping its fourth, which becomes a seventh to the new key note, and a fifth from the former key note; or by flatting its seventh, which becomes a fourth to the new key note, viz., the fourth of the former key. The minor key note is removed by sharping its sixth, which becomes a second to the new key note; or by flatting its second, which becomes a sixth to the new key note.

The following table exhibits a regular succession of keys, beginning with the natural, and continued till all the letters are sharped and flatted; together with the letters that represent *faw* and *law* in every transposition of the *me* by flats and sharps. More than four of either of these characters are seldom used.

	Letters for the me.	Major key.	Minor key.	Letters for faw.		Letters for faw.	Letters for law.		Letters for law.
NATURAL ♮, *me* is on...	B	C	A	C	and	F	A	and	E
BY SHARPS.									
1 sharp ♯, *me* is on..	F	G	E	C	and	G	E	and	B
2 sharps ♯♯, *me* is on	C	D	B	D	and	G	B	and	F
3 sharps ♯♯♯, *me* is on	G	A	F	A	and	D	F	and	C
4 sharps ♯♯♯♯, *me* is on	D	E	C	E	and	A	C	and	G
5 sharps ♯♯♯♯♯, *me* is on	A	B	G	B	and	E	G	and	D
6 sharps ♯♯♯♯♯♯, *me* is on..	E	F	D	F	and	B	D	and	A
7 sharps restores to the natural	B	C	A	C	and	F	A	and	E
BY FLATS.									
1 flat ♭, *me* is on.......................................	E	F	D	F	and	B	D	and	A
2 flats ♭♭, *me* is on.....................................	A	B	G	B	and	E	G	and	D
3 flats ♭♭♭, *me* is on	D	E	C	E	and	A	C	and	G
4 flats ♭♭♭♭, *me* is on ...,...............................	G	A	F	A	and	D	F	and	C
5 flats ♭♭♭♭♭, *me* is on	C	D	B	D	and	G	B	and	F
6 flats ♭♭♭♭♭♭, *me* is on	F	G	E	G	and	C	E	and	B
7 flats restores to the natural................................	B	C	A	C	and	F	A	and	E

OF THE KEYS.

51. *Q.* How many keys are there in music?
A. Two; the minor or flat key, and the major or sharp key.
Q. What are the natural letters for those keys?
A. A and C; A for the minor or flat key, and C for the major or sharp key.
Q. How are they known?
A. By the last note in the bass, which is always the key note or tonic. Should it be *law*, immediately below *me*, the tune is in a flat or minor key; but if *faw*, immediately above *me*, it is in a sharp or major key; observing that the semitones are always equally distant from the key note or tonic, whether it be natural, or assumes an artificial position.

ON THE MODULATION OF THE KEY.

52. The modulation or changing of the key note from one letter or given tone to another, is so frequent in regular composition, particularly in Anthems, that the performers will be very often embarrassed, unless they endeavour to acquire a knowledge or habit of discerning those changes.

The transition of the key from one letter to another is sometimes effected by gradual preparation, as by accidental flats, sharps, or naturals. When the change is gradual, the new key is announced by flats, sharps, or naturals. But if the change is sudden, the usual signs or signature at the beginning of the stave are either altered or removed, as in the Christian Song.

TRANSITION IN THE MAJOR MODE FROM ONE KEY OR LETTER TO ANOTHER.

TRANSITION IN THE MINOR MODE FROM ONE KEY OR LETTER TO ANOTHER.

MISCELLANEOUS DIRECTIONS.

53. It is as essential to good singing as to good speaking, that some words and syllables should have more stress of voice than others; and that the same syllable should be accented in singing as in speaking. Such words and syllables are called accented or emphatic. If the poetry is properly constructed, the emphatic syllable falls on the accented part of the measure; if otherwise, the emphasis of the words must be attended to, and the accent of the music neglected.

The teacher should require some lines to be rehearsed with the proper emphasis, and then sung with the same emphasis.

TAKING BREATH.

54. The breath should not be drawn in singing, any more than in speaking, in the middle of a word; nor when several notes come to one syllable should there be interruptions between them; but the several notes should be blended with smoothness, but not without distinctness. In fact, the breath should be no oftener drawn than fulness and firmness of tone require.

The practice of breathing regularly at a particular place in each measure should be specially guarded against; and also the habit of leaving the sound abruptly to take breath. The breath should be taken quickly, yet gently.

MUSICAL EXPRESSION.

55. Musical expression depends chiefly on the feeling which the singer possesses and imparts to the performance by the proper tones and correct delivery of words; hence, in singing, the teacher should select such pieces as would interest his singers, and then, by precept and example, be unwearied in his exertions to impress on them the importance of expressing the sentiment, and the great error of singing serious words in a thoughtless manner.

QUALITIES OF TONE.

56. The most essential qualities of a good tone are purity, fulness, firmness, and certainty.

Teachers should occasionally show the propriety of using correct sounds, by causing their pupils alternately to take two or more sounds which will produce discords, and then others that will produce concords; and thus exhibit the difference between them.

TO CORRECT FAULTS.

57. When a bad sound is heard from the pupil, the teacher should imitate that sound, and then contrast it with a correct sound, with the use of the appropriate organs; which will enable the pupil to see and correct the faulty sound. Teachers should, in this, be very careful to treat it in such a way as not to give umbrage, or embarrass the pupil.

RULE FOR BEATING TIME.

58. For common and compound time, confine the arm to the body, let the beat extend from the wrist forward, and perform the beat with the hand alone, straight down and straight up.

For triple time, for the first down beat, strike the edge of the hand, on the book or lap; second beat, throw the hand flat down; third beat, raise it straight up.

MELODY LESSONS.

INSTRUCTIONS TO THE TEACHER.

59. In performing melody lessons, the teacher should have his pupils to learn well the sound, the name, and the number of each note, from 1 to 8, so they can apply them in melody or harmony; take the eight notes, for instance, and apply them, 1, 2, 3, 4, 5, 6, 7, 8; 8, 7, 6, 5, 4, 3, 2, 1; the key note is numbered 1, the next 2, and so on to 8, either ascending or descending; and when you arrive at the 8th, if the piece should go beyond it, the 8th becomes 1, and is repeated as directed for the first octave.

Let your pupils take three notes, as *faw, sol, law*, or 1, 2, 3, and sound them successively, until they can sound them well; then let them alternately take 1 and 3, as *faw, law*, until they can sound them correctly; then let them go on to four notes, and teach well the difference between 2 and 3, and 3 and 4, for the first and second degrees are tones, and the next a semitone; (what is meant by a degree is the interval from one sound to another in immediate succession.) When you have thus trained the pupil, go on to the eighth sound, and another semitone will occur between the 7th and 8th sounds; (these occurrences are alone in the sharp key.) In performing flat keyed notes, you will observe that the semitones occur between the 2d and 3d, and 5th and 6th sounds, and are invariably between *me* and *faw*, and *law* and *faw*, find them where you may; (consequently, when represented by their natural letters, are between B and and E and F.)

Then take other melody lessons of different orders, and unite all the voices well, before you attempt to make harmony by a connection of other parts; for if pupils cannot make melody, it is impossible for them to make harmony; and an attempt of this kind, too soon, is injurious; for bad voices and jargon will be the result.

60. See, in the following scale of notes, where the semitones are indicated by a (*) star.

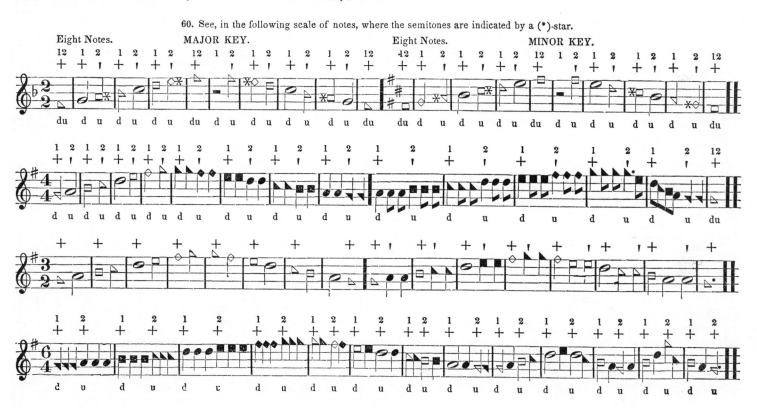

RUDIMENTS OF MUSIC.

INTERVALS.

Tenor.

When we sing, let's tune our voice; When we pray, let's train our words; When we sing, let's sing in faith; When we talk, we'll speak the truth;
When we talk, let's speak our joys; When our acts are for the Lord. When we pray, let's pray in faith; Thus becomes a noble youth.

Bass.

GENERAL OBSERVATIONS.

1. **PERSONS** may be well acquainted with all the various characters in psalmody, (or music;) they may also be able to sing their part in true time, and yet their performance be far from pleasing; if it is devoid of necessary embellishments, their manner and bad expression may conspire to render it disagreeable. A few plain hints, and a few general and friendly observations, we hope, will tend to correct these errors in practising vocal music.

2. Care should be taken that all the parts (when singing together) begin upon the proper pitch. If they are too high, difficulty, and perhaps discords, will be the consequence; if too low, dulness and languor. If the parts are not united by their corresponding degrees, the whole piece may be run into confusion and jargon before it ends; and perhaps the whole occasioned by an error of only one semitone in the pitch of one or more of the parts.

3. It is by no means necessary, to constitute good singers, that they should sing very loud. Each one should sing so soft as not to drown the teacher's voice, and each part so soft as will admit the other parts to be distinctly heard. If the teacher's voice cannot be heard, it cannot be imitated, (as that is the best way to modulate the voice and make it harmonious;) and if the singers of any one are so loud that they cannot hear the other parts, because of their own noise, the parts are surely not rightly proportioned, and ought to be altered.

4. When singing in concert, the bass should be sounded full, bold, and majestic, but not harsh; the tenor regular, firm, and distinct; the counter clear and plain; and the treble soft and mild, but not faint. The tenor and treble may consider the German flute, the sound of which they may endeavour to imitate, if they wish to improve the voice.

5. Flat-keyed tunes should be sung softer than sharp-keyed ones, and may be proportioned with a lighter bass; but for sharp-keyed tunes let the bass be full and strong, but never harsh.

6. The high notes, quick notes, and slurred notes, of each part, should be sung softer than the low notes, long notes, and single notes, of the same parts. All the notes included by one slur should be sung at one breath, if possible.

7. Learners should sing all parts of music somewhat softer than their leaders do, as it tends to cultivate the voice, and gives them an opportunity of following in a piece with which they are not well acquainted; but a good voice may be soon much injured by singing too loud.

8. When notes of the tenor fall below those of the bass, the tenor should be sounded strong, and the bass soft.

9. While first learning a tune, it may be sung somewhat slower than the true time or mood of time requires, until the notes can be named and truly sounded, without looking on the book.

10. Learners are apt to give the first note, where a fuge begins, nearly double the time it ought to have, sounding a crotchet almost as long as a minim in any other part of the tune, which puts the parts in confusion by losing time; whereas the fuges ought to be moved off lively, the time decreasing, (or the notes sung quicker,) and the sound of the engaged part or parts increasing in sound as the others fall in. All solos or fuges should be sung somewhat faster than when all the parts are moving together.

11. There are but few long notes in any tune but what might be swelled with propriety. The swell is one of the greatest ornaments of vocal music, if rightly performed. All long notes of the bass should be swelled, if the other parts are singing short or quick notes at the same time. The swell should be struck plain upon the first part of the note, increase to the middle, and then decrease softly, like an echo, or die away like the sound of a bell.

12. All notes (except some in syncopation) should be called plainly by their proper names, and fairly articulated; and in applying the words, great care should be taken that they be properly pronounced, and not torn to pieces between the teeth, nor forced through the nose. Let the mouth be freely opened, but not too wide, the teeth a little asunder, and let the sound come from the lungs, and be entirely formed where they should be only distinguished, viz., on the end of the tongue. The superiority of vocal to instrumental music is, that while one only pleases the ear, the other informs the understanding.

13. When notes occur one directly above another, (called choosing notes,) and there are several singers on the part where they are, let two sing the lower, while one does the upper notes, and in the same proportion to any other number.

14. Your singers should not join in concert, until each class can sing their own part correctly.

15. Learners should beat time by a pendulum, or with their teacher, until they can beat regular time, before they attempt to beat and sing both at once, because it perplexes them to beat, name time, and sound the notes at the same time, until they have acquired a knowledge of each by itself.

16. Too long singing at a time injures the lungs.*

---

* A cold or cough, all kind of spirituous liquors, violent exercise, too much bile on the stomach, long fasting, the veins overcharged with impure blood, &c. &c., are destructive to the voice of one who is much in the habit of singing. An excessive use of ardent spirits will speedily ruin the best voice.

17. Some teachers are in the habit of singing too long at a time with their pupils. It is better to sing but only eight or ten tunes at a lesson, or at one time, and inform the learners the nature of the pieces and the manner in which they should be performed; and continue at them until they are understood, than to run over forty or fifty in one evening, and at the end of a quarter of schooling, perhaps few besides the teacher know a flat-keyed tune from a sharp-keyed one, what part of the anthem, &c., requires emphasis, or how to give the pitch of any tune which they have been learning, unless some one inform them. It is easy to name the notes of a tune, but it requires attention and practice to sing them correctly.

18. Learners should not be confined too long to the parts that suit their voices best, but should try occasionally the different parts, as it tends greatly to improve the voice, and gives them a knowledge of the connection of the parts, and of harmony as well as melody.* The gentlemen can change from bass to tenor, or from tenor to bass, and the ladies from treble to tenor, &c.

19. Learners should understand the tunes well by note, before they attempt to sing them to verses of poetry.

20. If different verses are applied to a piece of music while learning, it will give the learners a more complete knowledge of the tune than they can have by confining it always to the same words. Likewise applying different tunes to the same words, will have a great tendency to remove the embarrassment created by considering every short tune as a set piece to certain words or hymns.

21. When the key is transposed, there are flats and sharps placed on the stave; and when the mood of time is changed, the requisite characters are placed upon the stave.

22. There should not be any noise indulged while singing, (except the music,) as it destroys entirely the beauty of harmony, and renders the performance very difficult, (especially to new beginners;) and if it is designedly promoted, is nothing less than a proof of disrespect in the singers to the exercise, to themselves who occasion it, and to the Author of our existence.

23. The apogiatura is placed in some tunes, which may be used with propriety by a good voice; also the trill over some notes; but neither should be attempted by any one until he can perform the tune well by plain notes, (as they add nothing to the time.) Indeed no one can add much to the beauty of a piece by using what are generally termed graces, unless they are in a manner natural to their voice.

24. When learning to sing, we should endeavour to cultivate the voice so as to make it soft, smooth, and round: so that, when numbers are performing in concert, there may on each part (as near as possible) appear to be but one uniform voice. Then, instead of confused jargon, it will be more like the smooth vibrations of the violin, or the soft breathings of the German flute. Yet how hard it is to make some believe soft singing is the most melodious; when, at the same time, loud singing is more like the hootings of the midnight bird than refined music.

25. The most important ornament in singing is strict decorum, with a heart deeply impressed with the great truth we utter while singing the lines, aiming at the glory of God, and the edification of one another.

26. All affectation should be banished, for it is disgusting in the performance of sacred music, and contrary to that solemnity which should accompany an exercise so near akin to that which will, through all eternity, engage the attention of those who walk in climes of bliss.

27. The nearest perfection in singing we arrive at, is to pronounce the words* and make the sounds as feeling as if the sentiments and sounds were our own. If singers, when performing a piece of music, could be as much captivated with the words and sounds as the author of the music is when composing it, the foregoing directions would be almost useless; they would pronounce, accent, swell, sing loud and soft where the words require it, make suitable gestures, and add every other necessary grace.

28. The great Jehovah, who implanted in our nature the noble faculty of vocal performance, is jealous of the use to which we apply our talents in that particular, lest we use them in a way which does not tend to glorify his name. We should therefore endeavour to improve the talent given us, and try to sing with the spirit and with the understanding, making melody in our hearts to the Lord.

---

* Melody is the agreeable effect which arises from the performance of a single part of music only. Harmony is the pleasing union of several sounds, or the performance of the several parts of music together.

* In singing there are a few words which should vary a little from common pronunciation, such as end in i and y; and these should vary two ways. The following method has been generally recommended: In singing, it is right to pronounce majesty, mighty, lofty, &c., something like majestee, mightee, loftee, &c.; but the sense of some other words will be destroyed by this mode of expressing them: such as sanctify, justify, glorify, &c.

DICTIONARY OF MUSICAL TERMS

Adagio, very slow; the first mood in common time.
Allegro, lively, quick; the third mood in common time.
Accent, a stress of the voice on a particular note or syllable.
Air, the tenor part; the inclination of a piece of music.
Alt, high above the stave.
Alto, or *Altus*, high counter.
Appetone, between a tone and semitone.
Affettuoso, tender; affecting; mournful; plaintive.
Andante, moderate.
Bass, the lowest part of music; grave; solemn.
Bassoon, a kind of wind instrument for bass.
Bass Viol, a large, or bass fiddle.
Breve, an ancient note, **II**, equal to two semibreves.
Canticles, divine or pious poems; songs.
Chant, to sing praises.
Chord, a sound; a concord; proportional vibrations.
Chorus, all the parts together.
Clefs, characters representing particular sounds or degrees.
Comma, a small part, as 1-4th, 1-5th, &c. of a tone.
Compose, to make tunes, or set notes for music.
Concert, many singers or instruments together.
Counter, is high treble performed in a female voice.
Couplet, both accents tied together in the same measure.
Crescendo, increasing in sounds, &c.
Da Capo, or *D. C.*, to return and close with the first strain.
Diagram, the gamut, or rudiments of music.
Diapason, an octave; an eighth degree.
Dissonance, discord; disagreement.
Duet, two parts only moving together.
Diminuendo, diminishing in sound; becoming louder.
Forte, or *For*, full; loud or strong.
Fuge, or *Fugha*, the parts of music following each other in succession.
Gamut, the scale, or rudiments of music.
Grand, full; great; complete; pleasing.
Grave, slow; solemn; mournful; most slow
Guido, a direct.
Harmony, a pleasing union of sounds.

Harmonist, a writer of harmony; a musician.
Hexameter, having six lines to a verse.
Hautboy, or *Hoboy*, a kind of wind instrument.
Inno, a hymn or song.
Intonation, giving the pitch or key of a tune.
Interval, the distance between two degrees or sounds.
Ionic, light and soft.
Keys, the most permanent sounds of the voice or instrument.
Key note, the principal or leading note of each octave.
Largo, one degree quicker than the second mood in common time.
Lima, the difference between major and minor.
Linto, slow.
Major mode, the sharp key; the great third; high; cheerful.
Major chord, an interval having more semitones than a minor chord of the same degrees.
Medius, is low treble performed in a man's voice.
Moods, certain proportions of time, &c.
Modulate, to regulate sounds; to sing in a pleasing manner
Musica, the art of music; the study or science of music.
Music, a succession of pleasing sounds; one of the liberal sciences.
Necessario, continuing like thorough-bass.
Octave, and eighth degree; five tones and two semitones.
Organ, the largest of all musical instruments.
Pastoral, rural; a shepherd's song; something pertaining to a shepherd.
Piano, or *Pia*, directs the performer to sing soft; a kind of instrument.
Pentemeter, five lines to each verse.
Pitchpipe, a small instrument for proving sounds.
Solo, one part alone.
Sonorous, loud and harmonious.
Symphony, a piece of music without words, which the instrument plays while the voices rest.
Syncope, cut off; disjointed; out of the usual order.
Syncopation, notes joined in the same degree in one position.
Trill, or *Tr.*, a tune like a shake or roll.
Transposition, the changing the place of the key note.
Trio, a tune in three parts.
Violoncello, a tenor viol, 1-8th above a bass viol.

SACRED HARP.

PART I.

CONSISTING OF PIECES USED BY WORSHIPPING ASSEMBLIES.

BETHEL.   C. M.   Psalmist, 691st Hymn.

1 Oh for a   clo-ser walk with God! A calm and heavenly frame!   A light to shine up-on the road That leads me   to the Lamb!

2 Where is the blessedness I knew When first I   saw the Lord!   Where is the soul-re-fresh-ing view Of Je-sus and his word!

3 What peaceful hours I then enjoy'd!
 How sweet their memory still!
But now I find an aching void
 The world can never fill

4 Return, O Holy Dove, return,
 Sweet messenger of rest;
I hate the sins that made thee mourn,
 And drove thee from my breast.

5 The dearest idol I have known,
 Whate'er that idol be,
Help me to tear it from thy throne,
 And worship only thee.

6 So shall my walk be close with God,
 Calm and serene my frame;
So purer light shall mark the road
 That leads me to the Lamb

AYLESBURY.   S. M

The God we worship now, Will guide us till we die: Will be our God while here be - low, And ours a - bove the sky.

WELLS.   L. M.

Life is the time to serve the Lord, The time t'ensure the great reward; And while the lamp holds out to burn, The vilest sinner may re - turn.

FAIRFIELD. C. M

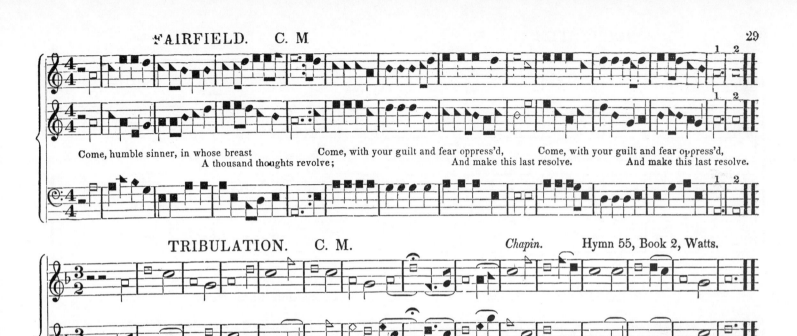

Come, humble sinner, in whose breast
A thousand thoughts revolve;

Come, with your guilt and fear oppress'd,
And make this last resolve.

Come, with your guilt and fear oppress'd,
And make this last resolve.

TRIBULATION. C. M.

Chapin. Hymn 55, Book 2, Watts.

Death, 'tis a me-lan-choly day, To those who have no God, When the poor soul is forced a - way, To seek her last a - bode.

2 In vain to heaven she lifts her eyes,
   For guilt, a heavy chain,
Still drags her downward from the skies,
   To darkness, fire, and pain.

3 Awake and mourn, ye heirs of hell,
   Let stubborn sinners fear;
You must be driven from earth, and dwell
   A long FOR EVER there.

4 See how the pit gapes wide for you,
   And flashes in your face;
And thou, my soul, look downward *two*
   And sing recovering grace.

ROCHESTER.   C. M.

Psalmist, 346th Hymn.

Come let us join our cheerful songs, With angels round the throne; Ten thousand thousand are their tongues, But all their joys are one.

PROSPECT.   L. M.

Psalmist, 1072d Hymn.   *Graham.*

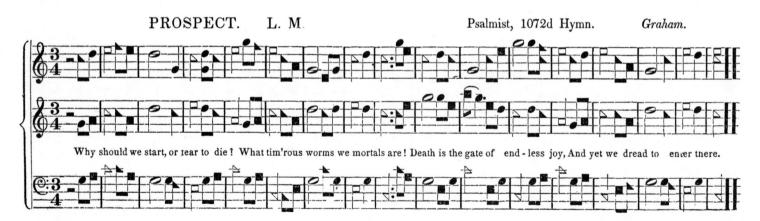

Why should we start, or rear to die? What tim'rous worms we mortals are! Death is the gate of end-less joy, And yet we dread to enter there.

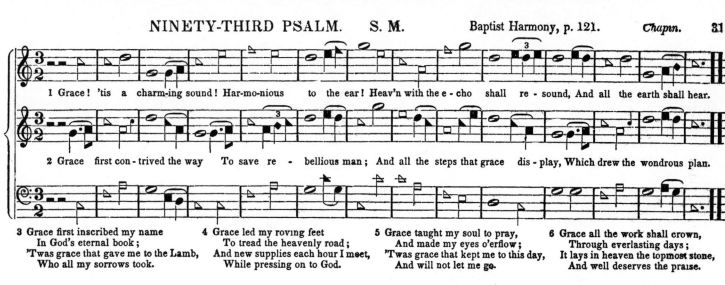

1 Grace! 'tis a charm-ing sound! Har-mo-nious to the ear! Heav'n with the e - cho shall re - sound, And all the earth shall hear.

2 Grace first con - trived the way To save re - bellious man; And all the steps that grace dis - play, Which drew the wondrous plan.

3 Grace first inscribed my name
   In God's eternal book;
'Twas grace that gave me to the Lamb,
   Who all my sorrows took.

4 Grace led my roving feet
   To tread the heavenly road;
And new supplies each hour I meet,
   While pressing on to God.

5 Grace taught my soul to pray,
   And made my eyes o'erflow;
'Twas grace that kept me to this day,
   And will not let me go.

6 Grace all the work shall crown,
   Through everlasting days;
It lays in heaven the topmost stone,
   And well deserves the praise.

WEBSTER. S. M.

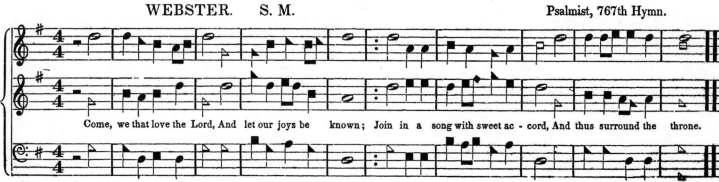

Come, we that love the Lord, And let our joys be known; Join in a song with sweet ac - cord, And thus surround the throne.

CORINTH. L. M.

Psalmist, 554th Hymn.   *John Massengale.*

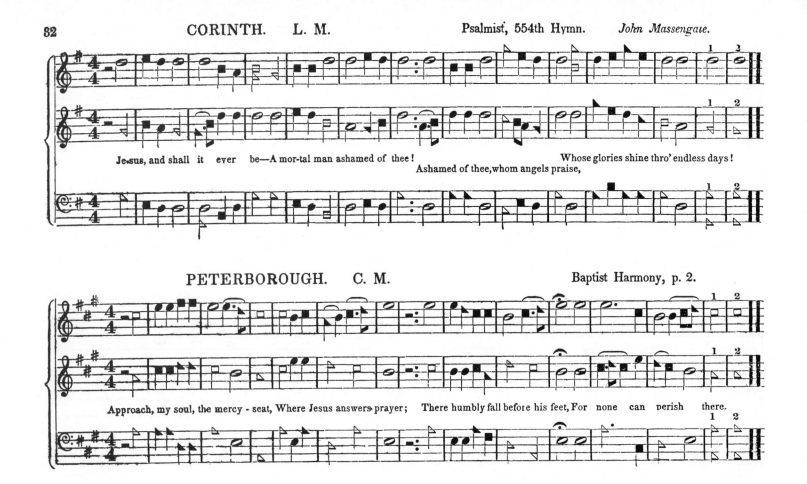

Je-sus, and shall it ever be—A mor-tal man ashamed of thee!   Whose glories shine thro' endless days!
Ashamed of thee, whom angels praise,

PETERBOROUGH.   C. M.

Baptist Harmony, p. 2.

Approach, my soul, the mercy - seat, Where Jesus answers prayer; There humbly fall before his feet, For none can perish there.

WEEPING SAVIOUR. S. M.

Psalmist, 471st Hymn. E. J. King.

Did Christ o'er sinners weep? And shall our cheeks be dry? Let floods of pen - i-ten-tial grief Burst forth from every eye.

ABBEVILLE. S. M.

Psalmist, 362d Hymn. E. J. King.

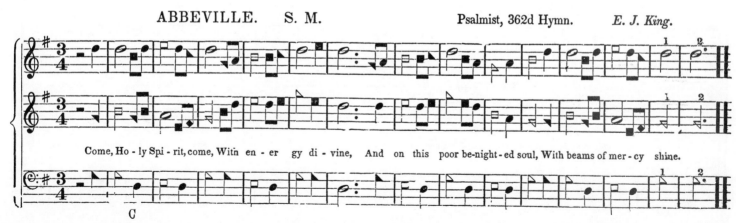

Come, Ho - ly Spi - rit, come, With en - er - gy di - vine, And on this poor be-night-ed soul, With beams of mer - cy shine.

HAMILTON. L. M.
Zion Songster, p. 222.   *B. F. White.*

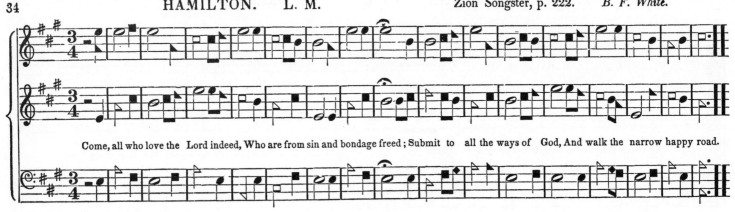

Come, all who love the Lord indeed, Who are from sin and bondage freed ; Submit to all the ways of God, And walk the narrow happy road.

BLEEDING SAVIOUR. C. M.
Psalmist, 472d Hymn.   *Z. Chambless.*

A las! and did my Saviour bleed, And did my Sovereign die ? Would he de - vote that sacred head For such a worm as I?

AUGUSTA.   C. M. D.

Psalmist, 248th Hymn.   *T. W. Carter.*

i O   for   a shout of   sa-cred joy   To God, the sovereign King!
Let eve-ry land their tongues employ, And hymns of triumph sing. } 2 Je-sus, our God, ascends on   high ; His heavenly guards a-

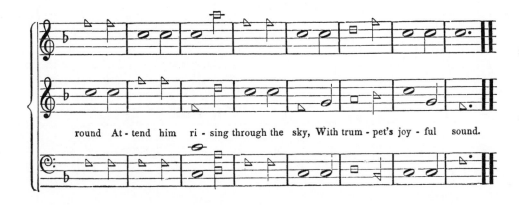

round At-tend him ri-sing through the sky, With trum-pet's joy-ful   sound.

3 While angels shout and praise their King,
   Let mortals learn their strains ;
Let all the earth his honours sing ;
   O'er all the earth he reigns.

4 Speak forth his praise with awe profound
   Let knowledge guide the song ;
Nor mock him with a solemn sound
   Upon a thoughtless tongue

AMERICA. S. M.

Psalmist, 183d Hymn. *Whitmore.*

Whose anger is, &c.

My soul, repeat his praise, Whose mercies are so great; Whose anger is so slow to rise, So rea-dy to a-bate.

Whose anger is, &c.

Whose anger is, &c. Whose

NINETY-FIFTH. C. M.

Psalmist, 1156th Hymn. *Colton.*

I'll bid, &c.

When I can read my title clear To mansions in the skies, I'll bid farewell to every fear, And wipe my weeping eyes.

to every fear, I'll bid

I'll bid, &c. I'll bid, &c.

CHINA.   C. M.

Psalmist, 1092d Hymn.

Why should we mourn departing friends, Or shake at death's alarms! 'Tis but the voice that Jesus sends, To call them to his arms.

LIVERPOOL.   C. M.

Mercer's Cluster, p. 146.   *M. C. H. Davis.*

1 Young people all, at - ten-tion give, And hear what I shall say;   I wish your souls with Christ to live, In ev - er-last-ing day.

2 Re-mem - ber you are hast'ning on To death's dark, gloomy shade;   Your joys on earth will soon be gone, Your flesh in dust be laid.

WINTER.   C. M.

His hoary frost, his flee - cy snow, Descend and clothe the ground; The liquid streams for - bear to flow, In i - cy fet - ters bound.

WINDHAM.   L. M.

Read.   Psalmist, 686th Hymn.

Broad is the road that leads to death, And thousands walk together there; But wisdom shows a narrow path, With here and there a tra - vel - ler.

DETROIT.　C. M

Do not I love thee, O my Lord! Behold my heart, and see, And turn each cur - sed i - dol out, That dares to rival thee.

WATCHMAN.　S. M.

Meth. H. B. 149.

A charge to keep I have, A God to glori - fy, A nev - er-dy-ing soul to save, And fit it for the sky.

LENOX. P. M.

Edson. Baptist Harmony, p. 356.

Blow ye the trumpet, blow, The glad - ly solemn sound, Let all the nations know, To earth's remotest bounds,

The year Re - turn,

The year The year Re - turn,

The year of ju - bi - lee is come, The year of ju - bi - lee is come; Re - turn, ye ran - som'd sin - ners, home.

Come, humble sinner, in whose breast A thousand thoughts revolve;
Come, with your guilt and fear oppress'd,
And make this last resolve, And

make this last re-solve, Come with your guilt and fear oppress'd, And make this last re-solve, :|:

Say, now, ye love - ly, so - cial band, Who walk the way to Ca - naan's land;
Ye who have fled from So - dom's plain, Say, do you wish to turn a - gain!

Oh! have you ven - tured

to the field, Well arm'd, with helmet, sword, and shield! And shall the world, with dread alarms, Com - pel you now to ground your arms?

When I can read my ti - tle clear To mansions in the skies, I'll bid fare - well to eve-ry fear, And wipe my weep-ing eyes.

I'll bid fare - well to eve-ry fear, I'll bid fare - well to eve-ry fear, And wipe my weep-ing eyes.

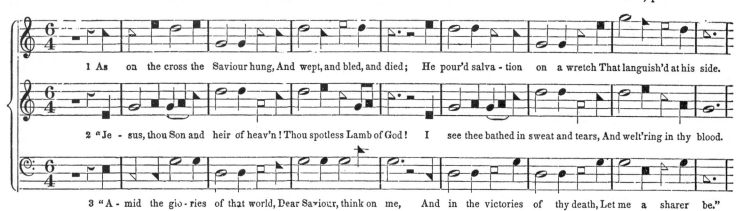

1 As on the cross the Saviour hung, And wept, and bled, and died; He pour'd salva - tion on a wretch That languish'd at his side.

2 "Je - sus, thou Son and heir of heav'n! Thou spotless Lamb of God! I see thee bathed in sweat and tears, And welt'ring in thy blood.

3 "A - mid the glo - ries of that world, Dear Saviour, think on me, And in the victories of thy death, Let me a sharer be."

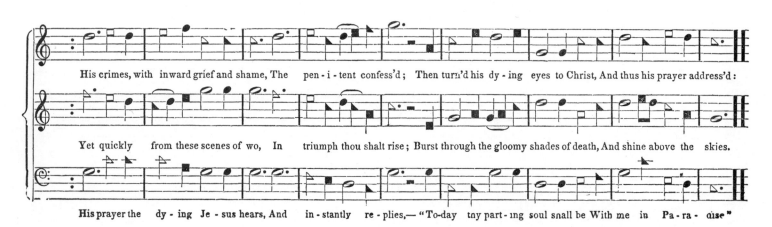

His crimes, with inward grief and shame, The pen - i - tent confess'd; Then turn'd his dy - ing eyes to Christ, And thus his prayer address'd:

Yet quickly from these scenes of wo, In triumph thou shalt rise; Burst through the gloomy shades of death, And shine above the skies.

His prayer the dy - ing Je - sus hears, And in - stantly re - plies,— "To-day thy part - ing soul shall be With me in Pa - ra - dise"

NEW BRITAIN. C. M.

Baptist Harmony, p. 123.

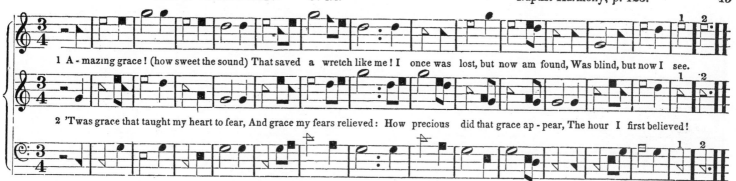

1 A-mazing grace! (how sweet the sound) That saved a wretch like me! I once was lost, but now am found, Was blind, but now I see.

2 'Twas grace that taught my heart to fear, And grace my fears relieved: How precious did that grace ap-pear, The hour I first believed!

8 Through many dangers, toils, and snares, | 4 The Lord has promised good to me, | 5 Yes, when this flesh and heart shall | 6 The earth shall soon dissolve like snow,
I have already come; | His word my hope secures; | And mortal life shall cease, [fail, | The sun forbear to shine;
'Tis grace has brought me safe thus far, | He will my shield and portion be, | I shall possess, within the veil, | But God, who call'd me here below,
And grace will lead me home. | As long as life endures. | A life of joy and peace. | Will be for ever mine.

SUPPLICATION. L. M.

Psalmist, 467th Hymn. 51st Psalm, Watts.

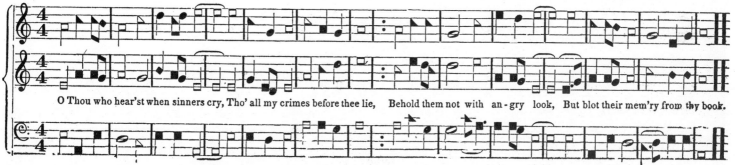

O Thou who hear'st when sinners cry, Tho' all my crimes before thee lie, Behold them not with an-gry look, But blot their mem'ry from thy book.

DUBLIN C. M.

Lord, what is man, poor feeble man? Born, of the earth at first; His life a shadow, light and vain, Still hast'ning to the dust.

HANOVER. C. M.

Baptist Harmony, p. 247.

Come, humble sinner, in whose breast
A thousand thoughts revolve,
Come, with your guilt and fear oppress'd,
:||:
And make this last resolve.

PRIMROSE.   C. M.   Hymn 88, B 2. Watts.   *Chapin.*   47

1 Salvation! Oh, the joy-ful sound! 'Tis pleasure to our ears; A sovereign balm for eve-ry wound A cordial for our fears.

2 Buried in sor-row and in sin, At hell's dark door we lay, But we a-rise by grace divine, To see a heav'nly day.

3 Sal-vation! let the echo fly The spacious earth a-round, While all the ar-mies of the sky Conspire to raise the sound.

IDUMEA.   S. M.   Meth. H. B. p. 231.   *Davison.*

And am I born to die? To lay this bo-dy down? And must my trem-bling spi-rit fly In-to a world un-known?

DEVOTION. L. M.

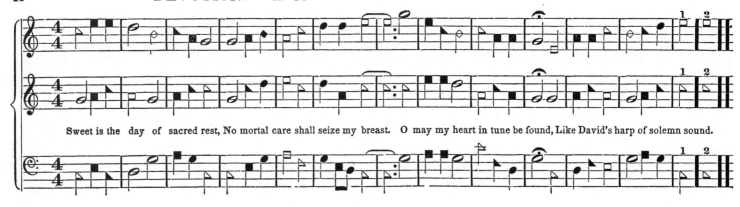

Sweet is the day of sacred rest, No mortal care shall seize my breast. O may my heart in tune be found, Like David's harp of solemn sound.

KEDRON. L. M.

Dare.

Thou Man of grief, remember me ; Thou never canst thyself forget Thy last ex - piring ag - o - ny—Thy fainting pangs and bloody sweat.

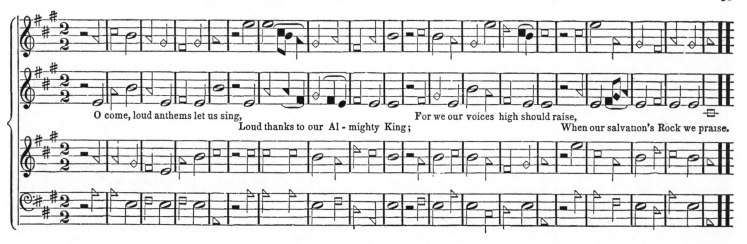

O come, loud anthems let us sing,
Loud thanks to our Al - mighty King;
For we our voices high should raise,
When our salvation's Rock we praise.

MEAR.   C. M.

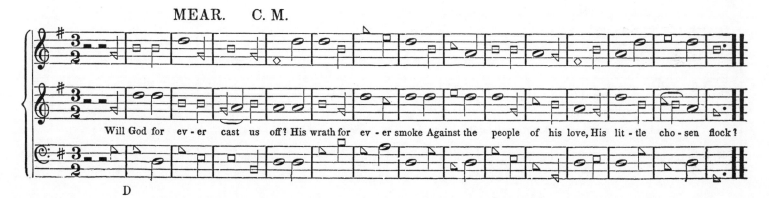

Will God for ev - er cast us off? His wrath for ev - er smoke Against the people of his love, His lit - tle cho - sen flock?

D

CONSOLATION. C. M.

Hymn 6, B. 2, Watts. *Dean.*

1 Once more, my soul, the ris-ing day Salutes thy wak-ing eyes; Once more, my voice, thy tri-bute pay To him that rules the skies.

2 Night un-to night his name re-peats, The day renews the sound, Wide as the heav'n on which he sits, To turn the sea-sons round

3 'Tis he supports my mortal frame,	4 On a poor worm thy pow'r might tread,	5 A thousand wretched souls are fled,	6 Dear God, let all my hours be thine,
My tongue shall speak his praise;	And I could ne'er withstand;	Since the last setting sun,	Whilst I enjoy the light,
My sins would rouse his wrath to flame,	Thy justice might have crush'd me dead,	And yet thou length'nest out my thread,	Then shall my sun in smiles decline
And yet his wrath delays.	But mercy held thine hand.	And yet my moments run.	And bring a pleasant night.

DISTRESS. L. M.

Psalmist, 1088th Hymn.

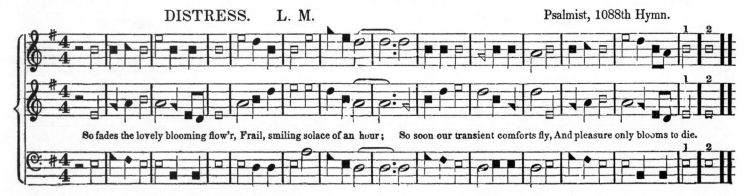

So fades the lovely blooming flow'r, Frail, smiling solace of an hour; So soon our transient comforts fly, And pleasure only blooms to die.

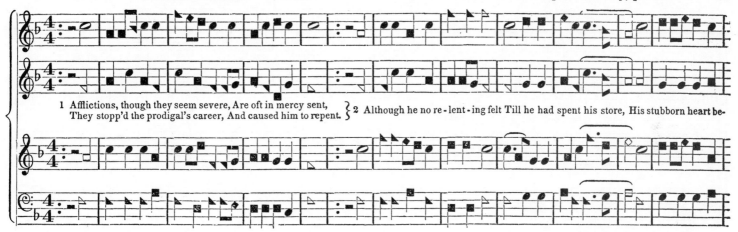

1 Afflictions, though they seem severe, Are oft in mercy sent,
They stopp'd the prodigal's career, And caused him to repent. } 2 Although he no re-lent-ing felt Till he had spent his store, His stubborn heart be-

gan to melt When famine pinch'd him sore.

3 What have I gain'd by sin, he said,
   But hunger, shame, and fear?
My father's house abounds with bread,
   Whilst I am starving here.

4 I'll go and tell him all I've done,
   Fall down before his face,
Not worthy to be call'd his son,
   I'll ask a servant's place.

5 He saw his son returning back,
   He look'd, he ran, he smiled,
And threw his arms around the neck
   Of his rebellious child.

6 Father, I've sinn'd, but O forgive!
   And thus the father said:
Rejoice, my house! my son's alive,
   For whom I mourn'd as dead.

7 Now let the fatted calf be slain,
   Go spread the news around,
My son was dead, but lives again,
   Was lost, but now is found.

8 'Tis thus the Lord himself reveals,
   To call poor sinners home;
More than the father's love he feels,
   And bids the sinner come.

ALBION. S. M.

Psalmist, 767th Hymn. *Boyd.*

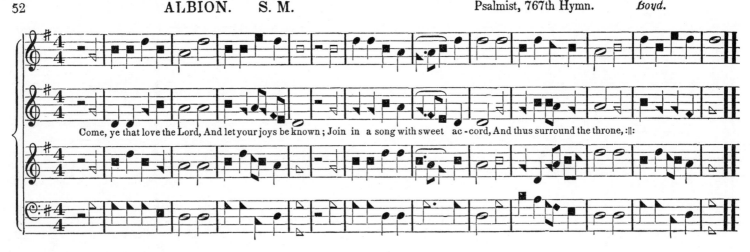

Come, ye that love the Lord, And let your joys be known; Join in a song with sweet ac-cord, And thus surround the throne, :‖:

CHARLESTOWN. 8, 7.

Mercy, O thou Son of Da-vid, Thus poor blind Bar-timeus pray'd; O-thers by thy grace are sav-ed, Now to me af-ford thine aid.

1 Je - sus, my all, to heav'n is gone, He whom I fix my hopes up - on;
His track I   see, and I'll pur - sue The narrow way till him I   view.

2 The way the ho - ly   prophets went; The road that leads from banishment;
The King's highway of ho - li - ness, I'll go, for all   his paths are peace.

I'm   on my journey home, to the new Jeru-

I'm on my journey home, to the new Je - ru - salem.

sa - lem. :||:   So   fare you well, :||:   :||:   I am   go - ing home.

3 This is the way I long have sought,
And mourn'd because I found it not;
My grief a burden long has been,
Because I was not saved from sin.

4 The more I strove against its power,
I felt its weight and guilt the more,
Till late I heard my Saviour say,
" Come hither, soul, I AM THE WAY."

5 Lo! glad I come, and thou, blest Lamb,
Shalt take me to thee, whose I am;
Nothing but sin have I to give,
Nothing but love shall I receive.

6 Then will I tell to sinners round,
What a dear Saviour I have found;
I'll point to thy redeeming blood,
And say, "Behold the way to God!"

GEORGIA. C. M.

Re-turn, O God of love, re - turn, Earth is a tire - some place ; How long shall we, thy children, mourn Our absence from thy face ?

IMANDRA NEW. 11s.

Dover Selection, p. 196.

Farewell, my dear brethren, the time is at hand,   Our several engagements now call us away,
When we must be parted from this social band :   Our parting is needful, and we must obey.

PARIS. L. M.

This spacious earth is all the Lord's, And men, and worms, and beasts, and birds; He rais'd the buildings on the seas, And gave it for their dwelling-place.

VERNON. L. M.

Come, O thou travel - ler unknown, Whom still I hold, but cannot see;
My company be - fore is gone, And I am left alone with thee: } With thee, all night, I mean to stay, And wrestle till the break of day.

1 How sweet the name of Jesus sounds In a be-liever's ear; It soothes his sorrows, heals his wounds, And drives away his fear.

2 It makes the wounded spi - rit whole, And calms the troubled breast; 'Tis manna to the hungry soul, And to the weary rest.

And drives a-way his fear. :|: It soothes his sorrows, heals his wounds, And drives a-way his fear.

And to the wea - ry rest. :|: 'Tis man-na to the hungry soul, And to the wea-ry rest.

3 Dear name! the rock on which I build, 4 Jesus! my shepherd, husband, friend, 5 Weak is the effort of my heart, 6 Till then I would thy love proclaim
My shield and hiding-place; My prophet, priest, and king; And cold my warmest thought; With every fleeting breath;
My never-failing treasury, fill'd My Lord, my life, my way, my end, But when I see thee as thou art, And may the music of thy name
With boundless stores of grace. Accept the praise I bring. I'll praise thee as I ought. Refresh my soul in death.

1 Am I a sol - dier of the cross, A follower of the Lamb?
And shall I fear to own his cause, Or blush to speak his name?

2 Must I be car - ried to the skies On flow'ry beds of ease, While

others fought to win the prize, And sail'd through bloody seas?

3 Are there no foes for me to face?
    Must I not stem the flood?
Is this vile world a friend to grace,
    To help me on to God?

4 Sure I must fight, if I would reign:—
    Increase my courage, Lord;
I'll bear the toil, endure the pain,
    Supported by thy word.

5 Thy saints, in all this glorious war,
    Shall conquer, though they die;
They see the triumph from afar,
    And seize it with their eye.

6 When that illustrious day shall rise,
    And all thine armies shine
In robes of victory through the skies,
    The glory shall be thine.

PISGAH. C. M

Baptist Harmony, p. 250.

Low, g.

Second Treble.

Je - sus, thou art the sinner's friend, As such I look to thee; Now in the bowels of thy love, O Lord, remember me!

Soft.

O Lord, remem-ber me! O Lord, remem - ber me! Now in the bowels of thy love, O Lord, re - mem - ber me.

1 Brethren, we have met to worship, And a - dore the Lord our God; All is vain. unless the Spirit Of the Holy One come down;
Will you pray with all your power, While we try to preach the word?

Brethren, pray, and

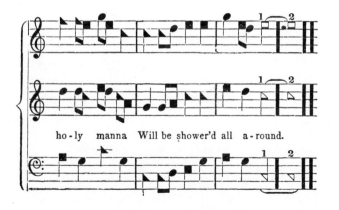

ho - ly manna Will be shower'd all a - round.

2 Brethren, see poor sinners round you,
Trembling on the brink of wo;
Death is coming, hell is moving,—
Can you bear to let them go?
See our fathers, see our mothers,
And our children sinking down;
Brethren, pray, and holy manna
Will be shower'd all around.

3 Sisters, will you join and help us?
Moses' sisters aided him;
Will you help the trembling mourners,
Who are struggling hard with sin?
Tell them all about the Saviour,
Tell them that he will be found;
Sisters, pray, and holy manna
Will be shower'd all around.

4 Is there here a trembling jailer,
Seeking grace, and fill'd with fears?
Is there here a weeping Mary,
Pouring forth a flood of tears?
Brethren, join your cries to help them;
Sisters, let your prayers abound;
Pray, O pray that holy manna
May be scatter'd all around.

5 Let us love our God supremely,
Let us love each other too;
Let us love and pray for sinners,
Till our God makes all things new:
Then he'll call us home to heaven,
At his table we'll sit down;
Christ will gird himself, and serve us
With sweet manna all around.

PORTUGAL. L. M.

Thorley.

1 How pleasant, How di - vine - ly fair, O Lord of hosts, thy dwell-ings are! With long de - sire my spi - rit faints,

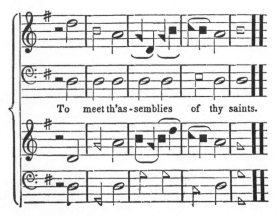

To meet th'as - semblies of thy saints.

2 My flesh would rest in thine abode,
My panting heart cries out for God;
My God! my King! why should I be
So far from all my joys and thee!

3 Blest are the souls that find a place
Within the temple of thy grace;
There they behold thy gentler rays,
And seek thy face, and learn thy praise.

4 Blest are the men whose hearts are set
To find the way to Zion's gate;
God is their strength; and through the road
They lean upon their helper, God.

5 Cheerful they walk with growing strength,
Till all shall meet in heav'n at length,
Till all before thy face appear,
And join in nobler worship there.

Sweet ri - vers of re - deem-ing love, Lie just be - fore mine eye, ⎬ I'd rise su - pe - ri - or to my pain,
Had I the pi - nions of a dove, I'd to those ri - vers fly; ⎬

With joy out - strip the wind, I'd cross o'er Jor-dan's storm - y waves, And leave the world be - hind.

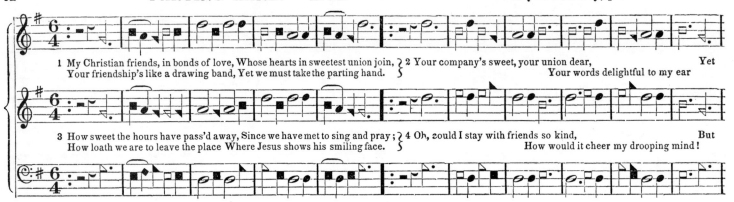

1 My Christian friends, in bonds of love, Whose hearts in sweetest union join, 2 Your company's sweet, your union dear,
Your friendship's like a drawing band, Yet we must take the parting hand.   Your words delightful to my ear   Yet

3 How sweet the hours have pass'd away, Since we have met to sing and pray; 4 Oh, could I stay with friends so kind,
How loath we are to leave the place Where Jesus shows his smiling face.   How would it cheer my drooping mind!   But

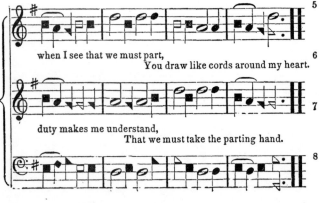

when I see that we must part,
      You draw like cords around my heart.

duty makes me understand,
      That we must take the parting hand.

5 And since it is God's holy will,
   We must be parted for a while,
   In sweet submission, all as one,
   We'll say, our Father's will be done.

6 My youthful friends, in Christian ties,
   Who seek for mansions in the skies,
   Fight on, we'll gain that happy shore,
   Where parting will be known no more.

7 How oft I've seen your flowing tears,
   And heard you tell your hopes and fears !
   Your hearts with love were seen to flame,
   Which makes me hope we'll meet again.

8 Ye mourning souls, lift up your eyes
   To glorious mansions in the skies;
   O trust his grace—in Canaan's land
   We'll no more take the parting hand

9 And now, my friends, both old and young,
   I hope in Christ you'll still go on ;
   And if on earth we meet no more,
   O may we meet on Canaan's shore.

10 I hope you'll all remember me,
   If you on earth no more I see;
   An interest in your prayers I crave,
   That we may meet beyond the grave

11 O glorious day ! O blessed hope !
   My soul leaps forward at the thought,
   When, on that happy, happy land,
   We'll no more take the parting hand.

12 But with our blessed, holy Lord,
   We'll shout and sing with one accord ;
   And there we'll all with Jesus dwell,
   So, loving Christians, fare you well!

All hail the power of Je - sus' name, Let an - gels prostrate fall; Bring forth the roy - al di - a - dem, And

crown him Lord of all. Bring forth the roy - al di - a - dem, And crown him Lord of all.

NASHVILLE. 8, 8, 6. *Johnson.*

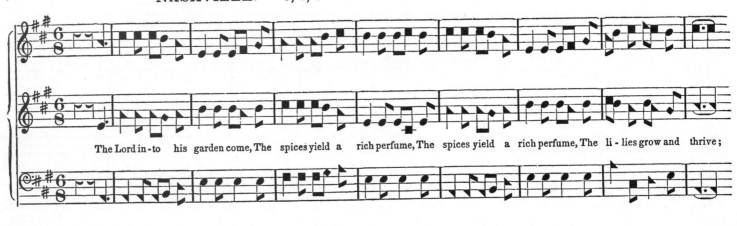

The Lord in-to his garden come, The spices yield a rich perfume, The spices yield a rich perfume, The li - lies grow and thrive;

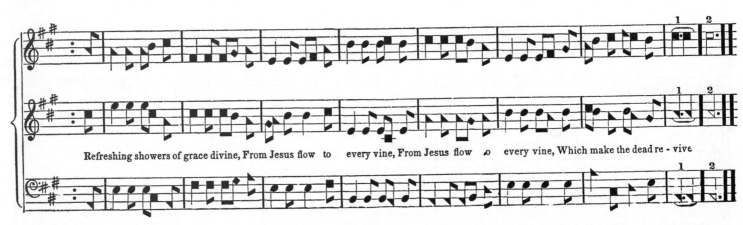

Refreshing showers of grace divine, From Jesus flow to every vine, From Jesus flow to every vine, Which make the dead re - vive

On   Jor - dan's stormy banks I stand, And cast   a   wish - ful eye,
To   Ca - naan's fair and hap - py land, Where my pos - ses - sions lie.

Oh   the trans - port - ing, rapturous scene, That

ri - ses   to   my   sight, Sweet fields ar - ray'd in   liv - ing green, And   ri - vers of   de - light.

KINGWOOD. 8, 8, 6.

Humphreys.

My days, my weeks, my months, my years, Fly rapid as the whirling spheres, :||: Around the stea-dy pole; Time, like the tide, its motion

keeps, And I must launch thro' endless deeps, :||: Where endless a - ges roll.

2 The grave is near the cradle seen,
  How swift the moments pass between!
    And whisper, as they fly,
  Unthinking man, remember this,
  Though fond of sublunary bliss,
    That you must groan and die.

3 My soul, attend the solemn call,
  Thine earthly tent must shortly fall,
    And thou must take thy flight
  Beyond the vast expansive blue,
  To sing above, as angels do,
    Or sink in endless night.

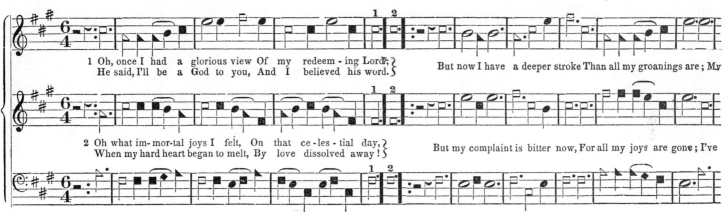

1 Oh, once I had a glorious view Of my redeem-ing Lord; }
He said, I'll be a God to you, And I believed his word. }
But now I have a deeper stroke Than all my groanings are; My

2 Oh what im-mor-tal joys I felt, On that ce-les-tial day, }
When my hard heart began to melt, By love dissolved away! }
But my complaint is bitter now, For all my joys are gone; I've

God has me of late for-sook,—He's gone, I know not where.

stray'd!—I'm left!—I know not how: The light's from me withdrawn.

3 Once I could joy the saints to meet,
   To me they were most dear;
I then could stoop to wash their feet,
   And shed a joyful tear:
But now I meet them as the rest,
   And with them joyless stay;
My conversation's spiritless,
   Or else I've naught to say.

4 I once could mourn o'er dying men,
   And long'd their souls to win;
I travail'd for their poor children,
   And warn'd them of their sin:
But now my heart's so careless grown,
   Although they're drown'd in vice,
My bowels o'er them cease to yearn—
   My tears have left mine eyes.

5 I forward go in duty's way,
   But can't perceive him there;
Then backwards on the road I stray,
   But cannot find him there:
On the left hand, where he doth work,
   Among the wicked crew,
And on the right, I find him not,
   Among the favour'd few.

6 What shall I do!—shall I lie down,
   And sink in deep despair?
Will he for ever wear a frown,
   Nor hear my feeble pray'r?
No: he will put his strength in me,
   He knows the way I've stroll'd;
And when I'm tried sufficiently,
   I shall come forth as gold.

SALEM.　L. M.

Meth. H. B. p. 455, and Psalmist, 232d Hymn.

He dies, the Friend of sinners dies! Lo, Salem's daughters weep around; A solemn darkness veils the skies, A sudden trembling shakes the ground.

MIDDLEBURY.　6, 6, 9.

Meth. Hymn Book, p. 357.

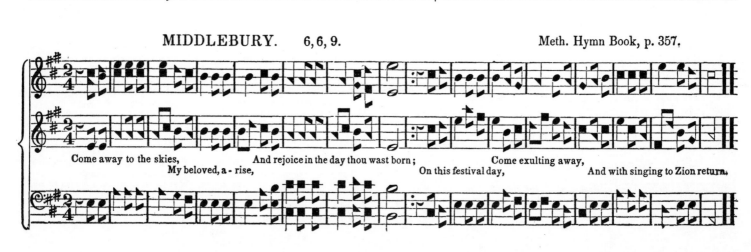

Come away to the skies, 　　　And rejoice in the day thou wast born; 　　　Come exulting away,
　　My beloved, a - rise, 　　　　　On this festival day, 　　　　And with singing to Zion return.

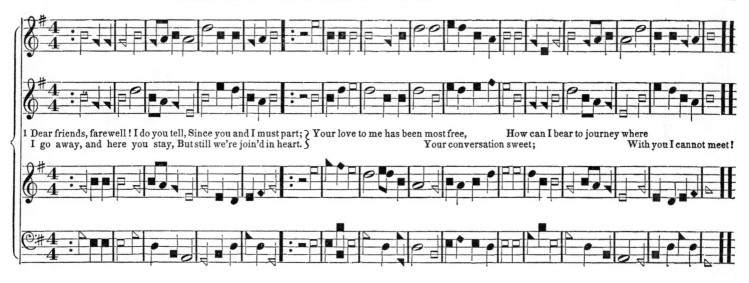

1 Dear friends, farewell ! I do you tell, Since you and I must part; } Your love to me has been most free,   How can I bear to journey where
  I go away, and here you stay, But still we're join'd in heart. }   Your conversation sweet;   With you I cannot meet !

2 Yet do I find my heart inclined
    To do my work below:
  When Christ doth call, I trust I shall
    Be ready then to go.
  I leave you all, both great and small,
    In Christ's encircling arms,
  Who can you save from the cold grave,
    And shield you from all harms.

3 I trust you'll pray, both night and day,
    And keep your garments white,
  For you and me, that we may be
    The children of the light.
  If you die first, anon you must,
    The will of God be done ;
  I hope the Lord will you reward,
    With an immortal crown.

4 If I'm call'd home whilst I am gone,
    Indulge no tears for me ;
  I hope to sing and praise my King,
    To all eternity.
  Millions of years over the spheres
    Shall pass in sweet repose,
  While beauty bright unto my sight
    Thy sacred sweets disclose.

5 I long to go,—then farewell, wo,
    My soul will be at rest ;
  No more shall I complain or sigh,
    But taste the heavenly feast.
  O may we meet, and be complete,
    And long together dwell,
  And serve the Lord with one accord;
    And so, dear friends, farewell !

RHODE ISLAND   8, 8, 3.

Thou great, mys - te - rious God unknown, Whose love hath gen - tly led me on,   E'en from my in - fant days;

My inmost soul ex - pose to view, And tell me if I   ev - er knew Thy jus - ti - fy - ing grace.

My soul forsakes her vain delight, And bids the world farewell, Base as the dirt beneath thy feet, And mischievous as hell. No longer will I

ask your love, Nor seek your friend-ship more; The hap-pi-ness that I ap-prove Is not with-in your pow'r.

THE WEARY SOULS. C. M.

Zion Songster, p. 117.   J. T. White.

Ye weary, heavy-laden souls, Who are oppress'd and sore, } Tho' chilling winds and beating rains,   And enemies surrounding us,
Ye travellers thro'the wilderness To Canaan's peaceful shore }   And waters deep and cold,   Take courage and be bold.

BELLEVUE. 11s.

Mercer's Cluster, p. 411.   Z. Chambless.

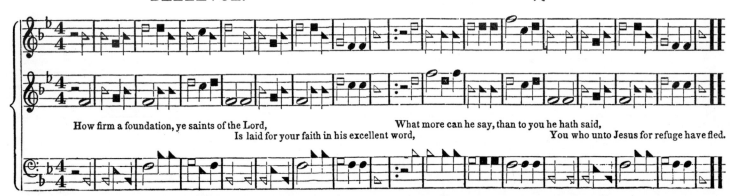

How firm a foundation, ye saints of the Lord,   What more can he say, than to you he hath said,
    Is laid for your faith in his excellent word,   You who unto Jesus for refuge have fled.

CUSSETA.　L. M.

Psalmist, 484th Hymn.　*Jno. Massengale.*

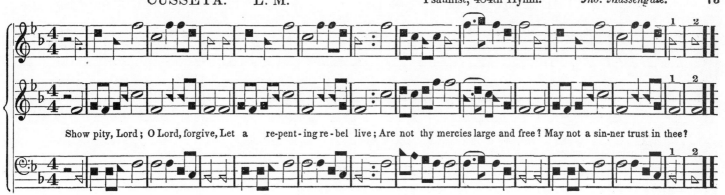

Show pity, Lord; O Lord, forgive, Let a　re-pent-ing re-bel live; Are not thy mercies large and free? May not a sin-ner trust in thee?

ARLINGTON.　C. M.

Jesus, with all　thy　saints above My tongue would bear her part; Would sound a-loud　thy　saving　love, And sing thy bleed-ing heart.

THE INQUIRER. C. M.

Psalmist, 552d Hymn.   *B. F. White.*

I'm not ashamed to own my Lord, Or to defend his cause,   Jesus, my God, I know his name;   Nor will he put my soul to shame, Nor
Maintain the honour of his word, The glory of his cross.   His name is all my trust;

KING OF PEACE.   7s.

Baptist Harmony, p. 329.   *F. Price.*

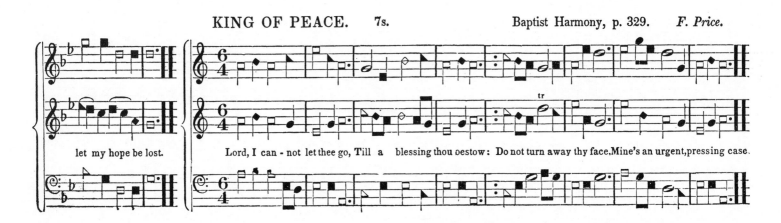

let my hope be lost.   Lord, I can-not let thee go, Till a   blessing thou bestow: Do not turn away thy face, Mine's an urgent, pressing case.

PARADISE. C. M

1 There is a land of pure de - light, Where saints im - mor - tal reign; In - fi - nite day ex - cludes the night,

And plea - sures ban - ish pain, And plea - sures ban - ish pain.

2 There everlasting spring abides,
  And never-withering flowers;
Death, like a narrow sea, divides
  This heavenly land from ours.

3 Sweet fields beyond the swelling flood
  Stand dress'd in living green;
So to the Jews old Canaan stood,
  While Jordan roll'd between.

4 But timorous mortals start and shrink,
  To cross this narrow sea;
And linger, shivering, on the brink,
  And fear to launch away.

5 Oh! could we make our doubts remove,
  Those gloomy doubts that rise,
And see the Canaan that we love
  With unbeclouded eyes!

6 Could we but climb where Moses stood,
  And view the landscape o'er,
Not Jordan's stream nor death's cold flood
  Should fright us from the shore

HOLINESS. 6 Lines, 7s.

Zion Songster, p. 7. *E. J. King.*

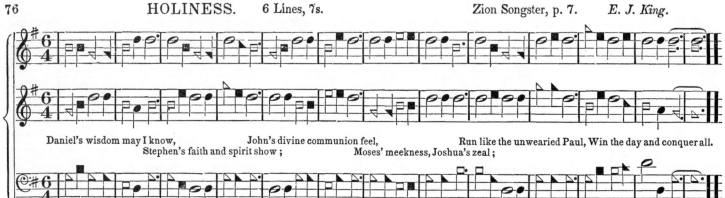

Daniel's wisdom may I know, John's divine communion feel, Run like the unwearied Paul, Win the day and conquer all.
Stephen's faith and spirit show ; Moses' meekness, Joshua's zeal ;

DESIRE FOR PIETY.

Baptist Harmony, p. 479. *B. F. White.*

CHORUS.

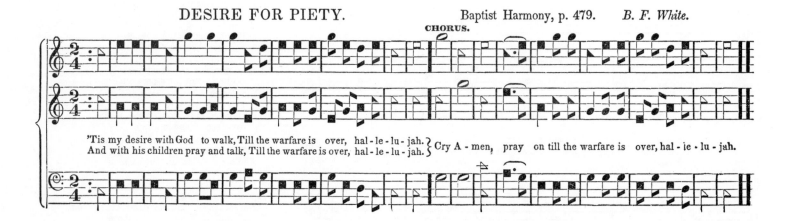

'Tis my desire with God to walk, Till the warfare is over, hal-le-lu-jah. ⎰ Cry A-men, pray on till the warfare is over, hal-le-lu-jah.
And with his children pray and talk, Till the warfare is over, hal-le-lu-jah. ⎱

THE CHILD OF GRACE. C. M. D

Mercer's Cluster, p. 246.   E. J. King.   77

How happy's every child of grace, Who feels his sins forgiven; } A country far from mortal sight,   The land of rest, the saints' delight,
This world, he cries, is not my place, I seek a place in heaven. }   Yet, oh! by faith I see   A heaven prepared for me.

TALBOTTON. 7s.

Baptist Harmony, p. 141.   E. J. King.

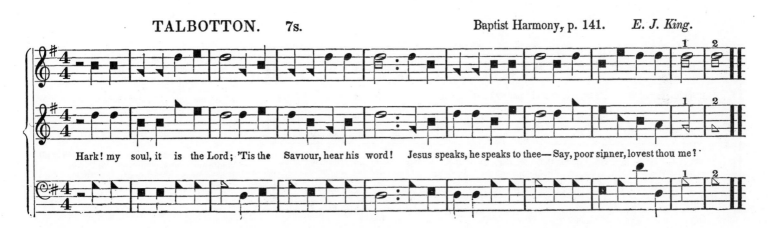

Hark! my soul, it is the Lord; 'Tis the   Saviour, hear his word!   Jesus speaks, he speaks to thee—Say, poor sinner, lovest thou me?

THE HEBREW CHILDREN.

B. F. White.

1 Where are the Hebrew children? :‖: :‖: Safe in the promised land. Tho' the furnace flamed around them,
God, while in their

2 Where are the twelve apostles? :‖: :‖: Safe in the promised land. They went up through pain and sighing,
Scoffing, scourging,

troubles, found them, He with love and mer-cy bound them, Safe in the pro-mised land.

cruci - fy - ing, No - bly for their Master dy - ing, Safe in the pro-mised land.

3 Where are the holy martyrs? :‖: :‖:
Safe in the promised land.
They went up through flaming fire,
Trusting in their great Messiah,
Who by grace will raise them higher,
Safe in the promised land.

4 Where are the holy Christians? :‖: :‖.
Safe in the promised land.
Those who've wash'd their robes, and made them
White and spotless pure, and laid them
Where no earthly stain can fade them,
Safe in the promised land.

THE OLD SHIP OF ZION.

CHORUS.

What ship is this that will take us all home, Oh! glo-ry, hal-le-lu-jah!
And safe-ly land us on Canaan's bright shore? Oh! glo-ry, hal-ie-lu-jah!
Oh! the old ship of Zi-on, hal-le-lu', hal-le-

lu', Oh! the old ship of Zion, hallelujah!

2 The winds may blow and the billows may foam,
   Oh! &c.
   But she is able to land us all home. Oh, &c.
   Oh! the old ship, &c.

3 She landed all who are gone before, Oh! &c.
   And yet she's able to land still more. Oh! &c.
   Oh! the old ship, &c.

4 No wrecks on sand-bars or dangers attend,
   Oh! &c.
   For Jesus is our Captain and Friend. Oh! &c.
   Oh! the old ship, &c.

5 She's waiting now for a heavenward gale, Oh! &c.
   Methinks I see her now hoisting her sail. Oh! &c.
   Oh! the old ship, &c

6 Her sails are spread, see how swiftly she moves,
   Oh! &c.
   Her landing harbour is Heaven above. Oh! &c.
   Oh! the old ship, &c.

7 What will the glad Christians do when above, Oh! &c.
   They'll shout, they'll sing, they'll be wrapt up in love.
   Oh! &c.
   Oh! the old ship, &c.

8 Should you arrive there then before I do, Oh! &c.
   Inform them that I am coming there too. Oh! &c.
   Oh! the old ship, &c.

9 If I arrive there then before you do, Oh! &c.
   I'll tell them that you are coming up too. Oh! &c.
   Oh! the old ship, &c.

SHOUTING SONG. 7 & 8.

B. F. White

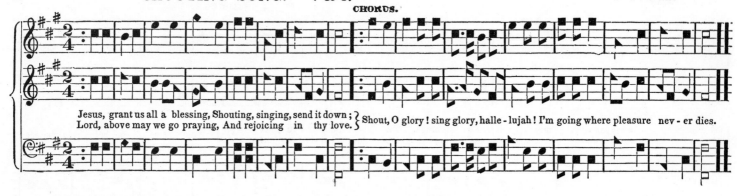

Jesus, grant us all a blessing, Shouting, singing, send it down; Shout, O glory! sing glory, halle - lujah! I'm going where pleasure nev - er dies.
Lord, above may we go praying, And rejoicing in thy love.

SERVICE OF THE LORD

E. J. King.

1 Farewell, vain world, I'm going home; I am bound to die in the army. I am bound to live in the service of my Lord, I am bound to die in the ar - my.
My Saviour smiles and bids me come; I am bound to die in the army.

2 Sweet angels beckon me away; I am bound to die in the ar - my. I am bound to live in the service of my Lord, I am bound to die in the ar - my.
To sing God's praise in endless day; I am bound to die in the army.

BEACH SPRING. 8, 5, 7.

J. F. White.

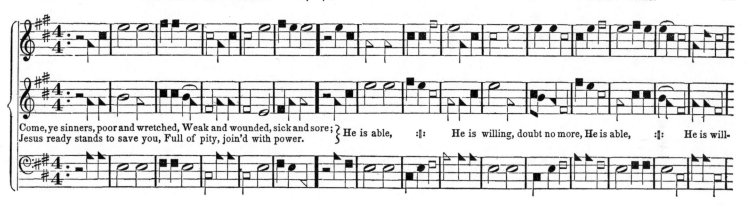

Come, ye sinners, poor and wretched, Weak and wounded, sick and sore; } He is able, :||: He is willing, doubt no more, He is able, :||: He is will-
Jesus ready stands to save you, Full of pity, join'd with power.

COOKHAM. 7s.

Psalmist, 207th Hymn.

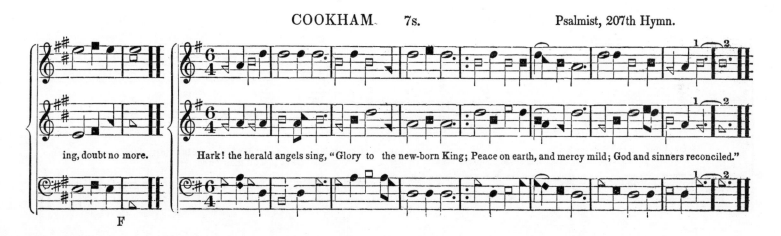

ing, doubt no more.

Hark! the herald angels sing, "Glory to the new-born King; Peace on earth, and mercy mild; God and sinners reconciled."

F

BOUND FOR CANAAN.

Mercer's Cluster, p. 356.

E. J. King.

CHORUS.

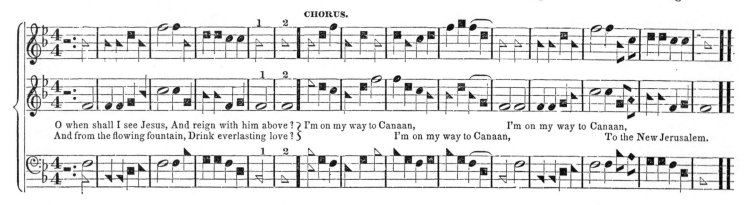

O when shall I see Jesus, And reign with him above? }
And from the flowing fountain, Drink everlasting love? }
I'm on my way to Canaan,
I'm on my way to Canaan,
I'm on my way to Canaan,
To the New Jerusalem.

EDGEFIELD.   8s.

J. T. White.

How tedious and tasteless the hours
When Jesus no longer I see !
Sweet prospects, sweet birds, and sweet flowers,
Have lost all their sweetness to me,
Have lost all their sweetness to me.

VALE OF SORROW. P. M.

Baptist Harmony, p. 448. *B. F. White.*

While in this vale of sorrow, I travel on in pain;
My heart is fix'd on Jesus, I hope the prize to gain; } But when I come to bid adieu To those I dearly love, My heart is often melted—It is the grief of love.

HARRIS. C. M.

Zion Songster, p. 140. *J. T. White.*

In e - vil long I took de-light, Un-awed by shame or fear Till a new ob - ject struck my sight, And stopp'd my wild career.

MOUNTVILLE. 7, 6.

1 Throughout our wide-spread union, / What cheering scenes arise— / The temp'rance flag is waving / Where'er we turn our eyes. / Bright in the south 'tis floating, / The north has raised it high, / The east and west unfurl it, :‖: :‖: / In glo-ry to the skies.

2 Ten thousand times ten thousand
Around her banner stand,
Resolved to drive intemp'rance
From our beloved land.
From every rolling river,
From city, town, and plain—
The cry is heard, Deliver :‖: :‖.
From rum's destructive reign.

3 What, though the gifts of Heaven
On every hand abound,
And God's abundant blessing
Our dear-loved nation crown—
In vain, with lavish'd kindness,
Do all these blessings come,
While drunkards, in their blindness, :‖: :‖:
Bow down. the slaves of rum.

4 Shall we, whose souls are lighted
With ardour from on high,—
Shall we, to men benighted,
The helping hand deny ;
No, no ! our tongues, unceasing,
Deliverance shall proclaim,
Till not one erring mortal :‖: :‖:
Shall bear the drunkard's shame.

5 Waft, waft, ye winds, the story,
And you, ye waters, roll,
Till, like a sea of glory,
It spreads from pole to pole,—
Till the last wretched drunkard
His liberty shall gain,
And temp'rance, all-victorious, :‖: :‖.
Throughout the nation reign.

THE MORNING TRUMPET.

CHORUS.

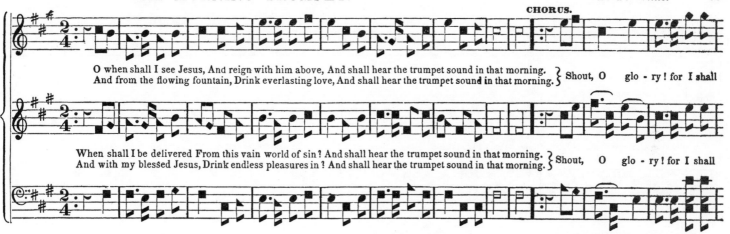

O when shall I see Jesus, And reign with him above, And shall hear the trumpet sound in that morning. } Shout, O glo - ry ! for I shall
And from the flowing fountain, Drink everlasting love, And shall hear the trumpet sound in that morning. }

When shall I be delivered From this vain world of sin ? And shall hear the trumpet sound in that morning. } Shout, O glo - ry ! for I shall
And with my blessed Jesus, Drink endless pleasures in ? And shall hear the trumpet sound in that morning. }

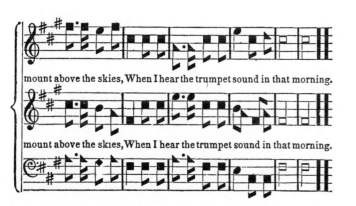

mount above the skies, When I hear the trumpet sound in that morning.

mount above the skies, When I hear the trumpet sound in that morning.

2 But now I am a soldier,
  My Captain's gone before;
He's given me my orders,
  And bids me ne'er give o'er;
His promises are faithful—
  A righteous crown he'll give,
And all his valiant soldiers
  Eternally shall live.
    Shout, &c.

3 Through grace I feel determined
  To conquer, though I die,
And then away to Jesus,
  On wings of love I'll fly:
Farewell to sin and sorrow,
  I bid them both adieu!
And O, my friends, prove faithful,
  And on your way pursue.
    Shout, &c

4 Whene'er you meet with troubles
  And trials on your way,
Then cast your care on Jesus,
  And don't forget to pray.
Gird on the gospel armour
  Of faith, and hope, and love,
And when the combat's ended,
  He'll carry you above.
    Shout, &c.

5 O do not be discouraged,
  For Jesus is your friend;
And if you lack for knowledge,
  He'll not refuse to lend.
Neither will he upbraid you.
  Though often you request.
He'll give you grace to conquer,
  And take you home to rest.
    Shout, &c.

Come, lit - tle children, now we may Par - take a lit - tle mor - sel,   For lit - tle songs and lit - tle ways Adorn'd   a great a - pos - tle.

A lit - tle drop of   Jesus' blood Can make a feast of   u - nion;   It is by lit - tle steps we move In - to   a full communion.

CHORUS.

Oh who will come and go with me! I am bound for the land of Ca - naan.} O! Ca - naan, sweet Canaan, I'm
I'm bound fair Canaan's land to see, I am bound for the land of Ca - naan.

I'll join with those who're gone be - fore, I am bound for the land of Ca - naan.} O! Ca - naan, sweet Ca -naan, I'm
Where sin and sor - row are no more, I am bound for the land of Ca - naan.

bound for the land of Ca - naan, Sweet Ca - naan, 'tis my hap - py home; I am bound for the land of Ca - naan.

88

DONE WITH THE WORLD. L. M.

B. F. White.

CHORUS.

Jesus, my all, to heaven is gone, And I don't expect to stay much longer here. } I am done with the world, and I want to serve the Lord,
He whom I fix my hopes upon, And I don't expect to stay much longer here. } And I don't expect to stay much longer here.

MOUNT ZION. C. M.

CHORUS.

Meth. Hymn Book, p. 7.   J. Massengale.

O for a thousand tongues to sing My great Redeemer's praise, } O Christians, praise him, :||.   Methinks I hear the gospel sounding
The glories of my God and King, The triumphs of his grace. }   For more volunteers.

J. T. White.

1 Well may thy servants mourn, my God, The church's desolation; The state of Zi - on calls aloud For grief and lamentation. Once she was all a-live to thee, And thousands were con-verted; But now a sad re-

verse we see, Her glo-ry is de-part-ed.

2 Her pastors love to live at ease,
   They covet wealth and honour;
And while they seek such things as these,
   They bring reproach upon her.
Such worthless objects they pursue
   Warmly and undiverted;
The church they lead and ruin too—
   Her glory is departed.

3 Her private members walk no more
   As Jesus Christ has taught them;
Riches and fashion they adore,
   With these the world has bought them.
The Christian name they still retain
   Absurdly and false-hearted;
And while they in the church remain,
   Her glory is departed.

4 And has religion left the church,
   Without a trace behind her?
Where shall I go, where shall I search,
   That I once more may find her?
Adieu, ye proud, ye light and gay,
   I'll seek the broken-hearted,
Who weep when they of Zion say,
   Her glory is departed.

5 Some few, like good Elijah, stand,
   While thousands have revolted,
In earnest for the heavenly land;
   They never yet have halted.
With such, religion doth remain,
   For they are not perverted;
O may they all through them regain
   The glory that's departed.

LOOK OUT. P. M.

B. F. White.

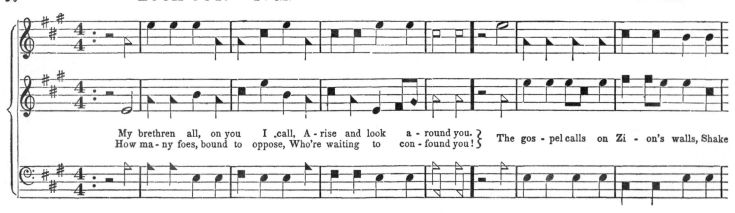

My brethren all, on you I .call, A - rise and look a - round you.
How ma - ny foes, bound to oppose, Who're waiting to con - found you! } The gos - pel calls on Zi - on's walls, Shake

off your sleep and slum - ber; A - rise and pray, we'll win the day, Tho' we are few in num - ber.

Dover Selection, p. 77.   *T. W. Carter.*   91

Head of the church triumphant,
We joyful - ly a - dore   thee:

Till thou appear, thy members here,
Shall sing like those in glo - ry.

We lift our hearts and voi-

ces, With blest anti - ci - pa - tion, And cry aloud, and give to God

The praise of our salva - tion,

And cry aloud, and give to God

The praise of our salva - tion.

BURK. 7, 6.

B. F. White

The glorious light of Zi - on Is spreading far and wide;
The glo-ry of King Je - sus Tri - umph-ant doth a - rise,
And sinners now are com-ing Un - to the gos - pel tide.
And sinners crowd a - round it With bit-ter groans and cries.

CHORUS.

To see the saints in glo-ry, And the angels stand in - vit - ing, And the angels stand in - vit - ing, To welcome sinners home.

Lord, shed a beam of heaven - ly day, To melt this stubborn stone a - way; And thaw, with rays of love divine, This

heart, this fro - zen heart of mine, This heart, this fro - zen heart of mine, This heart, this fro - zen heart of mine.

OAK BOWERY. L. M. 6 lines.

Meth. Hymn Book, p. 181.   *T. W. Carter.*

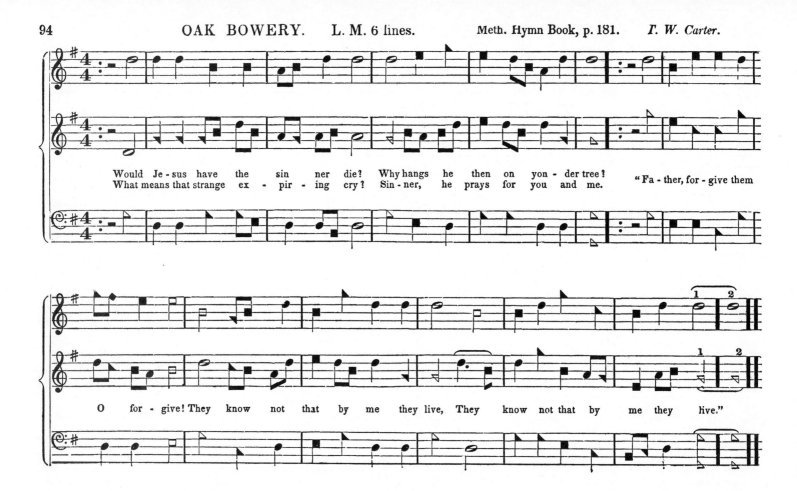

Would Je - sus have the sin - ner die? Why hangs he then on yon - der tree? "Fa - ther, for - give them

What means that strange ex - pir - ing cry? Sin - ner, he prays for you and me.

O for - give! They know not that by me they live, They know not that by me they live."

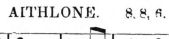

O thou, that hear'st the pray'r of faith, Wilt thou not save a soul from death, That casts it - self on thee?

I have no mer - it of my own, But fly to what my Lord hath done, And suf - fer'd once for me.

HAPPY MATCHES. 8, 8, 6, or C. P. M. Psalmist, 1143d Hymn. *B. F. White & King.*

1 When thou, my righteous Judge, shalt come
To take thy ransom'd people home,

Shall I a-mong them stand? Shall such a worthless worm as I,
Who sometimes am a -

fraid to die, Be found at thy right hand?

2 I love to meet thy people now,
Before thy feet with them to bow,
　Though vilest of them all;
But—can I bear the piercing thought?—
What if my name should be left out,
　When thou for them shalt call?

3 O Lord, prevent it by thy grace;
Be thou my only hiding-place,
　In this th' accepted day;

Thy pardoning voice, O, let me hear,
To still my unbelieving fear,
　Nor let me fall, I pray.

4 And when the final trump shall sound,
Among thy saints let me be found,
　To bow before thy face:
Then in triumphant strains I'll sing,
While heaven's resounding mansions ring
　With praise of sovereign grace.

1 We're travelling home to heaven above, Will you go? will you go?
To   sing our Saviour's   dy - ing love, Will you go? :||:   Our sun shall then no more go down, Our moon shall be no more withdrawn, Our

days of mourning past and gone, Will you go? :||:

2 We're going to reap the great reward,
    Will you go? :||:
Which Jesus Christ for us prepared,
    Will you go? :||:
A rich supply of milk and wine,
And everlasting joys divine,
And robes that will the sun outshine,
    Will you go? :||:

3 We are going to strike the golden lyre,
    Will you go? ·||:
And shout in strains of heavenly fire,
    Will you go? :||·

And sing our God's redeeming grace,
And see our Saviour face to face,
And evermore we'll shout his grace;
    Will you go? :||:

4 We're going to walk in plains of light,
    Will you go? :||:
Where endless day excludes the night,
    Will you go? :||:
There crowns of glory we shall wear,
And palms of victory ever bear,
And all the joys of heaven shall share;
    Will you go? :||:

G

1 Why should we at our lots complain, Or grieve at our dis - tress; Ah! we're much to blame,   We're all the same—
Some think if they could rich - es gain, They'd gain true happi - ness.

A - like we're made of clay: Then, since we have a Sa - viour dear, Let's drive all cares a - way.

2 Why should the rich despise the poor?
    Why should the poor repine?
A little time will make us all
    In equal friendship join.
        Ah! we're much to blame,—
        We're all the same,—
    Alike, we're made of clay:
Then, since we have a Saviour dear,
    Let's drive all cares away

3 The only circumstance of life
    That ever I could find
To soften cares and temper strife
    Was a contented mind:
        When we've this in store,
        We have much more
    Than wealth could e'er convey:
Then, since we have a Saviour dear,
    Let's drive all cares away

4 When age, old creeping age comes on,
    And we are young no more—
Let's all repent the sins we've done,
    Nor grieve that youth is o'er;
        More faithful be
        Than formerly,
    And constantly to pray:—
Then, since we have a Saviour dear
    Let's drive all cares away

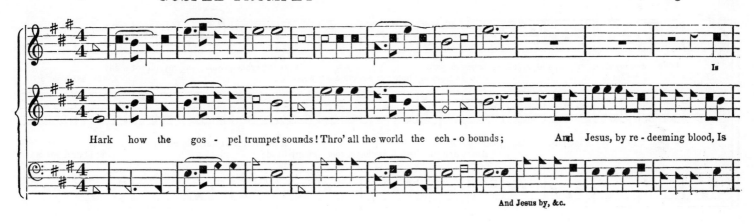

Hark how the gos - pel trumpet sounds! Thro' all the world the ech - o bounds; And Jesus, by re - deeming blood, Is

And Jesus by, &c.

bring - ing sin - ners home to God, And guides them safe - ly by his word, To end - less day.

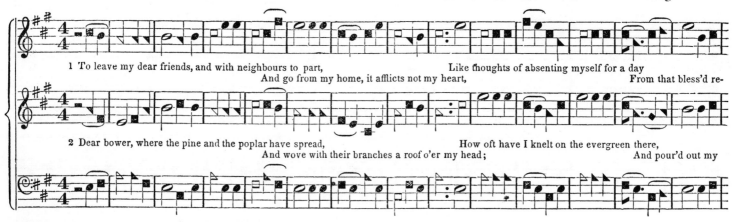

1 To leave my dear friends, and with neighbours to part,   Like thoughts of absenting myself for a day
And go from my home, it afflicts not my heart,   From that bless'd re-

2 Dear bower, where the pine and the poplar have spread,   How oft have I knelt on the evergreen there,
And wove with their branches a roof o'er my head;   And pour'd out my

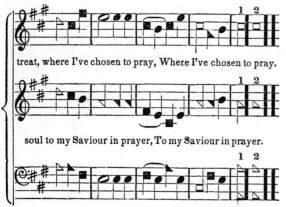

treat, where I've chosen to pray, Where I've chosen to pray.

soul to my Saviour in prayer, To my Saviour in prayer.

3 The early shrill notes of the loved nightingale,
That dwelt in my bower, I observed as my bell,
To call me to duty, while birds of the air
Sang anthems of praises, as I went to prayer, As I went to **prayer.**

4 How sweet were the zephyrs perfumed by the pine,
The ivy, the balsam, and wild eglantine;
But sweeter, ah! sweeter, superlative were
The joys I have tasted in answer to prayer, In answer to **prayer.**

5 For Jesus, my Saviour, oft deign'd there to meet,
And bless'd with his presence my humble retreat;
Oft fill'd me with rapture and blessedness there,
Indicting, in heaven's own language, my prayer, Own language **my prayer.**

6 Dear bower, I must leave you and bid you adieu,
And pay my devotion in parts that are new;
For Jesus, my Saviour, resides everywhere,
And can in all places give answer to prayer, Give answer to **prayer.**

CANAAN'S LAND.　C. M. D.

Zion Songster, p. 155.　　*E. J. King.*

Oh for a breeze of heavenly love, To waft my soul away } Eternal Spirit, deign to be My pilot here below, To steer through life's tempestuous sea,
To that celestial world above, Where pleasures ne'er decay! } Where stormy winds do blow.

HOLY CITY.　7, 6.

Zion Songster, p. 140.　　*B. F. White.*

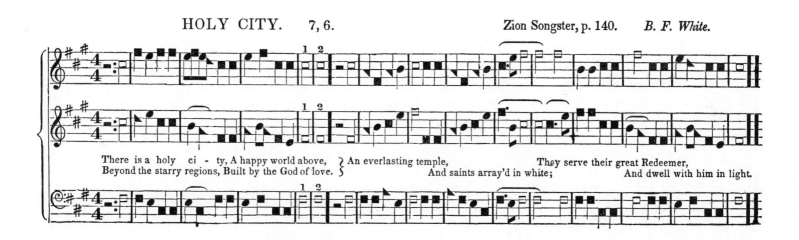

There is a holy ci - ty, A happy world above, } An everlasting temple, They serve their great Redeemer,
Beyond the starry regions, Built by the God of love. } And saints array'd in white; And dwell with him in light.

101

FULFILMENT. 9, 8. Zion Songster, p. 129. *E. J. King.*

See how the Scrip-tures are ful - fill - ing, Poor sin-ners are re - turn-ing home. }
The time that pro - phets were fore - tell-ing, With signs and won - ders now is come. }
The gos - pel trum - pets

now are blowing From sea to sea, from land to land ; God's Ho - ly Spi - rit down is pour - ing, And Christians join - ing heart and hand.

And let this fee-ble bo-dy fail, And let it faint or die; My soul shall quit this mournful vale, And soar to worlds on high.

And soar to worlds on high, And soar to worlds on high, My soul shall quit this mournful vale, And soar to worlds on high.

THE LOVELY STORY. 8s.

Mercer's Cluster, p. 56.   *E. J. King*

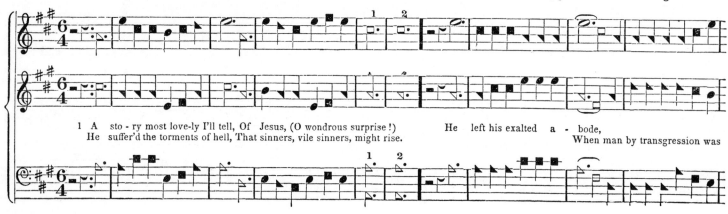

1 A sto - ry most love-ly I'll tell, Of Jesus, (O wondrous surprise!)
He suffer'd the torments of hell, That sinners, vile sinners, might rise.

He left his exalted a - bode,
When man by transgression was

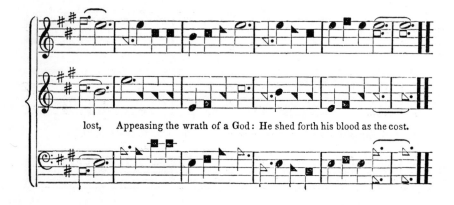

lost,   Appeasing the wrath of a God: He shed forth his blood as the cost.

2 Oh! did my dear Jesus thus bleed,
  And pity a ruin'd, lost race?
Oh, whence did such mercy proceed,
  Such boundless compassion and grace?
His body bore anguish and pain,
  His spirit most sunk with the load,
A short time before he was slain,
  His sweat was as great drops of blood.

3 Oh, was it for crimes I had done,
  The Saviour was hail'd with a kiss,
By Judas the traitor alone?
  Was ever compassion like this?
The ruffians all join'd in a band,
  Confined him, and led him away;
The cords wrapp'd around his sweet hands
  Oh, sinners, look at him, I pray

REDEMPTION. 6, 5.

Leonard P. Breedlove.

Come, friends and relations,
Let's join hearts and hands,—
The voice of the turtle
Is heard in our land;
Let's all walk together,
And follow the sound,
And march to the place
Where redemption is found.

TURN, SINNER, TURN.

CHORUS.

E. J. King.

To-day, if you will hear his voice, Now is the time to make your choice;
Say, will you to mount Zion go? Say, will you have this Christ, or no?
Oh! turn, sinner, turn,
May the Lord help you turn!
Oh! turn, sinner, turn,
Why will you die?

ECSTASY

T. W. Carter.

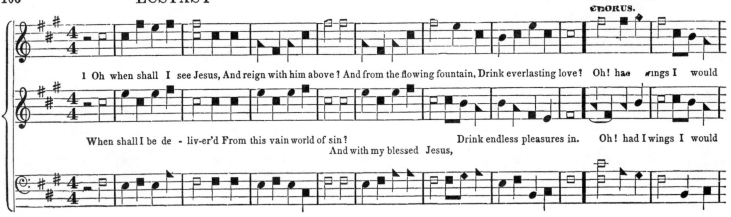

1 Oh when shall I see Jesus, And reign with him above? And from the flowing fountain, Drink everlasting love? Oh! had wings I would

When shall I be de - liv-er'd From this vain world of sin? Drink endless pleasures in. Oh! had I wings I would

And with my blessed Jesus,

fly a-way and be at rest, And I'd praise God in his bright abode.

2 But now I am a soldier,
    My Captain's gone before;
He's given me my orders,
    And bids me ne'er give o'er;
His promises are faithful—
    A righteous crown he'll give,
And all his valiant soldiers
    Eternally shall live.

3 Through grace I feel determined
    To conquer, though I die,
And then away to Jesus,
    On wings of love I'll fly:
Farewell to sin and sorrow
    I bid them both adieu!
And oh, my friends, prove faithful,
    And on your way pursue.

4 Whene'er you meet with troubles
    And trials on your way,
Then cast your care on Jesus,
    And don't forget to pray.
Gird on the gospel armour
    Of faith, and hope, and love,
And when the combat's ended,
    He'll carry you above.

5 Oh do not be discouraged,
    For Jesus is your friend;
And if you lack for knowledge,
    He'll not refuse to lend.
Neither will he upbraid you,
    Though often you request,
He'll give you grace to conquer
    And take you home to rest.

1 Here, in thy name, e - ter - nal God, We build this earthly house for thee;
Oh, choose it for thy fix'd abode, And guard it long from er - ror free!

2 Here, when thy people seek thy face,
And dying sinners pray to live;

Hear thou, in heaven, thy dwelling-place,
And when thou hearest, Lord, forgive.

3 Here, when thy messengers proclaim
The blessed gospel of thy Son,
Still by the power of his great name
Be mighty signs and wonders done.

4 When children's voices raise the song,
Hosanna! to their heavenly King,
Let heaven with earth the strain prolong
Hosanna! let the angels sing.

5 But will, indeed, Jehovah deign
Here to abide, no transient guest?
Here will our great Redeemer reign,
And here the Holy Spirit rest?

6 Thy glory never hence depart,
Yet choose not, Lord, this house alone;
Thy kingdom come to every heart;
In every bosom fix thy throne.

NIGHT WATCHMAN 7s.

Psalmist, 893d Hymn. *T. W. Carter.*

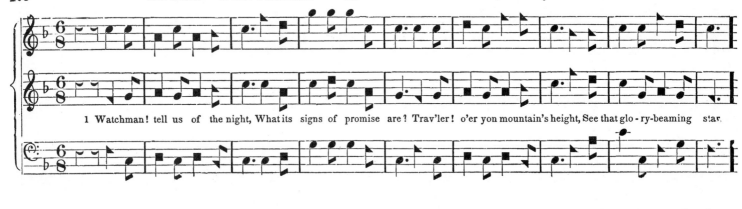

1 Watchman! tell us of the night, What its signs of promise are? Trav'ler! o'er yon mountain's height, See that glo-ry-beaming star.

2 Watchman! does its beauteous ray Aught of hope or joy fore-tell? Trav'ler! yes; it brings the day, Promised day of Is-ra-el.

3 Watchman! tell us of the night;
   Higher yet that star ascends.
Trav'ler! blessedness and light,
   Peace and truth, its course portends.

4 Watchman! will its beams alone
   Gild the spot that gave them birth?
Trav'ler! ages are its own;
   See! it bursts o'er all the earth.

5 Watchman! tell us of the night,
   For the morning seems to dawn.
Trav'ler! darkness takes its flight;
   Doubt and terror are withdrawn.

6 Watchman! let thy wanderings cease;
   Hie thee to thy quiet home.
Trav'ler! lo! the Prince of Peace,
   Lo! the Son of God is come!

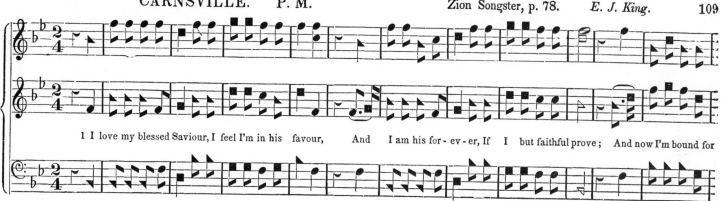

1 I love my blessed Saviour, I feel I'm in his favour, And I am his for - ev - er, If I but faithful prove; And now I'm bound for

Canaan, I feel my sins for - giv - en, And soon snall get to heaven, To sing redeeming love.

2 Poor sinners may deride me,
And unbelievers chide me,
But nothing shall divide me
   From Jesus, my best friend.
Supported by his power,
I long to see the hour
That bids my spirit tower,
   And all my troubles end.

3 The pleasing time is hast'ning,
My tott'ring frame is wasting,
Whilst I'm engaged in praising,
   Impelled by his love.
When yonder shining orders,
Who sing on Canaan's borders,
Shall bear me to the Lord there,
   To praise his name above.

MOUNT VERNON. L. M. D.

What sol-emn sound the ear invades,   From heaven the awful mandate flies, The Father of his coun - try dies.   Where
  What wraps the land in sorrow's shade ?

Where shall our country

What help, &c.   Our,   Our, &c.

shall our country turn its eye,   Our friend, protector, strength, and trust,
  What help remains beneath the   sky ?   Lies low and mould'ring in the dust.

turn its eye, What help remains be-neath the   sky ?   Our friend, protector, strength, and trust, Our. &c.

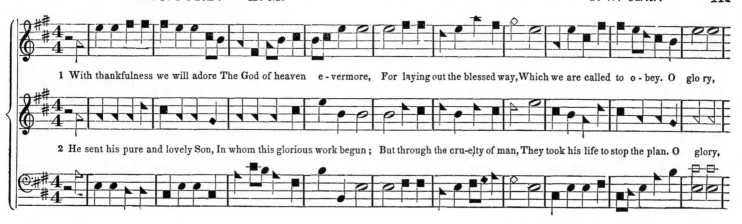

1 With thankfulness we will adore The God of heaven e-vermore, For laying out the blessed way, Which we are called to o-bey. O glory,

2 He sent his pure and lovely Son, In whom this glorious work begun; But through the cru-el-ty of man, They took his life to stop the plan. O glory,

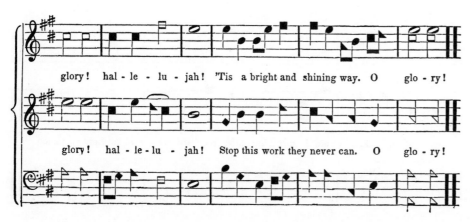

glory! hal-le-lu-jah! 'Tis a bright and shining way. O glo-ry!

glory! hal-le-lu-jah! Stop this work they never can. O glo-ry!

3 Thus God in mercy opes to me
The way of life and liberty;
He gives me strength to bear the cross,
And count all earthly things but dross.
  O glory, glory! hallelujah!
Peace and love come by the cross. O glory!

4 Then come, ye sinners, to the Lord,
Believe on him, believe his word,
Obey his call, all sin reject,
This love will all your souls protect.
  O glory, glory! hallelujah!
Love will all our souls protect. O glory!

5 Then heaven's joys we all shall feel;
Be fill'd with life, and love, and zeal,
And glory in each heart shall dwell,
Which mortal's tongue can never tell.
  O glory, glory! hallelujah!
Angel's tongue would fail to tell. O glory!

SANDTOWN. C. M.

Baptist Harmony, p. 223. *T. W. Carter.*

Urg'd by com-pas-sion, I look round U - pon my fel - low clay; See men re - ject the gospel sound, Good God, what shall I say ? My

bowels yearn o'er dy - ing men, Doom'd to e - ter - nal wo. Fain would I speak, but all is vain, Ex - cept the Lord speak too.

CHORUS.

1 Afflictions, though they seem severe,
Are oft in mercy sent;
They stopp'd the prodigal's career,
And caused him to repent.
Oh! I die with

hunger, here, he cries,
Oh! I die with hunger, here, he cries,
And starve in a foreign land:
My father's house hath large supplies,
And bounteous are his hands.

2 Although he no relenting felt
Till he had spent his store,
His stubborn heart began to melt,
When famine pinch'd him sore.

3 What have I gain'd by sin, he said
But hunger, shame, and fear?
My father's house abounds with bread,
Whilst I am starving here.

4 I'll go and tell him all I've done,
Fall down before his face;
Not worthy to be called his son,
I'll ask a servant's place.

5 He saw his son returning back,
He look'd, he ran, he smiled,
And threw his arms around the neck
Of his rebellious child.

H

SUFFIELD. C. M.

Psalmist, 1055th Hymn.

Teach me the measure of my days, Thou Maker of my frame, I would sur - vey life's narrow space, And learn how frail I am.

THE MIDNIGHT CRY, 7, 6, 7, 6, 7, 6, 7, 7.

Baptist Harmony, p. 483.

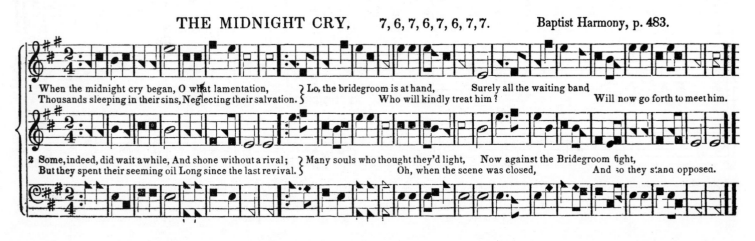

1 When the midnight cry began, O what lamentation,
Thousands sleeping in their sins, Neglecting their salvation.

Lo, the bridegroom is at hand,
Who will kindly treat him?

Surely all the waiting band
Will now go forth to meet him.

2 Some, indeed, did wait awhile, And shone without a rival;
But they spent their seeming oil Long since the last revival.

Many souls who thought they'd light,
Oh, when the scene was closed,

Now against the Bridegroom fight,
And so they stand opposed.

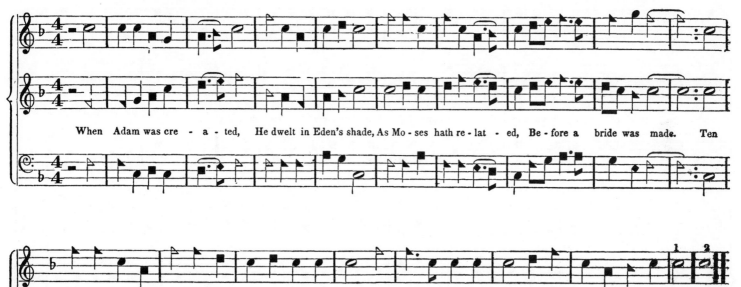

When Adam was cre - a - ted, He dwelt in Eden's shade, As Mo - ses hath re - lat - ed, Be - fore a bride was made. Ten

thousand times ten thou-sand Of creatures swarm'd a - round, Be - fore a bride was form - ed, Or a - ny mate was found.

1 Come, brothers and sis-ters who love one an-o-ther, And have done for years that are gone;
How oft-en we've met him in sweet, heavenly union, Which o-pens the way to God's throne.

With joy and thanksgiving we'll

praise him who loved us,   While we run the bright, shining way;

Though we part here in bo-dy, we're bound for one glory,

And bound for each other   to   pray.

2 There was Joshua and Joseph, Elias and Moses,
   That pray'd, and God heard from his throne;
There was Abraham, and Isaac, and Jacob, and David,
   And Solomon, and Stephen, and John;
There was Simeon, and Anna, and I don't know how many,
   That pray'd as they journey'd along;
Some cast among lions, some bound with rough irons,—
   Yet glory and praises they sung.

3 Some tell us that praying, and also that praising
   Is labour that's all spent in vain;
But we have such a witness that God hears with swiftness,
   From praying we will not refrain.
There was old father Noah, and ten thousand more,
   Who witness'd that God heard them pray;
There was Samuel, and Hannah, Paul, Silas, and Peter,
   And Daniel, and Jonah, we'll say.

4 That God, by his Spirit, or an angel doth visit
   Their souls and their bodies while praying;
Shall we all go fainting, while they all go praising,
   And glorify God in the flame?
God grant us to inherit the same pray'ng spirit,
   While we are a journeying below.
That when we cease praying, we shall not cease praising
   But round God's bright throne we shall bow

1 On Jor-dan's stormy banks I stand, And cast a wish-ful eye, On the o-ther side of Jor-dan, hal-le-lu-jah.
To Canaan's fair and hap-py land, Where my pos-ses-sions lie. On the o-ther side of Jor-dan, hal-le-lu-jah.

2 Oh the transport-ing, rapt'rous scene, That ri-ses to my sight! On the o-ther side of Jor-dan, hal-le-lu-jah.
Sweet fields, ar-ray'd in liv-ing green, And ri-vers of de-light. On the o-ther side of Jor-dan, hal-le-lu-jah.

CHORUS.

On the o-ther side of Jor-dan, hal-le-lu-jah, On the o-ther side of Jor-dan, hal-le-lu-jah.

3 O'er all those wide-extended plains	4 No chilling winds, nor pois'nous breath	5 When shall I reach that happy place,	6 Fill'd with delight my raptured soul
Shines one eternal day;	Can reach that healthful shore;	And be forever blest!	Would here no longer stay;
There God the Son for ever reigns	Sickness and sorrow, pain and death,	When shall I see my Father's face,	Though Jordan's waves should round me
And scatters night away.	Are felt and fear'd no more.	And in his bosom rest!	I'd fearless launch away. {roll

BALL HILL. 8, 7. *J. W. Davis.*

Come, thou Fount of eve - ry bless - ing, Tune my heart to sing thy grace;
Streams of mer - cy, nev - er ceas - ing, Call for songs of loud-est praise.
Sin - ners, come un - to the Sa - viour;

Don't you see that God is good! His arms are o - pen to re - ceive you, Taste and see that God is love.

How hap - py, how joy - ful, how love - ly I feel! I want to feel more love, yea, more love and zeal. I want my love

per - fect, I want my love pure, That all things with pa - tience I well may en - dure.

LUMPKIN. 7. 6.

Zion Songster, p. 107.   J. T. White

Sometimes a light sur - prises The Christian while he sings: It   is the Lord, who   rises With heal - ing in his

wings.   When com-forts are de - clin-ing, He grants the soul a - gain A   season of clear shin - ing, To cheer it af - ter rain.

FLORENCE. C. M.

Dr. T. W. Carter.

Not many years their rounds shall roll, Each moment brings it nigh,
Ere all its glo - ries stand re - veal'd, To our ad - mir - ing eye.

Ye wheels of na - ture,

speed your course, Ye mor - tal pow'rs, de - cay; Fast as ye bring the night of death, Ye bring e - ter - nal day.

ALL IS WELL. P. M.

J. T. White

Slow.

1 What's this that steals, that steals up-on my frame! Is it death? is it death? If this be death, I
That soon will quench, will quench this mor-tal flame. Is it death? is it death?

2 Weep not, my friends, my friends weep not for me, All is well! All is well! There's not a cloud that
My sins for-giv'n, for-giv'n, and I am free. All is well! All is well!

soon shall be From ev'-ry pain and sor-row free, I shall the King of glo-ry see. All is well! All is well!

doth a-rise, To hide my Je-sus from my eyes, I soon shall mount the up-per skies. All is well! All is well!

3 Tune, tune your harps, your harps ye saints on high.
        All is well, All is well!
I too will strike my harp with equal joy.
        All is well, All is well!
Bright angels are from glory come,
They're round my bed, they're in my room,
They wait to waft my spirit home.
        All is well. All is well!

4 Hark! hark! my Lord, my Lord and Master's voice,
        Calls away, Calls away!
I soon shall see—enjoy my happy choice,
        Why delay, Why delay?
Farewell, my friends, adieu, adieu.
I can no longer stay with you,
My glittering crown appears in view.
        All is well, All is well!

5 Hail! hail! all hail! all hail! ye blood-wash'd throng,
        Saved by grace, Saved by grace—
I come to join, to join your rapturous song,
        Saved by grace, Saved by grace!
All, all is peace and joy divine,
And heaven and glory now are mine,
Loud hallelujahs to the Lamb!
        All is well, All is well!

THE DYING CHRISTIAN. 11, 8.

Mercer's Cluster, p. 456.   *E. J. King.*

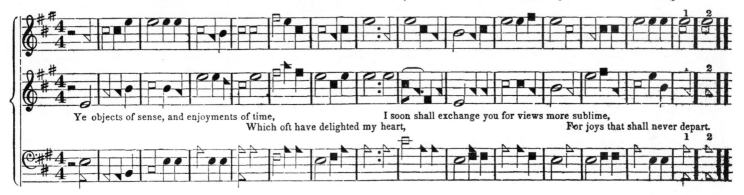

Ye objects of sense, and enjoyments of time,
Which oft have delighted my heart,
I soon shall exchange you for views more sublime,
For joys that shall never depart.

CROSS OF CHRIST. C. M. D.

L. P. Breedlove.

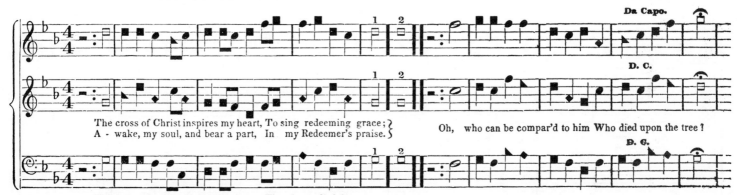

The cross of Christ inspires my heart, To sing redeeming grace;
A - wake, my soul, and bear a part, In my Redeemer's praise.
Oh, who can be compar'd to him Who died upon the tree!

This is my dear de - light - ful theme, That Jesus died for me

IRWINTON. C. M. *Dr. T. W. Carter.*

What poor, des-pis-ed com-pa-ny Of trav-el-ers are these,
That walk in yonder nar-row way, A - long the rug-ed maze? Ah! they are of a roy-al line, All

chil - dren of a King; Heirs of im - mor - tal crowns di - vine, And loud for joy they sing.

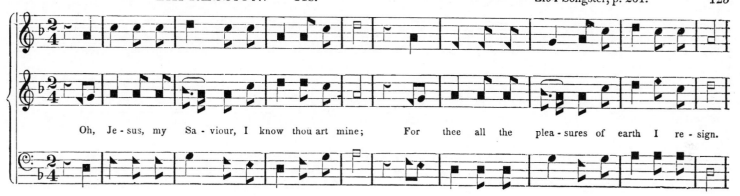

Oh, Je-sus, my Sa-viour, I know thou art mine; For thee all the plea-sures of earth I re-sign.

Of ob-jects most pleasing, I love thee the best; With-out thee I'm wretch-ed, but with thee I'm bless'd.

By Ba - bel's streams we sat and wept, While Zi - on we thought ' on; Amidst there - of we hung our harps, The willow trees up - on.

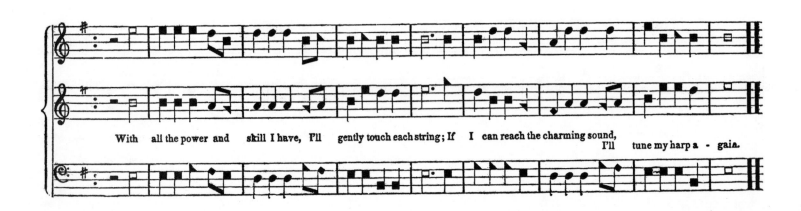

With all the power and skill I have, I'll gently touch each string; If I can reach the charming sound, I'll tune my harp a - gain.

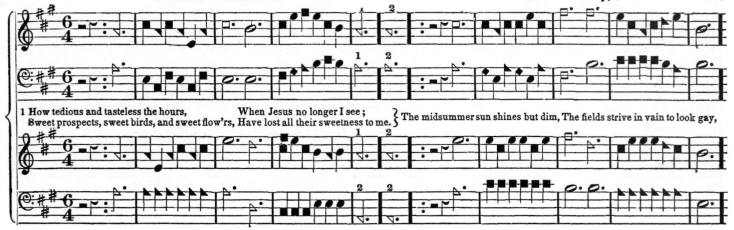

1 How tedious and tasteless the hours,   When Jesus no longer I see;
Sweet prospects, sweet birds, and sweet flow'rs, Have lost all their sweetness to me. } The midsummer sun shines but dim, The fields strive in vain to look gay,

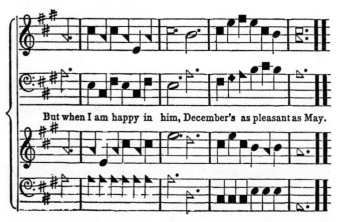

But when I am happy in him, December's as pleasant as May.

2 His name yields the richest perfume,
   And sweeter than music his voice;
His presence disperses my gloom,
   And makes all within me rejoice;
I should, were he always thus nigh,
   Have nothing to wish or to fear;
No mortal so happy as I,
   My summer would last all the year.

3 Content with beholding his face,
   My all to his pleasure resign'd;
No changes of season or place
   Would make any change in my mind·

While bless'd with a sense of his love,
   A palace a toy would appear,
And prisons would palaces prove,
   If Jesus would dwell with me there

4 Dear Lord, if indeed I am thine,
   If thou art my sun and my song,
Say, why do I languish and pine,
   And why are my winters so long?
Oh, drive these dark clouds from my sky,
   Thy soul-cheering presence restore;
Or take me unto thee on high,
   Where winter and clouds are no more.

THE PROMISED LAND. C. M.

Meth. H. B. p. 471.   *Miss M. Durham.*

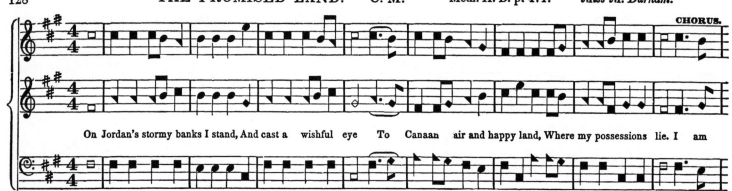

On Jordan's stormy banks I stand, And cast a wishful eye To Canaan air and happy land, Where my possessions lie. I am

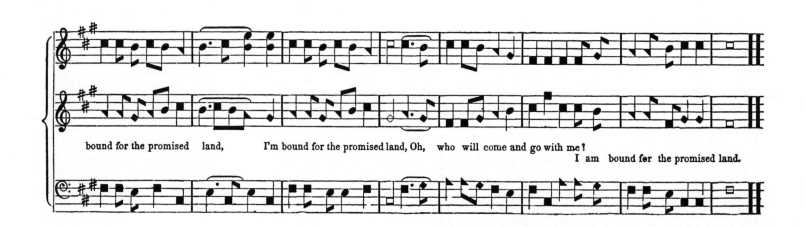

bound for the promised land, I'm bound for the promised land, Oh, who will come and go with me?

I am bound fer the promised land.

And if you meet with trou - bles, And tri - als on the way,
Then cast your care on Je - sus, And don't for - get to pray.

Gird on the heav'n - ly

ar - mour Of faith, and hope, and love; And when the com - bat s end - ed, He'll take you up a - bove.

I

The time is soon com - ing, by the prophets fore - told, When Zi - on in pu - ri - ty, the world shall be - hold.

When Je - sus' pure tes - ti - mo - ny will gain the day, De - no - mi - na - tions, self - ish - ness, will van - ish a - way.

MESSIAH. C. M.

He comes! he comes! to judge the world, Aloud th' archangel cries,
While thunders roll from pole to pole, And lightnings cleave the skies;
Th'affrighted nations hear the sound, And upward lift their eyes;

The slumb'ring tenants of the ground In living armies rise.

INVOCATION. 7, 6, 7, 6, 7, 7, 7, 6.

Rise, my soul, and stretch thy wings, Thy better portion trace,
Rise from transitory things, To heav'n, thy native place.
Sun, and moon, and stars decay, Rise, my soul, and haste away,
Time shall soon this earth remove, To seats prepared above.

EXULTATION. 6, 6, 9

Humphreys.

1 Come a - way to the skies, My be - loved, a - rise, And rejoice in the day thou wast born: On this fes - ti - val day, Come exulting a - way,

And with singing to Zion return.

2 We have laid up our love And our treasure above,
　Though our bodies continue below,
The redeem'd of the Lord Will remember his word,
　And with singing to paradise go.

3 Now with singing and praise, Let us spend all the days,
　By our heavenly Father bestow'd,
While his grace we receive From his bounty, and live
　To the honour and glory of God.

4 For the glory we were First created to share,
　Both the nature and kingdom divine!
Now created again That our souls may remain,
　Throughout time and eternity thine.

5 We with thanks do approve, The design of that love
　Which hath join'd us to Jesus's name;
So united in heart, Let us never more part,
　Till we meet at the feast of the Lamb.

6 There, Oh! there at his feet, We shall all likewise meet,
　And be parted in body no more;
We shall sing to our lyres, With the heavenly choirs,
　And our Saviour in glory adore.

7 Hallelujah we sing, To our Father and King,
　And his rapturous praises repeat;
To the Lamb that was slain, Hallelujah again,
　Sing, all heaven, and fall at his feet.

Treble by James Langston.

1 From Greenland's icy mountains,
From India's coral strand;
Where Afric's sunny fountains
Roll down their golden sand;
From many an ancient river,
From many a pa-my plain.

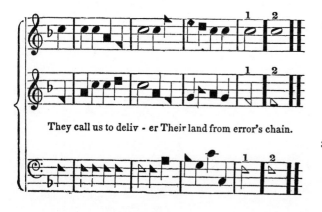

They call us to deliv - er Their land from error's chain.

2 What though the spicy breezes
    Blow soft o'er Ceylon's isle,
  Though every prospect pleases,
    And only man is vile;
  In vain, with lavish kindness,
    The gifts of God are strown:
  The heathen, in his blindness,
    Bows down to wood and stone.

3 Shall we, whose souls are lighted
    With wisdom from on high,
  Shall we, to men benighted,
    The lamp of life deny?

Salvation! O salvation!
    The joyful sound proclaim,
  Till earth's remotest nation
    Has learn'd Messiah's name.

4 Waft, waft, ye winds, his story,
    And you, ye waters, roll,
  Till, like a sea of glory,
    It spreads from pole to pole;
  Till o'er our ransom'd nature,
    The Lamb for sinner's slain,
  Redeemer, King, Creator,
    In bliss returns to reign.

THE CHRISTIAN'S HOPE. 8, 8, 8, 6, 8, 8, 8, 6.

Dover Sel. p. 173.

1 A few more days on earth to spend, And all my toils and cares shall end, And I shall see my God and friend, And praise his name on high

2 Then, O my soul, despond no more: The storm of life will soon be o'er, And I shall find the peaceful shore Of ev - erlast - ing rest.

No more to sigh nor shed a tear, No more to suf-fer pain or fear; But God, and Christ, and heav'n appear, Unto the raptured eye.

O happy day! O joyful hour! When, freed from earth, my soul shall tow'r Beyond the reach of Satan's pow'r, To be for-ev-er blest.

3 My soul anticipates the day,—
I'll joyfully the call obey,
Which comes to summon me away
  To seats prepared above.
There I shall see my Saviour's face,
And dwell in his beloved embrace,
And taste the fulness of his grace,
  And sing redeeming love.

4 Though dire afflictions press me sore,
And death's dark billows roll before,
Yet still by faith I see the shore
  Beyond the rolling flood:
The banks of Canaan, sweet and fair,
Before my raptured eyes appear:
It makes me think I'm almost there,—
  In yonder bright abode.

5 To earthly cares I bid farewell,
And triumph over death and hell,
And go where saints and angels dwell,
  To praise th' Eternal Three.
I'll join with those who're gone before,
Who sing and shout their sufferings o'er,
Where pain and parting are no more,
  To all eternity.

6 Adieu, ye scenes of noise and show,
And all this region here below,
Where naught but disappointments
    A better world's in view. [grow-
My Saviour calls! I haste away,
I would not here for ever stay;
Hail! ye bright realms of endless day,
  Vain world, once more adieu

Come, thou fount of ev' - ry bless - ing, Tune my heart to sing thy grace :
Streams of mer - cy nev - er ceas - ing, Call for songs of loud - est praise.

Teach me some me - lo - dious son-net,

Sung by flam - ing tongues a - bove. Praise the mount, O fix me on it, Mount of thy un - chang - ing love.

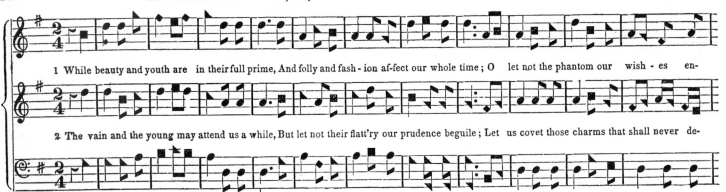

1 While beauty and youth are in their full prime, And folly and fash-ion af-fect our whole time; O let not the phantom our wish-es en-

2 The vain and the young may attend us a while, But let not their flatt'ry our prudence beguile; Let us covet those charms that shall never de-

gage; Let us live so in youth that we blush not in age.

cay, Nor lis-ten to all that de-ceivers can say.

3 I sigh not for beauty, nor languish for wealth,
But grant me, kind Providence, virtue and health;
Then, richer than kings, and far happier than they,
My days shall pass swiftly and sweetly away.

4 For when age steals on me, and youth is no more,
And the moralist Time shakes his glass at my door,
What pleasure in beauty or wealth can I find?
My beauty, my wealth, is a sweet peace of mind.

5 That peace! I'll preserve it as pure as 'twas given,
Shall last in my bosom an earnest of heaven;
For virtue and wisdom can warm the cold scene,
And sixty can flourish as gay as sixteen.

6 And when I the burden of life shall have borne,
And death with his sickle shall cut the ripe corn,
Reascend to my God without murmur or sigh.
I'll bless the kind summons, and lie down and **die**.

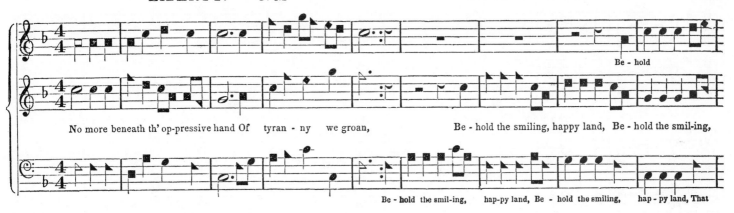

No more beneath th' op-pressive hand Of tyran - ny we groan,   Be - hold the smiling, happy land, Be - hold the smil-ing,

Be - hold the smil-ing, hap-py land, Be - hold the smiling, hap - py land, That

Be - hold   That

hap - py land, That free - dom calls her own.   That free - dom calls her own.

free - dom calls her own.

SOLITUDE IN THE GROVE. C. M

Oh, were I like a feather'd dove, And innocence had wings, I'd fly and make a long re - move From all these restless things. Let

me to some wild desert go, And find a peaceful home, Where storms of ma - lice ne - ver blow, And sorrows never come.

1 Burst, ye emerald gates, and bring To my raptured vis - ion
All th' ecstatic joys that spring Round the bright e - ly - sian.

Lo, we lift our longing eyes, Burst, ye in - tervening skies, Sun of

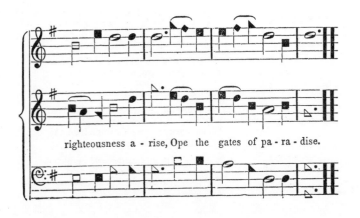

righteousness a - rise, Ope the gates of pa - ra - dise.

2 Floods of everlasting light
   Freely flash before him;
Myriads, with supreme delight,
   Instantly adore him:
Angel trumps resound his fame,
Lutes of lucid gold proclaim
All the music of his name,
Heav'n echoing with the theme.

3 Four-and-twenty elders rise
   From their princely station;
Shout his glorious victories,
   Sing the great salvation;

Cast their crowns before his **throne**,
Cry, in reverential tone,
Glory give to God alone;
"Holy, holy, holy One!"

4 Hark! the thrilling symphonies
   Seem, methinks, to seize us!
Join we too their holy lays,
   Jesus, Jesus, Jesus!
Sweetest sound in seraphs' song
Sweetest notes on mortal **tongue**
Sweetest carol ever sung·
Jesus, Jesus, roll along

SWEET SOLITUDE. L. M.

1 Hail, sol-itude! thou gentle queen, Of modest air and brow se-rene! 'Tis thou inspires the poet's theme,

Wrapp'd
Wrapp'd in sweet vision's airy dream;

in sweet vision's air-y dream, Wrapp'd in sweet vision's air-y dream.

2 Parent of virtue! muse of thought!
By thee are saints and patriots taught;
Wisdom to thee her treasures owes,
And in thy lap fair science grows.

3 Whate'er's in thee refines and charms,
Excites to thought, to virtue warms;
Whate'er is perfect, firm, and good,
We owe to thee, sweet solitude.

4 With thee the charms of life shall last,
E'en when the rosy bloom is past;
When slowly pacing Time shall spread
Thy silver blossoms o'er my head.

5 No more with this vain world perplex'd,
Thou shalt prepare me for the next:
The spring of life shall gently cease,
And angels waft my soul to peace.

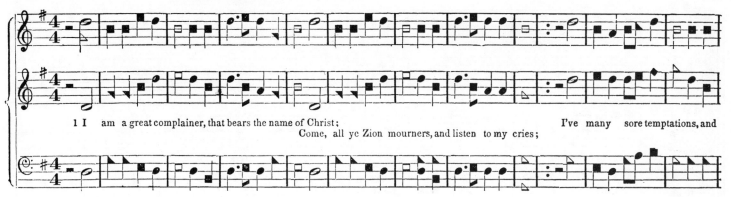

1 I am a great complainer, that bears the name of Christ;
Come, all ye Zion mourners, and listen to my cries;
I've many sore temptations, and

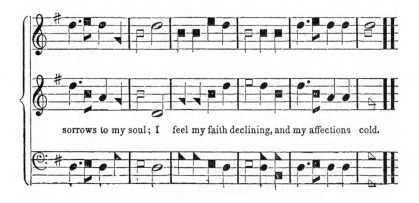

sorrows to my soul; I feel my faith declining, and my affections cold.

2 I wish it was with me now, as in the days of old,
When the glorious light of Jesus was flowing in my soul
But now I am distressed, and no relief can find,
With a hard, deceitful heart, and a wretched, wandering mind.

3 It is great pride and passion beset me on my way,
So I am fill'd with folly, and so neglect to pray;
While others run rejoicing, and seem to lose no time,
I am so weak I stumble, and so I'm left behind.

4 I read that peace and happiness meet Christians in their way,
That bear their cross with meekness, and don't neglect to pray;
But I, a thousand objects beset me in my way,
So I am fill'd with folly, and so neglect to pray.

STRATFIELD. C. M.

Through ev'ry age, e - ter - nal God, Thou art our rest, our safe a - bode; High was thy throne ere heav'n was made, Or

High Or

High was thy throne ere heav'n was made, Or earth thy humble

earth thy humble footstool laid. High Or

earth thy humble footstool laid. High was thy throne ere heav'n was made, Or earth thy humble footstool laid. :‖:

High

foot stool laid. High Or

While thee I seek, protecting Pow'r, Be my vain wish - es still'd, And may this con - se - crated hour With bet - ter hopes be fill'd.

Thy love the pow'r of thought bestow'd, To thee my thoughts would soar; Thy mercy o'er my life has flow'd, That mer - cy I a - dore.

1 Hark! the ju - bi - lee is sounding, O the joy - ful news is come; ⎬ Now we have an in - vi - tation To the meek and low-ly Lamb. Glory,
Free sal - va - tion is proclaimed In and through God's only Son; ⎬

ho - nour, and salvation; Christ, the Lord, is come to reign.

2 Come, dear friends, and don't neglect it,
  Come to Jesus in your prime;
Great salvation, don't reject it,
  O receive it, now's your time;
Now the Saviour is beginning
  To revive his work again.
    Glory, honour, &c.

3 Now let each one cease from sinning,
  Come and follow Christ the way;
We shall all receive a blessing,
  If from him we do not stray;
Golden moments we've neglected,
  Yet the Lord invites again!
    Glory, honour, &c.

4 Come, let us run our race with patience
  Looking unto Christ the Lord,
Who doth live and reign for ever,
  With his Father and our God;
He is worthy to be praised,
  He is our exalted King.
    Glory, honour, &c.

5 Come, dear children, praise your Jesus,
  Praise him, praise him evermore,
May his great love now constrain us
  His great name for to adore;
O then let us join together,
  Crowns of glory to obtain.
    Glory, honour, &c.

WARRENTON.   8, 7.

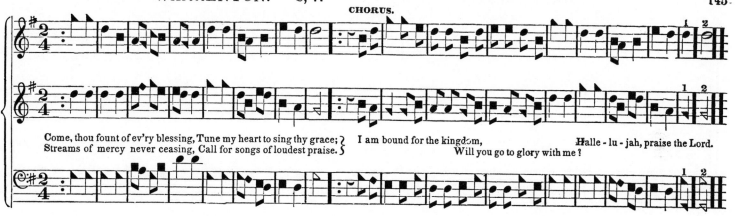

Come, thou fount of ev'ry blessing, Tune my heart to sing thy grace; } I am bound for the kingdom,   Halle - lu - jah, praise the Lord.
Streams of mercy never ceasing, Call for songs of loudest praise. } Will you go to glory with me ?

SWEET AFFLICTION.   8, 7.

Rippon's Hymns, p. 541.

In the floods of   tribu - la - tion, While the billows o'er me   roll, } Hal - le - lujah, Hal - le - lu - jah, Halle - lu - jah, praise the Lord.
Je-sus   whispers conso - la - tion, And supports my   faint - ing   soul. }

Halle - lu - jah, Halle - lu - jah, Halle - lu - jah, praise the Lord.

K

HALLELUJAH.   C. M   Dover Selection, p. 159.

And   let this   fee - ble bo - dy   fail, And let it   faint   and die;   And I'll sing hal - le - lu - jah, And
My   soul shall   quit this mournful   vale, And soar to   worlds   on high.

you'll sing hal - le - lu - jah,   And we'll all sing   hal - le - lu - jah, When we ar - rive   at   home.

Dis-miss us with thy blessing, Lord, Help us to feed up - on thy word; Though we are guil-ty, thou art good,
All that has been a-miss forgive, And let thy truth with-in us live.
Wash all our works in Jesus' blood

Give eve-ry fet - ter'd soul release, And bid us all de - part in peace. Give every fetter'd soul release, And bid us all de - part in peace.

Glo - rious things of thee are spo - ken, Zi - on, ci - ty of our God! }
He whose word can ne'er be bro - ken, Form'd thee for his own a - bode. } On the Rock of a - ges founded,

Who can shake thy sure re - pose? With sal - va - tion's wall sur - round - ed, Thou mayst smile at all thy foes.

1 The cha - riot! the cha - riot! its wheels roll in fire,

Lo! self-moving it drives on its pathway of

As the Lord cometh down in the pomp of his ire!

cloud, And the heav'ns with the burden of Godhead are bow'd.

2 The glory! the glory! around him are pour'd
Mighty hosts of the angels that wait on
the Lord;
And the glorified saints and the martyrs
are there,
And there all who the palm-wreaths of
victory wear.

3 The trumpet! the trumpet! the dead have
all heard,
Lo! the depths of the stone-cover'd char-
nel are stirr'd;
From the sea, from the earth, from the
south, from the north,
And the vast generations of man are come
forth.

4 The judgment! the judgment! the thrones
are all set,
Where the Lamb and the white-vested
elders are met;
There all flesh is at once in the sight of
the Lord,
And the doom of eternity hangs on his
word.

5 O mercy! O mercy! look down from
above,
Great Creator, on us, thy sad children,
with love;
When beneath to their darkness the wicked
are driv'n,
May our justified souls find a welcome in
heav'n.

THE SPIRITUAL SAILOR   7, 6.   Dover Selection, p. 133.   *I. Neighbours.*

1 The people called Christians
    Have many things to tell
        About the land of Canaan,
        Where saints and angels dwell;
            But here a dismal ocean, Enclosing them a-

2 Many have been impatient
    To work their passage through,
        And with united wisdom Have tried what they could do; But vessels built by human skill
            Have never sailed

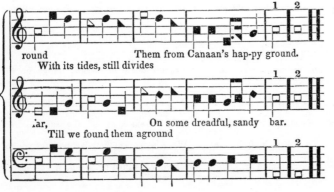

round   With its tides, still divides   Them from Canaan's hap-py ground.

.ar,   Till we found them aground   On some dreadful, sandy bar.

3 The everlasting gospel
    Hath launch'd the deep at last;
  Behold the sails expanded
    Around the tow'ring mast!
  Along the deck in order
    The joyful sailors stand,
  Crying, "Ho!—here we go
    To Immanuel's happy land."

4 We're now on the wide ocean;
    We bid the world farewell!
  And though where we shall anchor
    No human tongue can tell;
  About our future destiny
    There need be no debate,
  While we ride on the tide,
    With our Captain and his Mate.

5 To those who are spectators,
    What anguish must ensue,
  To hear their old companions
    Bid them a last adieu!
  The pleasures of your paradise
    No more our hearts invite;
  We will sail—you may rail,
    We shall soon be out of sight.

6 The passengers united
    In order peace and love ;—
  The wind is in our favour,
    How swiftly do we move!
  Though tempests may assail us,
    And raging billows roar
  We will sweep through the deep,
    Till we reach fair Canaan's shore

Behold the Judge descends, his guards are nigh; Tempests and fire attend him down the sky; Heav'n, earth, and hell draw near, let all things come To hear his

justice, and the sin-ner's doom: But gather first my saints, the Judge commands, Bring them, ye an - gels, from their distant lands.

BRUCE'S ADDRESS *Spiritualized.* 7, 7, 7, 5, 7, 7, 7, 5. Dover Sel. p. 152

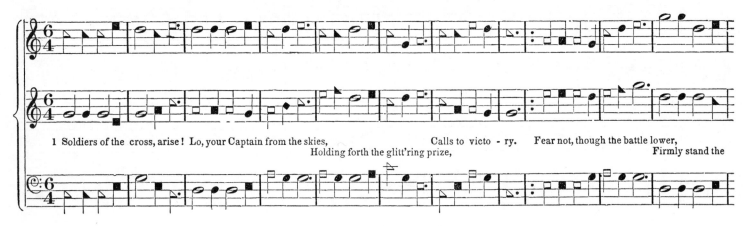

1 Soldiers of the cross, arise! Lo, your Captain from the skies,
Holding forth the glitt'ring prize, Calls to victo - ry. Fear not, though the battle lower,
Firmly stand the

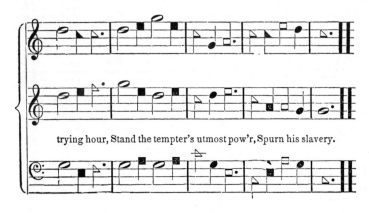

trying hour, Stand the tempter's utmost pow'r, Spurn his slavery.

2 Who the cause of Christ would yield?
Who would leave the battle-field?
Who would cast away his shield?—
Let him basely go:
Who for Zion's King will stand?
Who will join the faithful band?
Let him come with heart and hand,
Let him face the foe.

3 By the mercies of our God,
By Emmanuel's streaming blood,
When alone for us he stood,
Ne'er give up the strife:

Ever to the latest breath,
Hark to what your Captain saith ;—
" Be thou faithful unto death ;
Take the crown of life."

4 By the woes which rebels prove,
By the bliss of holy love,
Sinners, seek the joys above ;
Sinners, turn and live !
Here is freedom worth the name ·
Tyrant sin is put to shame ;
Grace inspires the hallow'd flame
God the crown will give.

1 Good morning, brother pilgrim, March you towards Jerusalem, Pray, wherefore are you smiling, We
What, bound for Canaan's coast? To join the heav'nly host? While tears run down your face?

soon shall cease from toiling, And reach that heav'nly place. And reach that heav'nly place.
And reach that heav'nly place, We soon shall cease from toiling,

2 To Canaan's coast we'll hasten,
To join the heavenly throng,
Hark! from the banks of Jordan,
How sweet the pilgrims' song!
Their Jesus they are viewing,
By faith we see him too,
We smile, and weep, and praise him,
And on our way pursue.

3 Though sinners do despise us,
And treat us with disdain,
Our former comrades slight us,
Esteem us low and mean:
No earthly joy shall charm us
While marching on our way,
Our Jesus will defend us
In the distressing day.

4 The frowns of old companions
We're willing to sustain,
And, in divine compassion,
To pray for them again;
For Christ, our loving Saviour,
Our Comforter and Friend,
Will bless us with his favour,
And guide us to the end.

5 With streams of consolation,
We're fill'd as with new wine,
We die to transient pleasures,
And live to things divine:
We sink in holy raptures,
While viewing things above,
Why glory to my Saviour,
My soul is full of love.

THE SAINTS' DELIGHT

65th hymn, 2d b. Watts   *F. Price.*

When I can read my ti-tle clear To mansions in the skies, I'll bid farewell to ev'-ry fear, And wipe my weeping eyes.

I feel like, I feel like I'm on my jour-ney home. I feel like, I feel like I'm on my jour-ney home.

2 Should earth against my soul engage,
   And fiery darts be hurl'd,
Then I can smile at Satan's rage,
   And face a frowning world.

3 Let cares like a wild deluge come,
   Let storms of sorrow fall;
So I but safely reach my home,
   My God, my heav'n, my all.

4 There I shall bathe my weary soul
   In seas of heavenly rest;
And not a wave of trouble roll
   Across my peaceful breast.

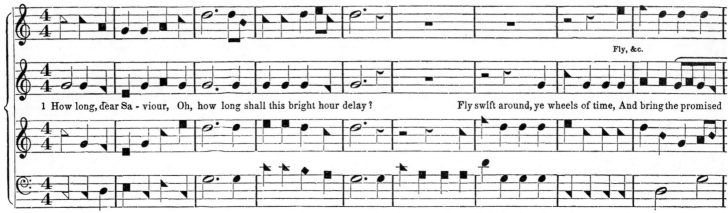

1 How long, dear Sa - viour, Oh, how long shall this bright hour delay?   Fly swift around, ye wheels of time, And bring the promised

Fly, &c.

Fly swift a - round, ye wheels of time, :||:

day, : And   bring   the   promised   day.

2 Lo, what a glorious sight appears
   To our believing eyes!
The earth and seas are pass'd away,
   And the old rolling skies.

From the third heaven,where God resides,
   That holy, happy place,
The New Jerusalem comes down,
   Adorn'd with shining grace.

4 Attending angels shout for joy,
   And the bright armies sing;

Mortals, behold the sacred seat
   Of our descending King!

5 The God of glory down to men
   Removes his blest abode;
Men, the dear object of his grace,
   And he the loving God.

6 His own soft hand shall wipe the tears
   From every weeping eye;
And pains and groans, and griefs and fears,
   And death itself shall die.

THE PILGRIM'S LOT. 8, 8, 6

Mercer's Cluster, p. 224. *H Graham.*

How happy is the pilgrim's lot, How free from anxious care and thought, How free from anxious care and thought,

From worldly hope and

fear; Confined to neither court nor cell, His soul disdains on earth to dwell.

His soul disdains on earth to dwell, He on-ly so-journs here.

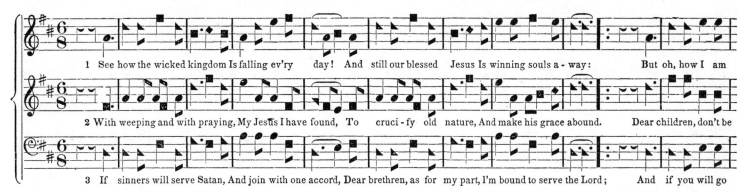

1 See how the wicked kingdom Is falling ev'ry day! And still our blessed Jesus Is winning souls a-way: But oh, how I am

2 With weeping and with praying, My Jesus I have found, To cruci-fy old nature, And make his grace abound.   Dear children, don't be

3 If sinners will serve Satan, And join with one accord, Dear brethren, as for my part, I'm bound to serve the Lord;   And if you will go

tempted, No mortal tongue can tell! So often I'm surrounded With enemies from hell.

weary, But march on in the way; For Jesus will stand by you, And be your guard and stay.

with me, Pray give to me your hand, And we'll march on together, Unto the promised land.

4 Through troubles and distresses,
    We'll make our way to God ;
Though earth and hell oppose us,
    We'll keep the heavenly road
Our Jesus went before us,
    And many sorrows bore,
And we who follow after,
    Can never meet with more.

5 Though dear to me, my brethren,
    Each one of you I find ;
My duty now compels me
    To leave you all behind:
But while the parting grieves us,
    I humbly ask your prayers,
To bear me up in trouble,
    And conquer all my fears.

6 And now, my loving brothers,
    I bid you all farewell !
With you, my loving sisters,
    I can no longer dwell.

Farewell to every mourner !
    I hope the Lord you'll find,
To ease you of your burden,
    And give you peace of mind.

7 Farewell, poor careless sinners !
    I love you dearly well ;
I've labour'd much to bring you
    With Jesus Christ to dwell ;
I now am bound to leave you—
    Oh, tell me, will you go ?
But if you won't decide it,
    I'll bid you all adieu !

8 We'll bid farewell to sorrow,
    To sickness, care, and pain ;
And mount aloft with Jesus,
    For evermore to reign ;
We'll join to sing his praises,
    Above th' ethereal blue ;
And then, poor careless sinners,
    What will become of you ?

1 Thou art gone to the grave—but we will not deplore thee,
   Though sorrows and darkness encompass the tomb;
The Saviour has pass'd thro' its portals before thee,
   And the

lamp of his love is thy guide thro' the gloom,
   And the lamp of his love is thy guide thro' the gloom.

2 Thou art gone to the grave—we no longer behold thee,
   Nor tread the rough paths of the world by thy side;
But the wide arms of mercy are spread to enfold thee,
   And sinners may hope, since the Saviour hath died.

3 Thou art gone to the grave—and thy cradle's forsaken,
   With us thy fond spirit did not tarry long,
But the sunshine of heaven beam'd bright on thy waking,
   And the sound thou didst hear was the seraphim's song

4 Thou art gone to the grave, but 'twere wrong to deplore thee,
   When God was thy ransom, and guardian, and guide;
He gave thee, and took thee, and soon will restore thee.
   Where death hath no sting, since the Saviour hath died.

What wondrous love is this! oh! my. soul! oh! my soul! What wondrous love is this oh! my soul! What wondrous love is this! That

caused the Lord of bliss To bear the dreadful curse for my soul, for my soul, To bear the dread-ful curse for my soul.

No more shall the sound of the war-whoop be heard,　　　The tomahawk, buried, shall rest in the ground,
The ambush and slaughter no longer be fear'd,　　　And peace and good-will to the nations abound.

MARYSVILLE.　L. M.

Jesus, my all, to heav'n is gone—He whom I fix my hopes upon ;　His track I see, and I'll pur-sue The narrow way till him I view.

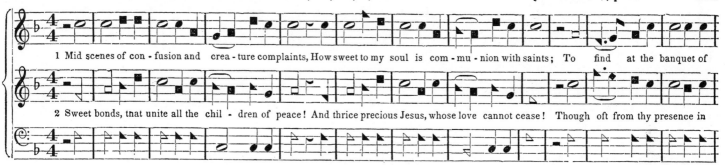

1 Mid scenes of con - fusion and crea - ture complaints, How sweet to my soul is com - mu - nion with saints; To find at the banquet of

2 Sweet bonds, tnat unite all the chil - dren of peace! And thrice precious Jesus, whose love cannot cease! Though oft from thy presence in

3 I sigh from this bo - dy of sin to be free, Which hinders my joy and com - mu - nion with thee; Though now my temptations like

CHORUS.

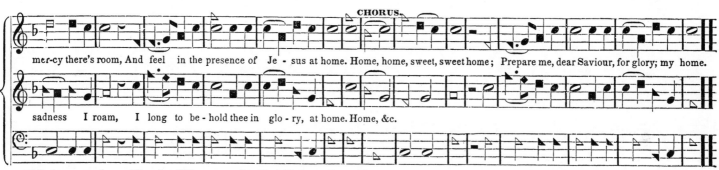

mer-cy there's room, And feel in the presence of Je - sus at home. Home, home, sweet, sweet home; Prepare me, dear Saviour, for glory; my home.

sadness I roam, I long to be - hold thee in glo - ry, at home. Home, &c.

bil - lows may foam, All, all will be peace, when I'm with thee at home. Home, &c.

4 While here in the valley of conflict I stay,
   O give me submission, and strength as my day;
   In all my afflictions to thee I would come,
   Rejoicing in hope of my giorious nome.
      Home. home. &c.
        L

5 Whate'er thou deniest, O give me thy grace,
   The Spirit's sure witness, and smiles of thy face;
   indulge me with patience to wait at thv throne,
   And find, even now, a sweet foretaste of home.
      Home. home, &c.

6 I long, dearest Lord, in thy beauties to shine,
   No more as an exile in sorrow to pine,
   And in thy dear image arise from the tomb,
   With glorified millions to praise thee, **at home.**
      Home, home, sweet sweet home;
      Receive me, dear Saviour, in glory, **my home.**

PLENARY. C. M.

A. Clark.

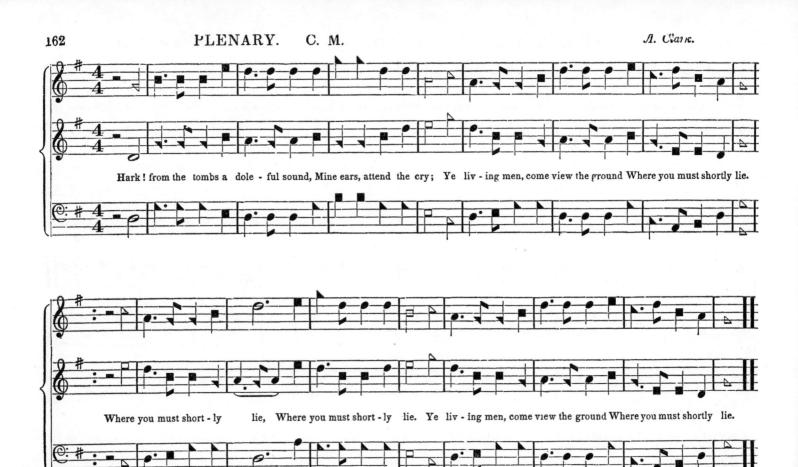

Hark! from the tombs a dole - ful sound, Mine ears, attend the cry; Ye liv - ing men, come view the ground Where you must shortly lie.

Where you must short - ly lie, Where you must short - ly lie. Ye liv - ing men, come view the ground Where you must shortly lie.

PART II.

CONSISTING PRINCIPALLY OF PIECES USED IN SINGING SCHOOLS AND SOCIETIES.

MORNING.　　L. M.

Psalmist, 232d Hymn.

A solemn darkness veils the skies,
A sudden tremb - - ling shakes the ground.

1 He dies, the friend of sinners dies,
Lo! Salem's daughters weep around;

A solemn darkness veils the skies,
A sudden trembling shakes the ground.

A solemn darkness veils the skies,
A solemn darkness veils the skies,

A sudden trembling shakes the ground.

2 Ye saints approach!—the anguish view
Of him who groans beneath your load;
He gives his precious life for you;
For you he sneds his precious blood

3 Here's love and grief beyond degree;
The Lord of glory dies for men;
But, lo! what sudden joys we see!
Jesus, the dead, revives again.

4 The rising God forsakes the tomb;
Up to his Father's court he flies;
Cherubic legions guard him home,
And shout him welcome to the skies.

DUANE STREET. L. M. D

Treble by J. T. White.

A poor wayfäring man of grief Hath often pass'd me on my way; Who sued so humbly for re - lief, That I could nev - er answer nay

I had not power to ask his name,
Whither he went or whence he came. Yet there was something in his eye
That won my love, I knew not why

1 How painful-ly pleas-ing the fond re-col-lec-tion Of youthful con-nec-tion and innocent joy,
While blest with pa-ren-tal ad-vice and af-fection, Surrounded with mercy and peace from on high;
I still view the chairs of my

2 The Bible, that vol-ume of God's in-spi-ration, At morning and-evening could yield us delight;
The prayers of our father, a sweet in-vo-ca-tion, For mercy by day and for safe-ty by night;
O hymns of thanksgiving with

father and mo-ther, The seats of their off-spring, as ranged on each hand, And the richest of books, which ex-cels ev'ry other, The fa-mi-ly

harmonious sweetness, As warm'd by the hearts of the fa-mi-ly band, Hath raised us from earth to that raptur-ous dwell-ing, De-scribed in the

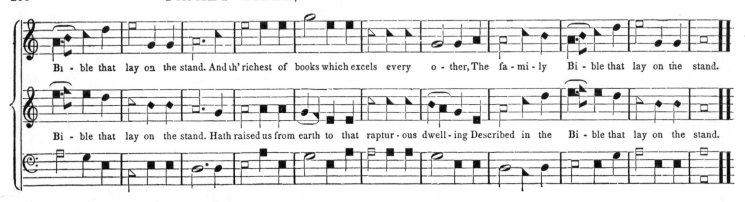

Bi - ble that lay on the stand. And th' richest of books which excels every o - ther, The fa - mi - ly Bi - ble that lay on the stand.

Bi - ble that lay on the stand. Hath raised us from earth to that raptur - ous dwell - ing Described in the Bi - ble that lay on the stand.

JOYFUL.   C. M.

B. F. White.

Treble by E. J. King.

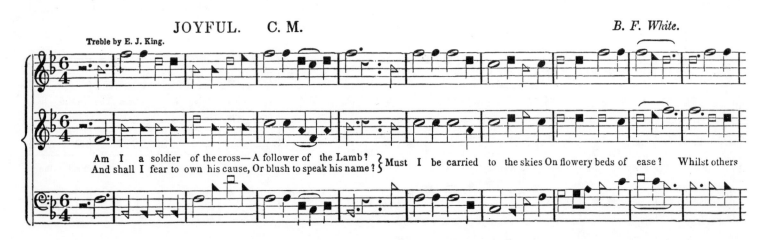

Am I a soldier of the cross—A follower of the Lamb!
And shall I fear to own his cause, Or blush to speak his name? } Must I be carried to the skies On flowery beds of ease! Whilst others

CHORUS.

fougnt to win the prize,   Oh, that will be   joyful,   joy - ful,   joy - ful! Oh, that will be joyful, To   meet to part   no
And sail'd through bloody seas.

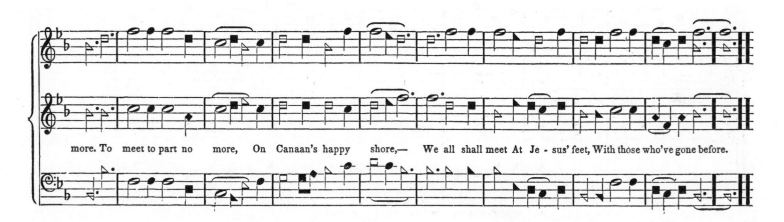

more. To   meet to part no   more,   On Canaan's happy   shore,—   We all shall meet At Je - sus' feet, With those who've gone before.

COWPER. L. M

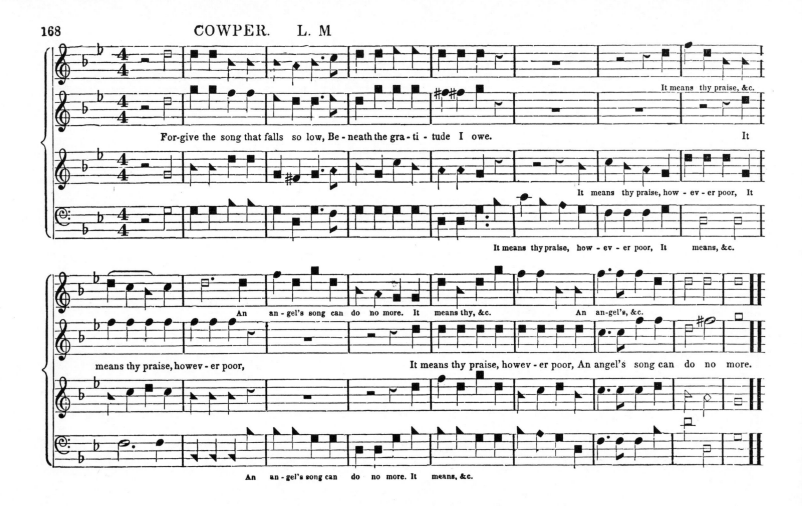

It means thy praise, &c.

For-give the song that falls so low, Be - neath the gra - ti - tude I owe.

It

It means thy praise, how - ev - er poor, It

It means thy praise, how - ev - er poor, It means, &c.

An an-gel's song can do no more. It means thy, &c. An an-gel's, &c.

means thy praise, howev - er poor,

It means thy praise, howev - er poor, An angel's song can do no more.

An an - gel's song can do no more. It means, &c.

DARTMOUTH. S. M.

Come sound his praise a - broad, And hyms of glo - ry sing, Je - ho - vah is the sov'reign God, The u - ni -

ver-sal King, He form'd the deep unknown, He gave the seas their bound, The wa - t'ry worlds are all his own, And all the sol - id ground.

EXHILARATION. L. M.

Dr. T. W. Carter.

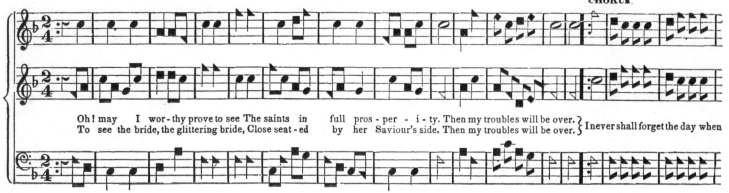

Oh! may I wor-thy prove to see The saints in full pros-per-i-ty. Then my troubles will be over.
To see the bride, the glittering bride, Close seat-ed by her Saviour's side. Then my troubles will be over. } I never shall forget the day when

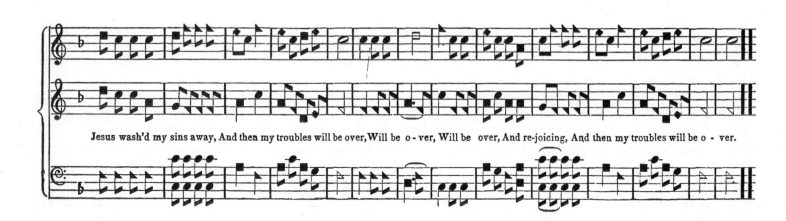

Jesus wash'd my sins away, And then my troubles will be over, Will be o-ver, Will be over, And re-joicing, And then my troubles will be o-ver.

Lord, in the morn-ing thou shalt hear My voice as-cend-ing high;

To thee will I di-

To thee will I di-rect my prayer, To thee lift up mine eye.

To thee will I di-rect my prayer, To thee lift up mine eye.

thee will I di-rect my prayer, To thee lift up mine eye. To thee will I di-rect my prayer, To thee lift up mine eye.

rect my prayer, To thee lift up mine eye. To thee will I di-rect my prayer, To thee lift up mine eye.

Wake, all ye soaring throngs, and sing, Ye cheerful war - blers of the spring, Harmonious anthems raise,   To him who shaped your

To him who shaped your finer mould, Who

him who shaped your finer mould,   To him, &c.   Who tipp'd, &c.   And tuned, &c.

Who tipp'd your glitt'ring wings with gold,

Who tipp'd your glitt'ring wings with gold,

finer mould,   To him who shaped your finer mould,   And tuned your voice to praise

tipp'd your glitt'ring wings with gold

Lord, in the morning thou shalt hear   To thee will I direct my prayer,   Up to the hills where Christ is gone
My voice ascending high;   To thee lift up mine eye;—   To

plead for all his saints, Presenting at his Father's throne, Pre - sent - ing at his Fa - ther's throne Our songs and our complaints.

PETERSBURG. L. M.

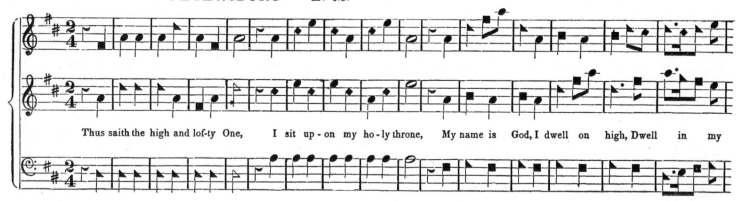

Thus saith the high and lof-ty One, I sit up-on my ho-ly throne, My name is God, I dwell on high, Dwell in my

own e-ter-ni-ty. But I descend to worlds be-low, On earth, I have a man-sion too, The

PETERSBURG. Continued.

hum - ble spi - rit and contrite, Is an a - bode, of my de - light, Is an a - bode of my de - light.

STAR IN THE EAST. 11s & 10s.

R. Herron.

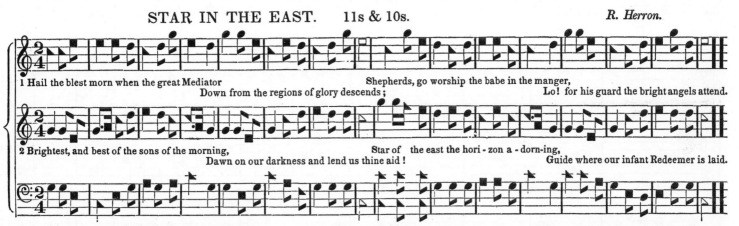

1 Hail the blest morn when the great Mediator
Down from the regions of glory descends;
Shepherds, go worship the babe in the manger,
Lo! for his guard the bright angels attend.

2 Brightest, and best of the sons of the morning,
Dawn on our darkness and lend us thine aid!
Star of the east the hori - zon a - dorn-ing,
Guide where our infant Redeemer is laid.

3 Cold on his cradle the dew-drops are shining,
Low lies his bed with the beasts of the stall;
Angels adore him in slumber reclining,
Maker, and Monarch, and Saviour of all.

4 Say, shall we yield Him in costly devotion,
Odours of Edom and offerings divine;
Gems of the mountain, and pearls of the ocean,
Myrrh from the forest, and gold from the mine.

5 Vainly we offer each ample oblation,
Vainly with gold would his favour secure·
Richer by far is the heart's adoration,
Dearer to God are the prayers of the poor

THE GOODLY LAND. P. M.

Zion Songster, p. 11.   *J. T. White.*

Though na - ture's strength de - cay, And earth and hell with - stand, To Canaan's bounds I urge my way,

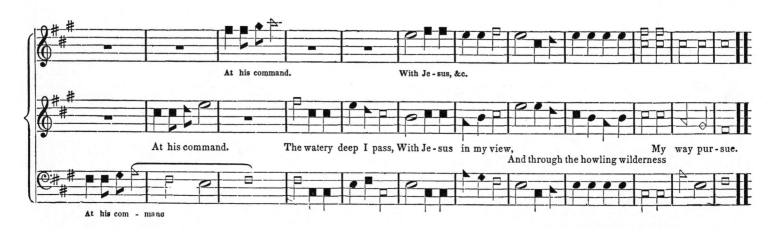

At his command.   With Je - sus, &c.

At his command.   The watery deep I pass, With Je - sus in my view,   My way pur - sue.
And through the howling wilderness

At his com - mand

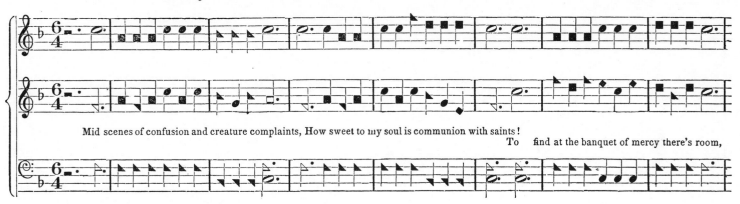

Mid scenes of confusion and creature complaints, How sweet to my soul is communion with saints!
To find at the banquet of mercy there's room,

And feel in the presence of Je - sus at home. Home, sweet home, Prepare me, dear Saviour, for glo - ry, my home.

M

HOSANNA. 7s, 6s.

1 When, his salvation bringing, To Zi - on Je - sus came, The children all stood singing Hosan - na to his name. Nor did there zeal of-

fend him, But as he rode a - long, He let them still attend him, And smiled to hear their song.

2 And since the Lord retaineth
His love for children still;
Though now as King he reigneth
On Zion's heavenly hill:
We'll flock around his banner,
Who sits upon the throne;
And cry aloud "Hosanna
To David's royal son."

3 For should we fail proclaiming
Our great Redeemer's praise,
The stones, our silence shaming,
Might well hosanna raise
But shall we only render
The tribute of our words?
No! while our hearts are tender.
They, too, shall be the Lord's

1 I find myself placed in a state of probation, Which God has commanded us well to improve; And I am re - solved to re - gard all his precepts, And on in the way of obedience to move. I know I must go through great tribulation,

And many sore conflicts on ev-e-ry hand; But grace will support and comfort my spirit, And I shall be a - ble for - ev - er to stand.

2 I'm call'd to contend with the powers of darkness,
   And many sore conflicts I have to pass through;
O Jesus, be with me in every battle,
   And help me my enemies all to subdue.
If thou, gracious Lord, will only be with me,
   To aid and direct me, then all will be right;
Apollyon, with all his powerful forces,
   In thy name and thy strength I shall soon put to flight

3 And when I must cross the cold stream of Jordan
   I'll bid all my sorrows a final adieu,
And hasten away to the land of sweet Canaan,
   Where, Christians, I hope I shall there meet with you.
That rest into which my soul shall then enter,
   Is perfectly glorious, and never shall end;
A rest of exemption from warfare and labour,
   A rest in the bosom of Jesus, my friend.

4 And more than exemption from fighting and hardship,
   My gracious Redeemer will grant unto me;
A portion of bliss he has promised to give me,
   And true to that promise he surely will be.
Yes, I shall receive and always inherit
   A happy reception and truly divine,
For which all the praises and glory, my Saviour,
   Are due unto thee, and shall ever be thine.

In vain we lavish out our lives, To ga - ther emp - ty wind; The choicest blessings earth can yield Will starve a hungry mind.

Come, and the Lord shall feed our souls With more substantial meat, With such as saints in glo - ry love, With such as an - gels eat.

Death, like an o - ver - flowing stream, Sweeps us a - way; our life's a dream,

An empty tale,

An empty tale, a morning flower, An empty

An empty, tale, a morn-ing flower, An empty tale, a

An empty tale, a morn-ing flower, :||:

An empty tale, &c.

Cut down

tale, a morning flower, An empty tale, a morn-ing flower, Cut down and wither'd in an hour.

morn - ing flower, :||:

flower, An emp - ty tale,

Cut down

2 Our age to seventy years is set;
  How short the time! how frail the **state**
  And if to eighty we arrive,
  We rather sigh and groan than live.

3 But oh how oft thy wrath appears,
  And cuts off our expected years,
  Thy wrath awakes our humble dread:
  We fear the power that strikes us dead.

4 Teach us, O Lord, how frail is man;
  And kindly lengthen out the span,
  'Till a wise care of piety
  Fit us to die and dwell with thee.

Watts, Psalm 90, pt. 1.

NEWBURGH. S. M.

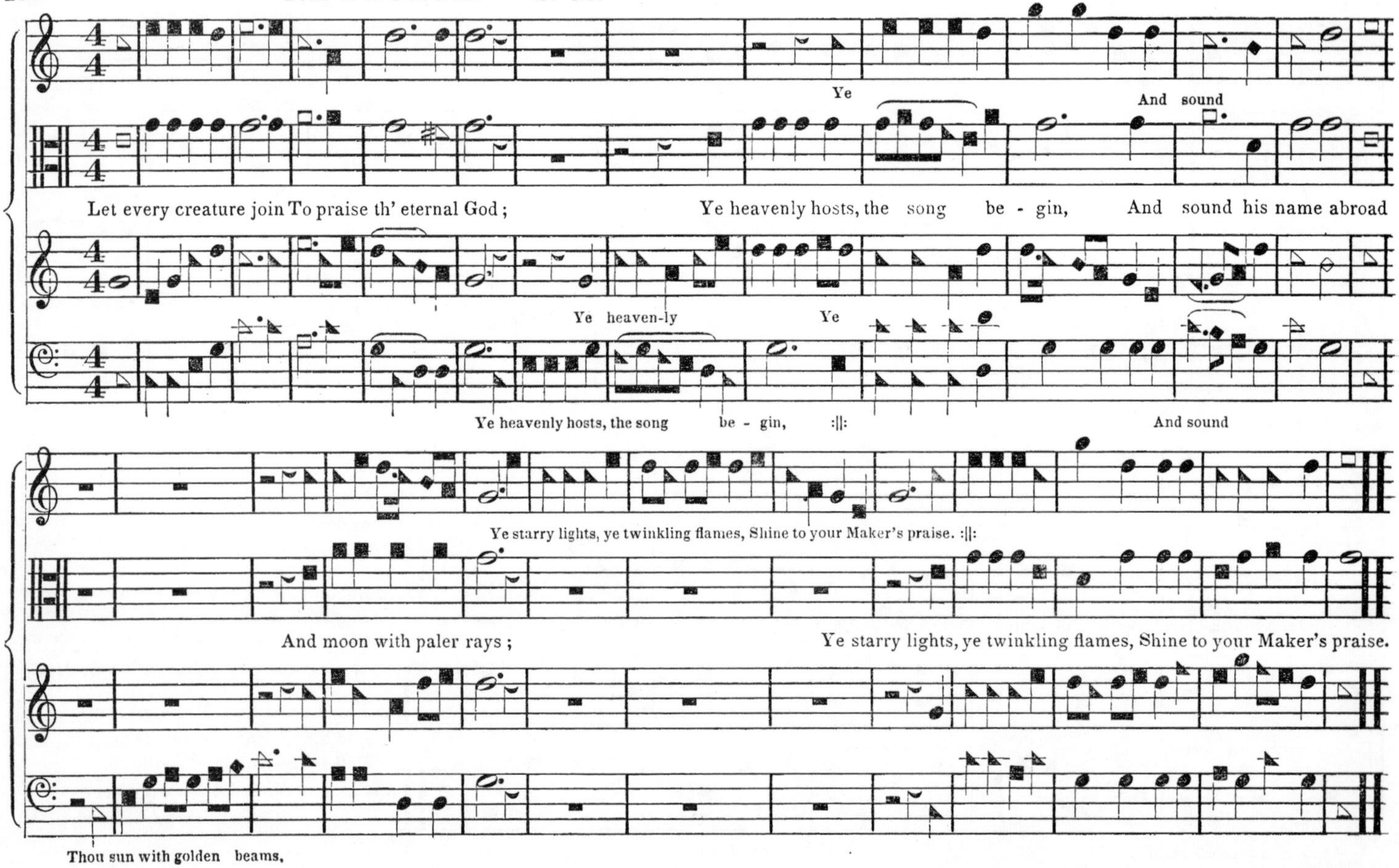
Ye
And sound
Let every creature join To praise th' eternal God ; Ye heavenly hosts, the song be - gin, And sound his name abroad
Ye heaven-ly
Ye
Ye heavenly hosts, the song be - gin, :||:
And sound
Ye starry lights, ye twinkling flames, Shine to your Maker's praise. :||:
And moon with paler rays ; Ye starry lights, ye twinkling flames, Shine to your Maker's praise.
Thou sun with golden beams,

Lord, what a thoughtless wretch was I, To mourn, and murmur, and repine, To see the wicked placed on high, In pride and   robes of   honour

shine. But, oh, their end, their dreadful end; Thy sanctu - a - ry taught me so, On slip'ry rocks I see them stand, And fiery   bil - lows roll be - low.

ENFIELD. C. M.

Be - fore the ro - sy dawn of day, To thee, my God, I'll sing; A - wake, my soft and tune-ful lyre, A - wake, each charming string: A -

wake, and let thy flow - ing strains Glide through the midnight air, While high a - midst, the silent orb, The sil - ver moon, rolls clear.

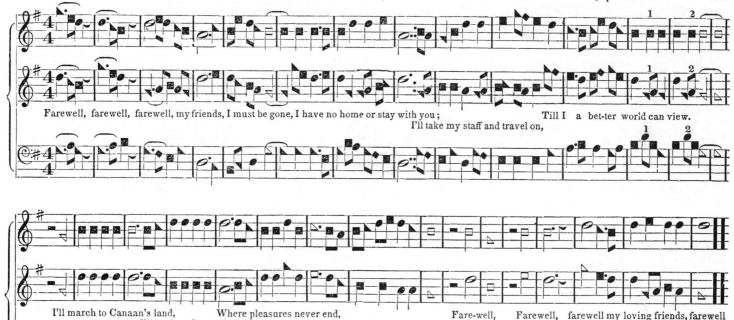

Farewell, farewell, farewell, my friends, I must be gone, I have no home or stay with you; Till I a bet-ter world can view.
I'll take my staff and travel on,

I'll march to Canaan's land, Where pleasures never end, Fare-well, Farewell, farewell my loving friends, farewell
I'll land on Canaan's shore, And trou - bles come no more.

2 Farewell, &c. my friends, time rolls along,
    Nor waits for mortal cares or bliss;
    I'll leave you here, and travel on,
    Till I arrive where Jesus is.
        I'll march, &c
        Farewell, &c.

3 Farewell, &c. dear brethren in the Lord,
    To you I'm bound with cords of love;
    But we believe his gracious word,
    We all ere long shall meet above.
        I'll march, &c.
        Farewell, &c

4 Farewell, &c. ye blooming sons of God,
    Sore conflicts yet remain for you;
    But dauntless keep the heavenly road,
    Till Canaan's happy land you view.
        I'll march, &c.
        Farewell, &c.

SHERBURNE. C. M.

While shepherds watch'd their flocks by night, All seat-ed on the ground,

The an-gel of the Lord came down, And glo - ry

The an-gel of the Lord, came down, And glo ry,

And glo - ry, And glo - ry, The angel, And glo - ry, 1 2

shone a - round. :||: The angel of the Lord came down, And glory shone around, And glory, &c.

hone around :||: The an-gel, And g.o - ry,

God, my supporter, and my hope, My help forever near; Thine arm of mer - cy held me up, When

Thine arm, &c.

Thine arm of mer - cy held me up, :‖:

Thine arm, &c.

sinking in de-spair. When sink-ing in de-spair.

2 Thy counsels, Lord, shall guide my feet
  Through life's bewilder'd race,
Thine hand conduct me near thy seat,
  To dwell before thy face.

3 Were I in heav'n without my God,
  'Twould be no joy to me;
And whilst this earth is my abode,
  I long for none but thee.

4 What if the springs of life should break,
  And flesh and heart should faint,

God is my soul's eternal rock,
  The strength of every saint.

5 Behold, the sinners that remove
  Far from thy presence die;
Not all the idol gods they love
  Can save them when they cry.

6 But to draw near to thee, my God,
  Shall be my sweet employ;
My tongue shall sound thy works abroad
  And tell the world my joy.

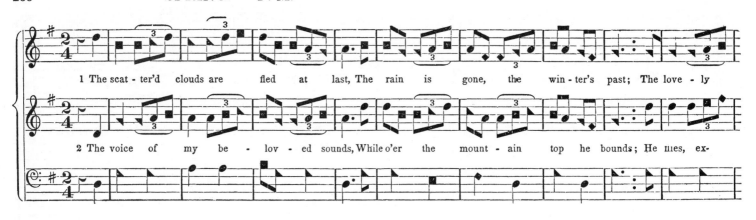

1 The scat - ter'd clouds are fled at last, The rain is gone, the win - ter's past; The love - ly

2 The voice of my be - lov - ed sounds, While o'er the mount - ain top he bounds; He flies, ex-

ver - nal flowers ap - pear, The warb - ling choirs en - chant our ear. Now, with sweetly pen - sive moan,

ult - ing, o'er the hills, And all my soul with trans - port fills. Gent - ly doth he chide my stay,

SPRING. *Concluded.*

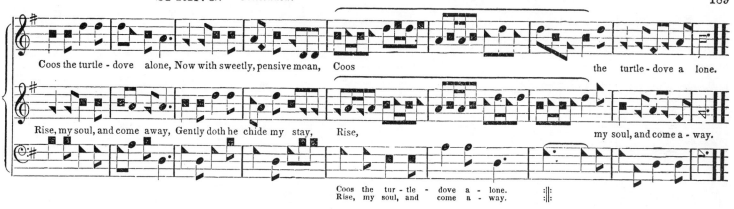

Coos the turtle - dove alone, Now with sweetly, pensive moan, Coos the turtle - dove a lone.

Rise, my soul, and come away, Gently doth he chide my stay, Rise, my soul, and come a - way.

Coos the tur - tle - dove a - lone.
Rise, my soul, and come a - way.

MONTGOMERY.   C. M.   Psalmist, 18th Hymn.   *More.*

Ear - ly, my God, without de - lay, I haste to seek thy face; My thirsty spirit faints a - way, With-

So pil - grims on the scorching sand, Be - neath a burn - ing sky, Long for a

out thy cheering grace ;   So pilgrims on the   scorch - ing   sand,   Be - neath a burning sky,

So pilgrims, &c.   :||:

So   pilgrims on the scorching sand, :||:

cool - ing   stream   at hand,   :||:

Long for a cooling   stream   at hand, And they must drink   or   die.   Long for a   cooling stream at hand, And they must drink or die.

Long for, &c.

Long for, &c.

Thy words the rag-ing   winds con-trol, And   rule   the boist'rous   deep;   Thou mak'st the sleeping

bil-lows roll, The   roll - - - ing bil-lows   sleep.   :‖:

SCHENECTADY. L. M.

Psalmist, 926th Hymn.   *Shumway.*

From all that dwell below the skies, Let the Cre - a - tor's praise arise; Let the Redeemer's name be sung, Thro' ev'ry land, by ev' - ry

E - ter - nal are   E - ter - nal truth   Thy

tongue.   E - ternal are thy mercies, Lord, E - ter - nal truth attends thy   word; Thy

E - ternal are   E - ternal truth   Thy

E - ter - nal are thy mercies, Lord, E - ter - nal truth at - tends thy word;   Thy praise shall sound from shore to shore

SCHENECTADY. *Concluded.*

shore to shore, Till suns shall rise and set no more. Till

praise shall sound from shore to shore, Till suns shall rise and set no more. Till suns shall rise and set no more.

shore, Till Till

suns shall rise and set no more. Till

HUNTINGTON. L. M.

Lord, what a thoughtless wretch was I, To mourn, and murmur, and repine; To see the wicked placed on high, In pride and robes

N

But, oh,   Thy   But— taught me so;

of honour shine.   But,   oh, their end, their dreadful end! Thy sanc - tu - a - ry taught me so; But—

But, oh,   Thy   But— taught me so;

But,   oh, their end, their dreadful end! Thy   sanctu - a - ry   taught me   so; But— taught me   so;

taught me so; On slip - pery rocks I see them stand, And fie - ry bil - lows roll be - low.

How beauteous are their feet
Who stand on Zion's hill;
Who bring salvation on their tongues,
And words of peace reveal!
Who bring, &c.
And, &c.
How charming, charming is their voice!

Zion   He   Zion

How sweet the tidings are! Zion, behold thy Saviour king, He reigns and triumphs here! Zion   He

Zion

ALABAMA. C. M.

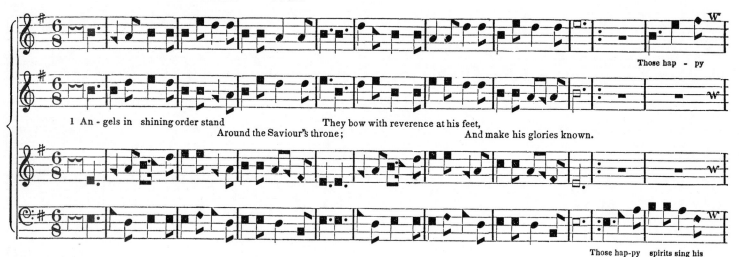

Those hap - py

1 An - gels in shining order stand

Around the Saviour's throne;

They bow with reverence at his feet,

And make his glories known.

Those hap-py spirits sing his

2 The cross of Christ inspires my heart
   To sing redeeming grace;
Awake, my soul, and bear a part
   In my Redeemer's praise.
Oh! what can be compared to him
   Who died upon the tree!
This is my dear, delightful theme,
   That Jesus died for me.

3 When at the table of the Lord
   We humbly take our place;
The death of Jesus we record,
   With love and thankfulness.

These emblems bring my Lord to view,
   Upon the bloody tree;
My soul believes and feels it's true
   That Jesus died for me.

4 His body broken, nail'd, and torn,
   And stain'd with streams of blood,
His spotless soul was left forlorn,
   Forsaken of his God.
'Twas then his Father gave the stroke
   That justice did decree;
All nature felt the dreadful stroke,
   When Jesus died for me.

5 Eli lama sabachthani,
   My God, my God, he cried,
Why hast thou thus forsaken me!
   And thus my Saviour died.
But why did God forsake his Son,
   When bleeding on the tree?
He died for sins, but not his own,
   For Jesus died for me.

6 My guilt was on my Surety laid,
   And therefore he must die;
His soul a sacrifice was made
   For such a worm as I.

spirits, &c. Those To all To all But I But I For For
Those To all But I For
praise, To all e - ter-ni - ty; But I can sing redeeming grace, For Jesus died for me.

Was ever love so great as this?
Was ever grace so free?
This is my glory, joy, and bliss,
That Jesus died for me.

7 He took his meritorious blood,
And rose above the skies,
And in the presence of his God,
Presents his sacrifice.
His intercession must prevail
With such a glorious plea;

My cause can never, never fail,
For Jesus died for me.

8 Angels in shining order sit
Around my Saviour's throne;
They bow with reverence at his feet,
And make his glories known.
Those happy spirits sing his praise
To all eternity;
But I can sing redeeming grace,
For Jesus died for me.

9 Oh! had I but an angel's voice
To bear my heart along,
My flowing numbers soon would rise
To an immortal song.
I'd charm their harps and golden lyres
In sweetest harmony,
And tell to all the heavenly choirs
That Jesus died for me.

STAR OF COLUMBIA. 11s.

Words by Dr. Dwight.   *Miss M. T. Durham*

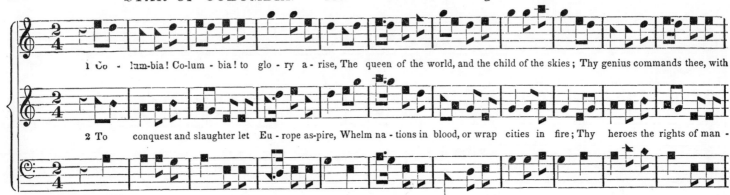

1 Co - lum-bia! Co-lum - bia! to glo - ry a - rise, The queen of the world, and the child of the skies; Thy genius commands thee, with

2 To conquest and slaughter let Eu - rope as-pire, Whelm na - tions in blood, or wrap cities in fire; Thy heroes the rights of man -

rap - tures behold, While a - ges on a - ges thy splendours unfold: Thy reign is the last and the no - blest of time, Most

kind shall de-fend, And tri - umph pur - sue them and glo - ry at - tend. A world is thy realm, for a world be thy laws, En-

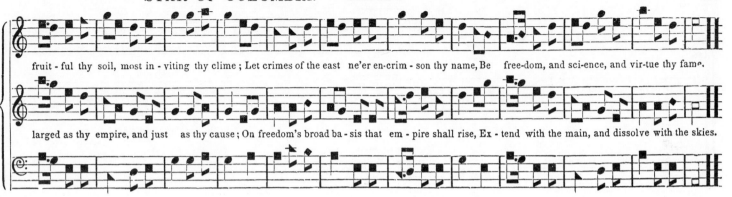

fruit - ful thy soil, most in - viting thy clime; Let crimes of the east ne'er en-crim - son thy name, Be free-dom, and sci-ence, and vir-tue thy fame.

larged as thy empire, and just as thy cause; On freedom's broad ba - sis that em - pire shall rise, Ex - tend with the main, and dissolve with the skies.

3 Fair science her gate to thy sons shall unbar,
And the east see thy morn hide the beams of her star;
New bards and new sages unrivall'd shall soar
To fame unextinguish'd, when time is no more.
To the last refuge of virtue design'd,
Shall fly from all nations, the best of mankind;
There, grateful to Heaven, with transport shall bring
Their incense, more fragrant than odours of spring.

4 Nor less shall thy fair ones to glory ascend,
And genius and beauty in harmony blend;
Their graces of form shall awake pure desire,
And the charms of soul still enliven the fire:
Their sweetness unmingled, their manners refined,
And virtue's bright image enstamp'd on the mind;
With peace and sweet rapture shall teach life to glow,
And light up a smile in the aspect of wo.

5 Thy fleets to all regions thy pow'r shall display;
The nations admire, and the ocean obey;
Each shore to thy glory its tribute unfold,
And the east and the south yield their spices and gold;
As the day-spring unbounded thy splendours shall flow,
And earth's little kingdoms before thee shall bow,
While the ensigns of union in triumph unfurl'd,
Hush anarchy's sway, and give peace to the world.

6 Thus down a lone valley with cedars o'erspread,
From the noise of the town I pensively stray'd,
The bloom from the face of fair heaven retired,
The wind ceased to murmur, the thunders expired,
Perfumes, as of Eden, flow'd sweetly along,
And a voice, as of angels, enchantingly sung,
Columbia! Columbia! to glory arise
The queen of the world, and the child of the skies.

EDOM. C. M.

With songs and honours sounding loud, Ad - dress the Lord on high, Over the heav'ns he spreads his clouds,
And waters veil the

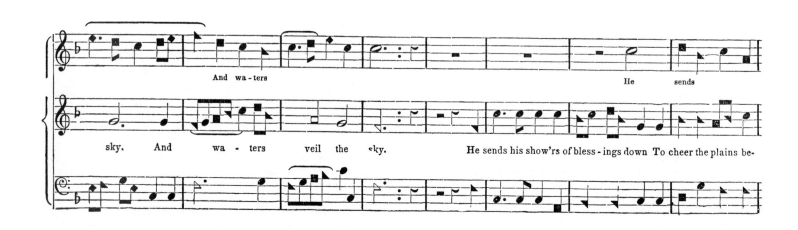

And wa - ters   sky.   And   wa - ters   veil the   sky.   He sends

He sends his show'rs of bless - ings down To cheer the plains be-

EDOM. *Concluded*

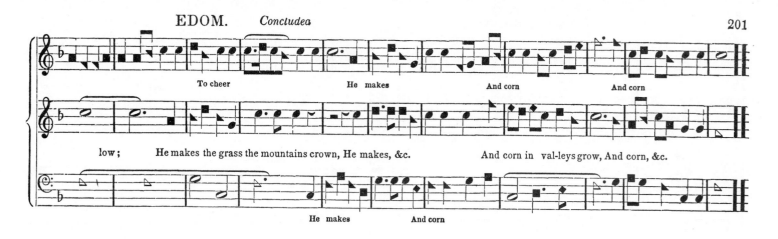

To cheer   He makes   And corn   And corn

low;   He makes the grass the mountains crown, He makes, &c.   And corn in val-leys grow, And corn, &c.

He makes   And corn

PILGRIM. 8, 6, 8, 6, 8, 6, 8, 6. C. M.

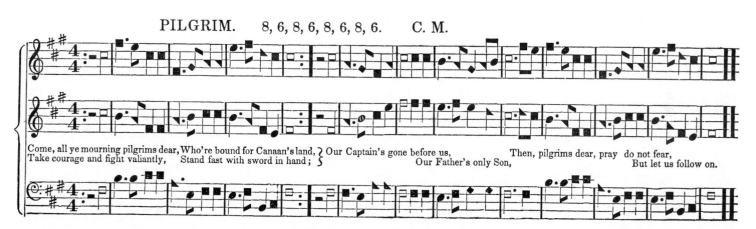

Come, all ye mourning pilgrims dear, Who're bound for Canaan's land, ⎰ Our Captain's gone before us,   Then, pilgrims dear, pray do not fear,
Take courage and fight valiantly,   Stand fast with sword in hand; ⎱   Our Father's only Son,   But let us follow on.

NEW LEBANON. 8s.

Sherman.

Great God, the heav'n's well-order'd frame Declares the glo - ries of thy name;

There thy rich

There thy rich works of wonder shine; A

There thy rich

There thy rich works of wonder shine;

thousand starry beauties there, A thou-sand radiant marks appear, Of boundless pow'r and skill divine, Of boundless pow'r and skill divine.

FLORIDA. S. M. Psalmist, 761st Hymn. *Witmore.* 203

Let sin-ners take their course, And choose the road to death; But in the wor-ship of my God, I'll spend my dai - ly

But

But

But

I'll

breath,

spend my dai - ly breath;

But in the wor - ship of my God, I'll spend my dai ly breath.

I'll

MISSION. L. M.

Baptist Harmony, p. 266.   *A. Gramstng.*

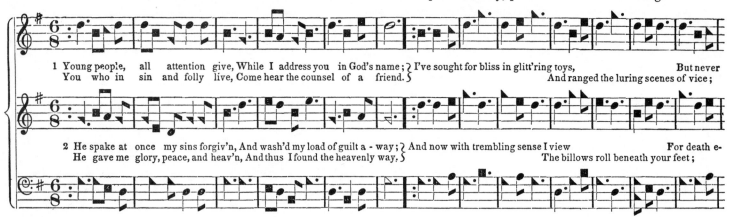

1 Young people, all attention give, While I address you in God's name; I've sought for bliss in glitt'ring toys, But never
  You who in sin and folly live, Come hear the counsel of a friend.

2 He spake at once my sins forgiv'n, And wash'd my load of guilt a - way; And now with trembling sense I view For death e-
  He gave me glory, peace, and heav'n, And thus I found the heavenly way. The billows roll beneath your feet;

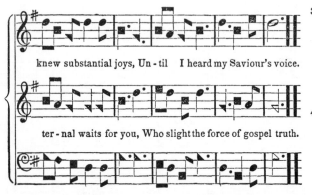

knew substantial joys, Un - til I heard my Saviour's voice.

ter - nal waits for you, Who slight the force of gospel truth.

3 Youth, like the spring, will soon be gone,
    By fleeting time or conquering death;
  Your morning sun may set at noon,
    And leave you ever in the dark.
  Your sparkling eyes and blooming cheeks
    Must wither like the blasted rose;
  The coffin, earth, and winding-sheet
    Will soon your active limbs enclose.

4 Ye heedless ones, that wildly stroll,
    The grave will soon become your bed,
  Where silence reigns, and vapours roll
    In solemn darkness round your head.
  Your friends will pass the lonesome place,
    And with a sigh move slow along;
  Still gazing on the spires of grass
    With which your graves are overgrown.

5 Your souls will land in darker realms,
    Where vengeance reigns and billows roar,
  And roll amid the burning flames,
    When thousand thousand years are o'er.
  Sunk in the shades of endless night,
    To groan and howl in endless pain,
  And never more behold the light,
    And never, never rise again.

6 Ye blooming youth, this is the state
    Of all who do free grace refuse;
  And soon with you 'twill be too late
    The way of life and Christ to choose.
  Come, lay your carnal weapons by,
    No longer fight against your God;
  But with the gospel now comply,
    And heav'n shall be your great reward.

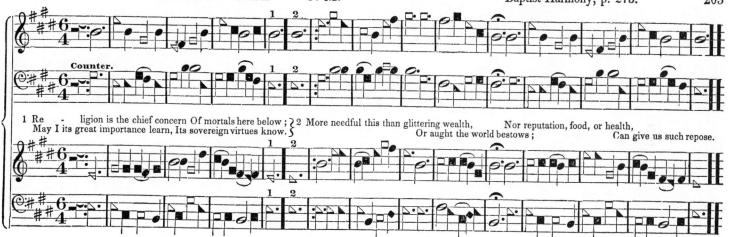

1 Re - ligion is the chief concern Of mortals here below ; 2 More needful this than glittering wealth,   Nor reputation, food, or health,
May I its great importance learn, Its sovereign virtues know.   Or aught the world bestows ;   Can give us such repose.

3 Religion should our thoughts engage
  Amidst our youthful bloom ;
'Twill fit us for declining age,
  And for the awful tomb.

4 O, may my heart, by grace renew'd,
  Be my Redeemer's throne ;
And be my stubborn will subdued
  His government to own.

5 Let deep repentance, faith, and love,
  Be join'd with godly fear ;
And all my conversation prove
  My heart to be sincere.

6 Preserve me from the snares of sin
  Through my remaining days ;
And in me let each virtue shine,
  To my Redeemer's praise.

7 Let lively hope my soul inspire,
  Let warm affections rise ;
And may I wait, with strong desire,
  To mount above the skies.

CONSOLATION NEW. S. S. E.

Come on, my partners in dis-tress, My comrades through the wilderness, Who still your bo-dies feel; A - while forget your

griefs and fears, And look beyond this vale of tears To that ce - les - tial hill, To that ce - les - tial hill.

1 Come, lit-tle children, now we may Par-take a lit-tle mor-sel,
For lit-tle songs and little ways A-dorn'd a great a-postle.
A lit-tle drop of Jesus' blood Can make a feast of u-nion; It

2 A little faith does mighty deeds, Quite past all my recount-ing;
Faith, like a lit-tle mustard seed, Can move a lof-ty mountain.
A lit-tle chari-ty and zeal, A lit-tle trib-u-la-tion, A

is by little steps we move In-to a full com-munion.

little patience makes us feel Great peace and conso-la-tion.

3 A little cross with cheerfulness,
    A little self-denial,
Will serve to make our troubles less,
    And bear the greatest trial.
The Spirit like a little dove
    On Jesus once descended;
To show his meekness and his love,
    The emblem was intended.

4 The title of the little Lamb
    Unto our Lord was given;
Such was our Saviour's little name,
    The Lord of earth and heaven.
A little voice that's small and still
    Can rule the whole creation;
A little stone the earth shall fill,
    And humble every nation.

5 A little zeal supplies the soul,
    It doth the heart inspire;
A little spark lights up the whole,
    And sets the crowd on fire.
A little union serves to hold
    The good and tender-hearted;
It's stronger than a chain of gold,
    And never can be parted.

6 Come, let us labour here below,
    And who can be the straitest;
For in God's kingdom, all must know
    The least shall be the greatest.
O give us, Lord, a little drop
    Of heavenly love and union;
O may we never, never stop
    Short of a full communion.

THE TURTLE DOVE. L. M.

Dover Selection, p. 154.

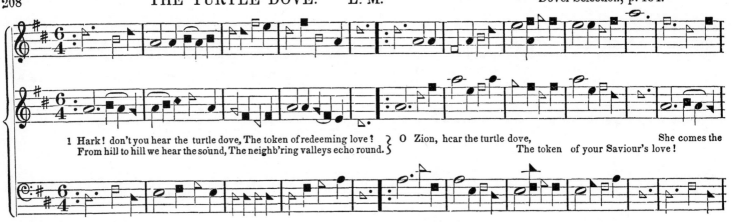

1 Hark! don't you hear the turtle dove, The token of redeeming love! } O Zion, hear the turtle dove,
From hill to hill we hear the sound, The neighb'ring valleys echo round. } The token of your Saviour's love!

She comes the

desert land to cheer, And welcome in the jubil-year.

2 The winter's past, the rain is o'er,
We feel the chilling winds no more;
The spring is come; how sweet the view,
All things appear divinely new.
On Zion's mount the watchmen cry,
"The resurrection's drawing nigh:"
Behold, the nations from abroad
Are flocking to the mount of God.

3 The trumpet sounds, both far and nigh;
O sinners, turn! why will ye die?
How can you spurn the gospel charms!
Enlist with Christ, gird on your arms.
These are the days that were foretold,
In ancient times, by prophets old;
They long'd to see this glorious light,
But all have died without the sight.

4 The latter days on us have come,
And fugitives are flocking home;
Behold them crowd the gospel road,
All pressing to the mount of God.
O yes! and I will join that band,
Now here's my heart, and here's my hand;
With Satan's band no more I'll be,
But fight for Christ and liberty.

5 His banner soon will be unfurl'd,
And he will come to judge the world;
On Zion's mountain we shall stand,
In Canaan's fair, celestial land.
When sun and moon shall darken'd be,
And flames consume the land and sea;
When worlds on worlds together blaze,
We'll shout, and loud hosannas raise

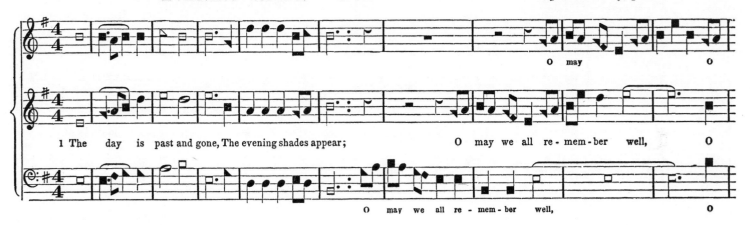

1 The   day   is   past and gone, The evening shades appear;   O may we all re - mem - ber well,   O

O   may   we   all re - mem - ber   well,

may we all re - mem - ber well, The night of death is   near.

2 We lay our garments by,
    Upon our beds to rest;
So death will soon disrobe us all
    Of what we here possess.

3 Lord, keep us safe this night,
    Secure from all our fears:
May angels guard us while we sleep,
    Till morning light appears.

4 And when we early rise,
    And view th' unwearied sun,
May we set out to win the prize,
    And after glory run.

5 And when our days are past,
    And we from time remove,
O may we in thy bosom rest,
    The bosom of thy love.

LENA. 8, 7.

See the Lord of glo - ry dy - ing! See him gasping! hear him cry-ing! See his burden'd bo-som heave!

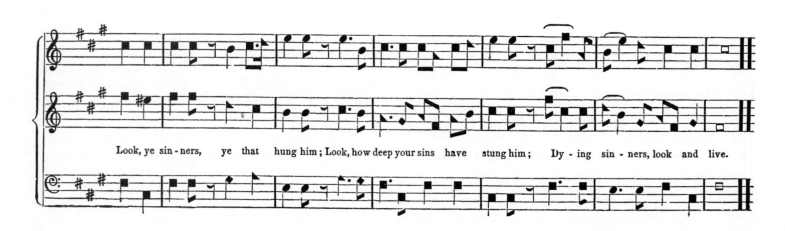

Look, ye sin - ners, ye that hung him; Look, how deep your sins have stung him; Dy - ing sin - ners, look and live.

Where nothing dwelt but beasts of prey, Or men as fierce and wild as they, He bids th'oppress'd and poor repair, And build them towns and cities there. They

They sow the fields, and

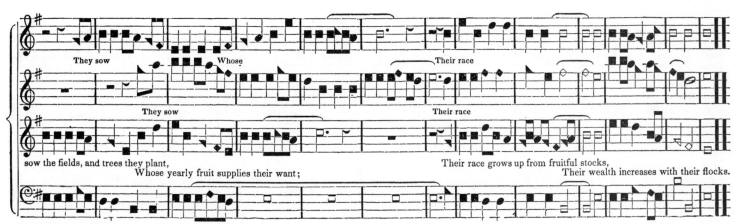

They sow

They sow

Whose

Their race

Their race

sow the fields, and trees they plant,

Whose yearly fruit supplies their want;

Their race grows up from fruitful stocks,

Their wealth increases with their flocks.

trees they plant, Whose yearly fruit supplies their want;

How pleasant 'tis to see Kindred and friends agree, Each in his pro-per station move, Each in his proper station move,

Each in his pro-per station move. :||:

And

And each fulfil his part, With sympathizing heart, In all the cares of life, In all the cares of life and love.

And With In

1 Lift up your heads, Immanuel's friends, O hal-le, hal-le-lu-jah,
And   taste the pleasure Jesus sends, O hal-le, hal-le-lu-jah.

Let nothing cause you to delay, O halle, hal-le-lu-jah;

2 Our conflicts here, though great they be, Shall not prevent our victory,
If we but watch, and strive, and pray, Like soldiers in the good old way.

And I'll sing halle-lujah, And glo-ry be to God   on high;

3 O good old way, how sweet thou art! May none of us from thee depart,
But may our actions always say, We're marching on the good old way.

And   I'll sing halle-lujah, And glo-ry be to God   on high;

But hasten on the good old way, O halle, halle-lu-jah!

And I'll sing halle-lujah, There's glory beaming from the sky.

And I'll sing halle-lujan, There's glory beaming from the sky.

4 Though Satan may his power employ
Our peace and comfort to destroy,
Yet never fear, we'll gain the day,
And triumph in the good old way.
And I'll sing, &c.

5 And when on Pisgah's top we stand,
And view by faith the promised land,
Then we may sing, and shout, and pray,
And march along the good old way.
And I'll sing, &c.

6 Ye valiant souls, for heaven contend;
Remember, glory's at the end;
Our God will wipe all tears away,
When we have run the good old way.
And I'll sing, &c.

7 Then far beyond this mortal shore,
We'll meet with those who're gone before;
And him we'll praise in endless day,
Who brought us on the good old way.
And I'll sing, &c.

REPENTANCE. C. M.

O, if my soul was form'd for wo, How would I vent my sighs! Repentance should like rivers flow, From both my streaming eyes. 'Twas

'Twas for my sins my

'Twas   Hung   And   For   For

for my sins my dearest Lord Hung on that cursed tree,   And groan'd away his dy-ing life,   For thee, my soul, for thee,

For thee, my soul, for thee.

dearest Lord   Hung   And   For   For

Young people all, attention give, I want your souls with Christ to live, Remember, you are hast'ning on
And hear what I do say; In ever - last - ing day; To death's dark, gloomy

Remember To

Remember To

shade; Your joys on earth will soon be gone, Your flesh in dust be laid. Your joys on earth will soon be gone, Your, &c.

Remember To

snade.

DELIGHT. P. M.

Coan, Guilford, Ct

Thou

No burning heats by day, Nor blasts of evening air, Shall take my health a-way, If God be with me there.

Thou art my sun and

Thou art my sun and thou my shade, To

art To guard

Thou art my sun and thou my shade, To guard my head by night or noon, by night or noon. Thou art my sun and thou my shade, To guard my head by night or noon.

thou my shade, To guard my head by night or noon.

guard my head by night or noon. Thou

Great God, at - tend while Zi-on sings The joy that from thy presence springs;

To

To spend one day with thee on earth, Ex-ceeds a thousand

thee on earth, Exceeds spend one day with thee on earth, Exceeds a thou - sand days of mirth. To spend one day with thee on earth, Exceeds a thousand days of mirth.

ceeds a thousand days of mirth.

days of mirth. To spend one day with thee on earth,

MOUNT PLEASANT. C. M

There is a house not made with hands, Eternal, and on high, And here my spi-rit waiting stands, Till God shall bid it fly.

And here

And

And

And here my spirit waiting stands, Till God shall bid it fly, Till God shall bid it

And

Till

Till

fly

Til

And here

MOUNT ZION. S M.

Brown.

The hill of Zi-on yields A thousand sa-cred sweets, Be-fore we reach the heav'nly fields, Or walk the golden streets.

Then let your songs, &c. And We're To

Then let your songs a - bound, And eve-ry tear be dry: We're marching through Immanuel's ground, To fairer worlds on

Then let your songs a - bound, And eve-ry tear be dry: We're marching through Immanuel's ground, To fair - er worlds on high.

fair - er worlds on high. We're, &c.

high. We're marching through Im - ma - nuel's ground, To fair - er worlds on high. To

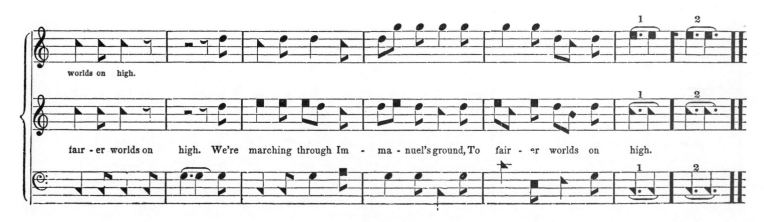

worlds on high.

fair - er worlds on high. We're marching through Im - ma - nuel's ground, To fair - er worlds on high.

Thy works of glory, mighty Lord,
That rul'st the boist'rous sea;
The sons of courage shall record,
Who tempt the dang'rous way.
At thy command the winds arise,
And

At
swell the tow'ring waves;
And
The
And
The men astonish'd mount the skies, And sink in gap - ing graves.

winds a-rise, And
The
And

1 Hither, ye faithful, haste with songs of triumph, To Beth-le-hem haste, the Lord of life to meet; To you this day is born a Prince and Saviour; O come, and let us worship, O come, and let us worship, O come, and let us wor-ship at his feet.

2 O Jesus, for such wondrous condescension,
   Our praises and reverence are an offering meet;
Now is the Word made flesh and dwells among us:
   O come, and let us worship at his feet.

3 Shout his almighty name, ye choirs of angels,
   And let the celestial courts his praise repeat,
Unto our God be glory in the highest;
   O come, and let us worship at his feet.

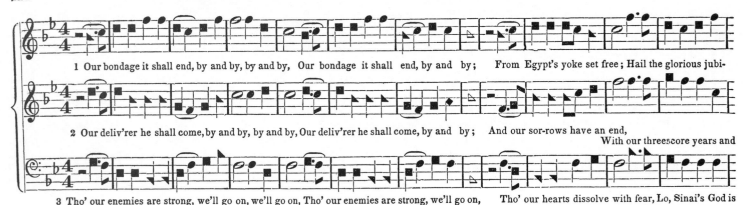

1 Our bondage it shall end, by and by, by and by, Our bondage it shall end, by and by;   From Egypt's yoke set free; Hail the glorious jubi-

2 Our deliv'rer he shall come, by and by, by and by, Our deliv'rer he shall come, by and by;   And our sor-rows have an end, With our threescore years and

3 Tho' our enemies are strong, we'll go on, we'll go on, Tho' our enemies are strong, we'll go on,   Tho' our hearts dissolve with fear, Lo, Sinai's God is

lee, And to Canaan we'll re-turn, by and by, by and by, And to Canaan we'll re - turn, by and by.

ten, And vast glory crown the day, by and by, by and by, And vast glory crown the day, by and by.

near, While the fiery pillar moves, we'll go on, we'll go on, While the fiery pillar moves, we'll go on.

4 Though Marah has bitter streams, we'll go on;
    Though Baca's vale be dry,
    And the land yield no supply;
To a land of corn and wine, we'll go on.

5 And when to Jordan's floods we are come,
    Jehovah rules the tide,
    And the waters he'll divide,
And the ransom'd host shall shout, We are come.

6 Then friends shall meet again, who have loved,
    Our embraces shall be sweet
    At the dear Redeemer's feet,
When we meet to part no more, who have loved

7 Then with all the happy throng, we'll rejoice,
    Shouting glory to our King,
    Till the vaults of heaven ring
And through all eternity we'll rejoice.

PART III.

CONSISTING OF ODES AND ANTHEMS.

CHRISTMAS ANTHEM.

Oh how charming, Oh how charming Are the radiant bands of mu - sic, mu - sic, music, mu - sic! Oh how charming

Are the radiant bands of music, Fly - ing in the air.   The church triumphant gives the tone,

In glo-ry, with ce - lestial

While they surround the holy throne,

arts, Angel - ic armies tune their harps,

And raptured seraphs play their parts:

Strike, strike, strike their notes at our Redeem - er's birth.

E. J. King.

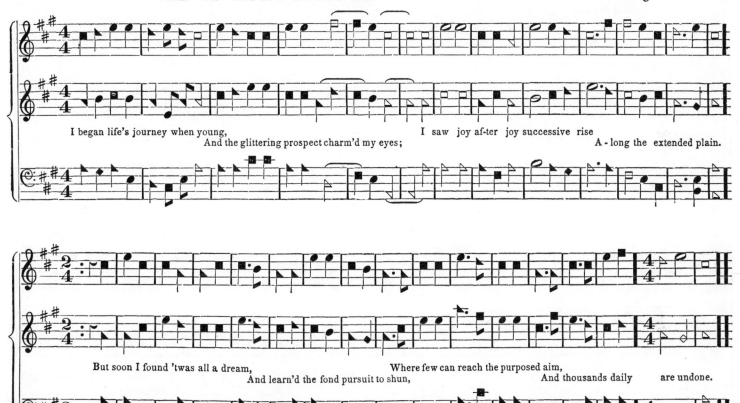

I began life's journey when young,

And the glittering prospect charm'd my eyes;

I saw joy af-ter joy successive rise

A - long the extended plain.

But soon I found 'twas all a dream,

And learn'd the fond pursuit to shun,

Where few can reach the purposed aim,

And thousands daily are undone.

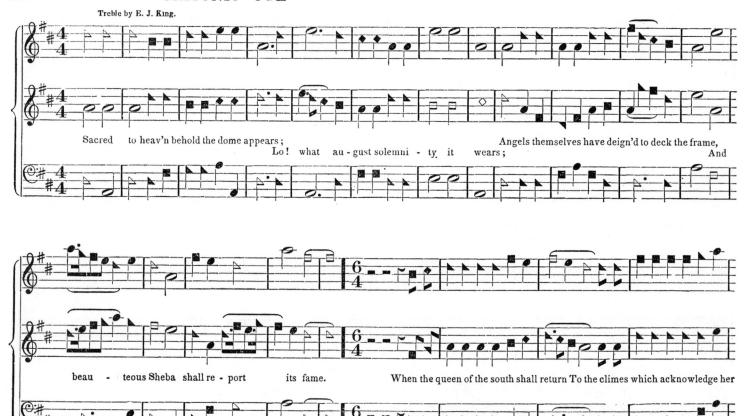

Treble by E. J. King.

Sacred to heav'n behold the dome appears; Lo! what au-gust solemni-ty it wears; Angels themselves have deign'd to deck the frame, And

beau-teous Sheba shall re-port its fame. When the queen of the south shall return To the climes which acknowledge her

sway,   Where the sun's warmer beams fiercely burn,   Well worthy my journey ! I've seen   De-
                        The princess, with transport, shall say   A monarch both graceful and wise,

serving the love of a queen,   And a temple well worthy the skies.   Open, ye gates, receive a queen who shares With equal sense your happiness and cares.

Of riches much, but more of wisdom see; Proportion'd workmanship and ma - son - ry.   Oh charming She - ba, there behold What

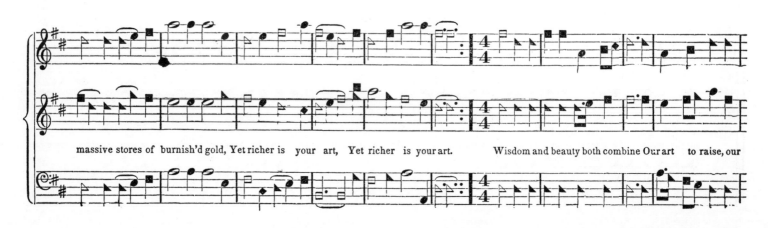

massive stores of burnish'd gold, Yet richer is your art, Yet richer is your art.   Wisdom and beauty both combine Our art to raise, our

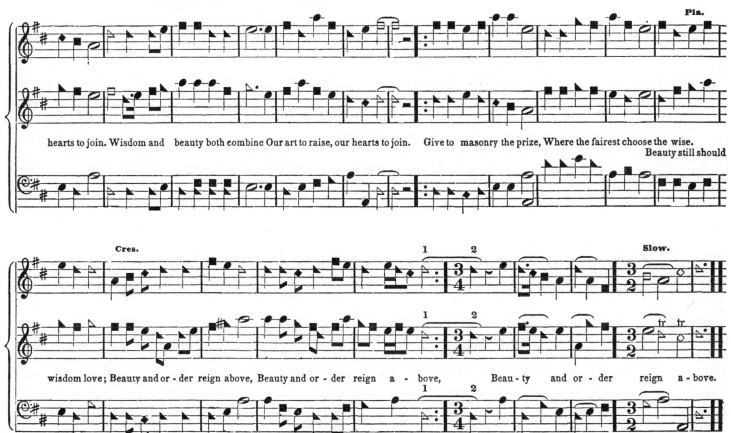

hearts to join. Wisdom and   beauty both combine Our art to raise, our hearts to join.   Give to masonry the prize, Where the fairest choose the wise.

Beauty still should

wisdom love; Beauty and or - der reign above, Beauty and or - der reign a - bove,   Beau - ty   and or - der   reign   a - bove.

BAPTISMAL ANTHEM.

Matthew 3d chapter.

B. F. White.

And say - ing, Re - pent ye;

In those days came John the Baptist, preaching in the wilderness of Judea,   And saying,   Re - pent ye;

And saying,

for the kingdom of heaven is at   hand,   For this is he that was spoken of by the prophet E-sa-ias,   saying, The voice of one

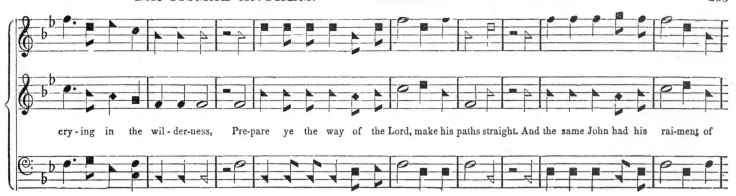

cry-ing in the wil-der-ness, Pre-pare ye the way of the Lord, make his paths straight. And the same John had his rai-ment of

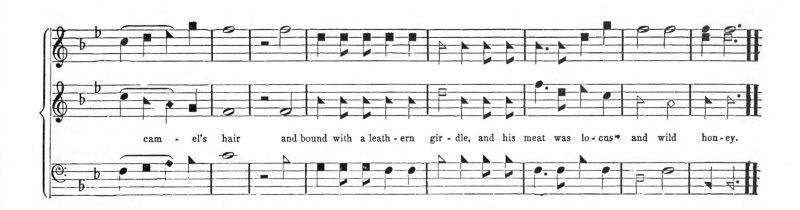

cam - el's hair   and bound with a leath-ern gir-dle, and his meat was lo-cust and wild   hon-ey.

96th Psalm.   E. J. King.

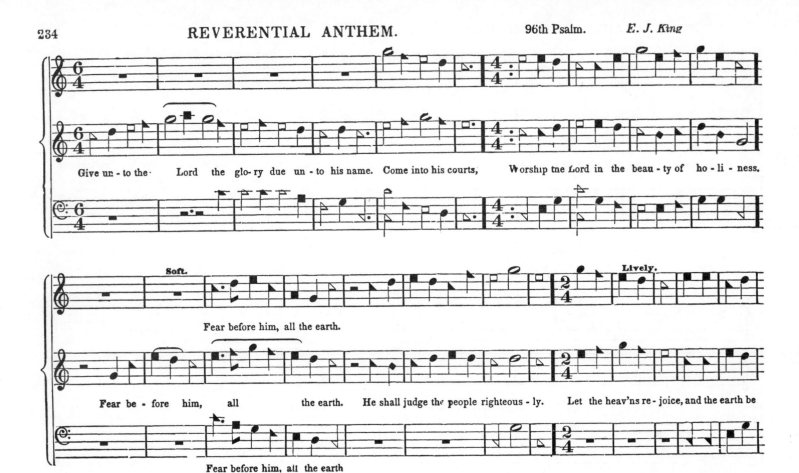

Give un-to the Lord the glo-ry due un-to his name. Come into his courts, Worship the Lord in the beau-ty of ho-li-ness.

Soft.

Fear before him, all the earth.

Lively.

Fear be-fore him, all the earth. He shall judge the people righteous-ly. Let the heav'ns re-joice, and the earth be

Fear before him, all the earth

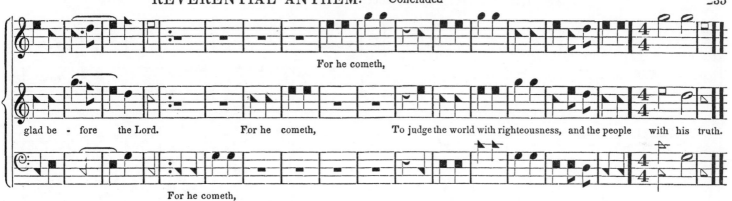

For he cometh,

glad be - fore the Lord.   For he cometh,   To judge the world with righteousness, and the people with his truth.

For he cometh,

EASTER ANTHEM.   Young's Night Thoughts, 4th Night.   *Billings.*

The   Lord is ris'n in - deed!   Hal - le - lujah! The Lord   is   ris'n in - deed! Hal - le - lu - jah!

Now is Christ ris'n from the dead, And become the first-fruit of them that slept.　　Now is Christ ris'n from the dead, And become the first-fruit of them that slept.

Halle - lujah, halle - lujah, halle - lu- jah.　　And did he rise?　　And did he rise?　　did he rise? hear it, ye

And did he rise?　　And did he rise?

nations! hear it, O ye dead! He rose, :||: :||: :||: He burst the bars of death! :||: :||: And triumph'd o'er the grave.

Then, then, then I rose, then I rose, then I rose, :||: then first hu-

mani - ty tri - umphant past the crystal ports of   light,   and   seiz'd   e - ter - nal youth.   Man   all im - mor - tal hail,

hail, Heaven, all lavish of strange gifts to man, Thine's all the glory, man's the boundless bliss; Thine's all the glo - ry, man's the boundless bliss.

David the king was grieved and moved, He went to his chamber, his chamber, and wept; And as he went he wept, and said,

O my son! :||: Would to God I had died, :||: :||: For thee, O Ab-salom, my son, my son!

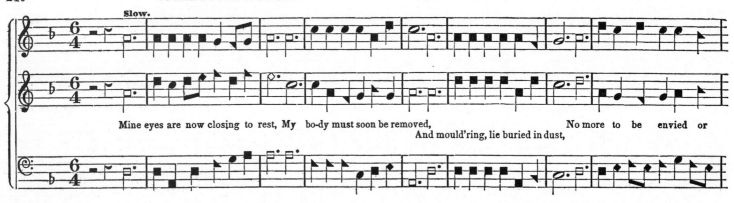

Mine eyes are now closing to rest, My bo-dy must soon be removed,
And mould'ring, lie buried in dust,
No more to be envied or

loved, No more to be envied or loved. Ah! what is this drawing my breath, And steal-ing my sen-ses a-way!

O tell me,

O tell me,

O tell me, my soul, is it death, Releasing me kindly from clay? Now mounting, my soul shall de-

O tell me,

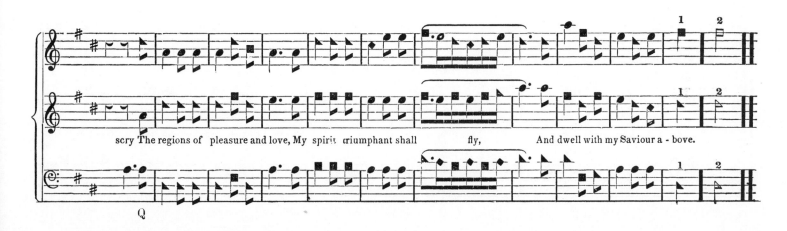

scry The regions of pleasure and love, My spirit triumphant shall fly, And dwell with my Saviour a - bove.

Q

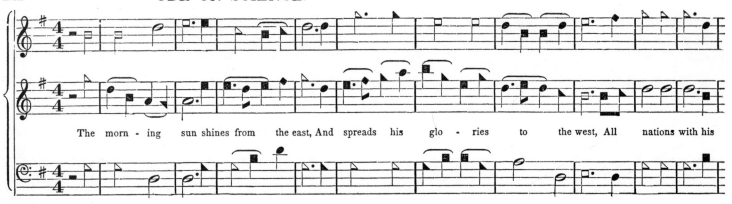

The morn - ing sun shines from the east, And spreads his glo - ries to the west, All nations with his

beams are blest, Where'er the ra - diant light ap - pears. So sci - ence spreads her lu - cid ray O'er lands which

long in darkness lay; She vi - sits fair Co - lum - bi - a, And sets her sons a - mong the stars.

Fair freedom her at - tend - ant waits, To bless the por - tals of her gates, To crown the young and ris - ing states With

lau-rels　of　im - mor - tal day:　The　Brit - ish　yoke,　the　Gal - lic chain, Was urged up - on　our

necks in　vain, All haugh-ty　ty - rants　we　dis - dain,　And shout, Long live　A - me - ri　ca.

Vital spark of heav'nly flame, Quit, oh! quit this mortal frame; Trembling, hoping, ling'-ring, fly - ing, fly - ing, fly ing.

Oh the pain, the bliss of dy-ing! Cease, fond nature, cease thy strife, And let me languish in - to life, And let me languish in - to life.

Hark! Hark! Hark! they whisper; angels say, Sister spirit, come away; Sis-ter spi-rit,

Hark! they whisper; angels say, Sis-ter spi-rit, come a-way.

come away. What is this absorbs me quite—Steals my senses, shuts my sight? Drowns my spirit, draws my breath? Tell me, my soul, can

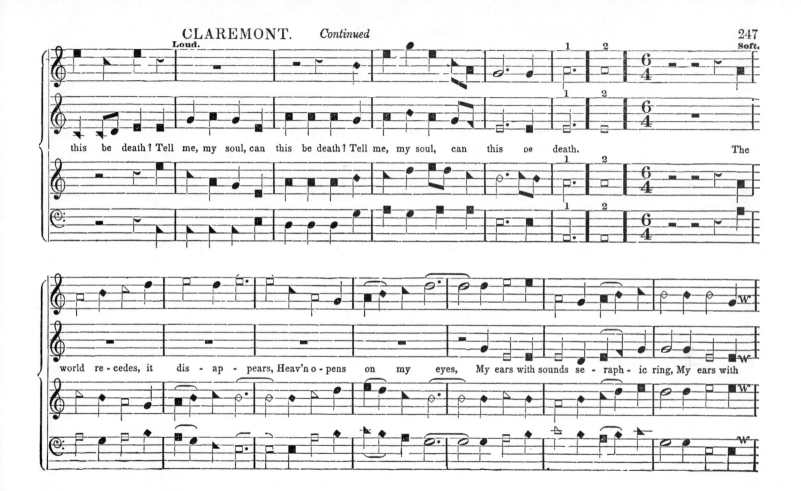

this be death? Tell me, my soul, can this be death? Tell me, my soul, can this oe death. The

world re-cedes, it dis-ap-pears, Heav'n o-pens on my eyes, My ears with sounds se-raph-ic ring, My ears with

CLAREMONT. *Continued.*

sounds se - raph - ic   ring,   My ears with sounds se - raph - ic   ring.   Lend, lend your wings! I

mount! I fly!   I   mount! I fly! O grave! where is thy   vic - to - ry! thy vic - to - ry! O grave! where is thy

vic-to - ry? thy vic - to - ry? O death! where is thy sting? Lend, lend your wings! I mount! I fly! I mount! I fly! I

mount! I fly, I fly! O grave! where is thy victory?
O death! where is thy sting?
I mount! I fly! I mount! I fly! O grave! where is thy vic - to - ry?
O death! where is thy sting?

hands, and they cease not day nor night, saying, Holy, ho-ly, ho-ly, ho-ly, ho-ly, Lord God Al-mighty, Which was, and is, and

is to come, Which was, &c. And I heard a mighty an-gel fly - ing thro' the midst of heav'n,

cry - ing with a loud voice, Wo, wo, wo, wo, Be un - to the earth by reason of the trumpet which is

yet to sound. And when the last trumpet sounded, the great men and nobles, rich men and poor, bond and free, ga - ther - ed themselves to-

gether, and cri -ed to the rocks and mountains to fall up - on them, and hide them from the face of Him that sitt - eth on the throne;

For the great day of the Lord is come, and who shall be a - ble to stand? And who shall be a - ble to stand?

ROSE OF SHARON

Sol. Song ii.   *Billings.*

I   am the rose of Sharon, and the li - ly of the   valley;   I   am the rose of Sharon, and the li - ly of the   val-ley;

As the lily among the thorns, so is my love among the daughters; As the apple tree, the ap-ple tree a - mong   the   trees   of the   wood,

so is my beloved among the sons, so is my beloved among the sons.   I sat down un-der his shadow with great delight,

I sat

I sat

I sat

And his fruit was sweet to my taste; And his fruit, and his fruit was sweet to my taste.

And his frui. was sweet to my taste.

And his fruit, and his fruit was sweet to my taste, And his fruit, and his fruit, &c.

He brought me to the banqueting house,

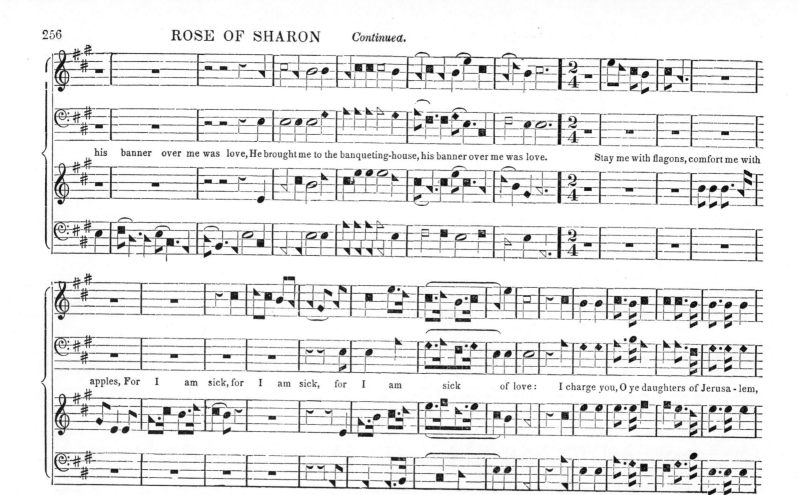

his banner over me was love, He brought me to the banqueting-house, his banner over me was love.   Stay me with flagons, comfort me with

apples, For I am sick, for I am sick, for I am sick of love: I charge you, O ye daughters of Jerusa-lem,

By the roes, and by the hinds of the field, That you stir not up, that you stir not up, that you stir not up, that you stir not up, nor a-

wake, awake, a-wake, a-wake my love, till he please. The voice of my beloved, Be-hold! he cometh,

R

leaping upon the mountains, skipping, :||:   :||:   :||:   leaping upon the mountains, skipping up - on the hills.   My beloved spake, and

said un - to me,   Rise up, rise up, rise up,   rise   up,   my love,   my fair one, and come a - way.   For   lo, the winter is

past, the rain is over and gone. For lo, the winter is past, the rain is over and gone, the rain is over, the

rain is over, the rain is over and gone. For lo, the winter is past, the rain is over and gone.

FAREWELL ANTHEM

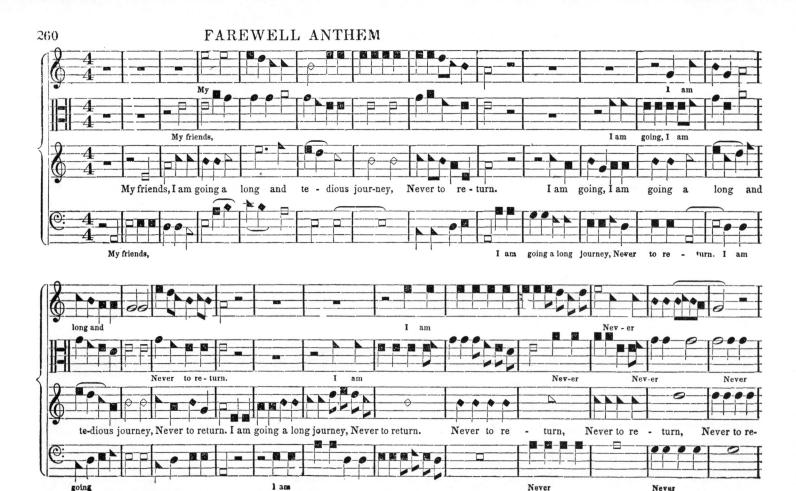

Hark! hark! my dear friends, for death hath call - ed me, And I must go, and lie down in the cold and si - lent grave,

Where the mourners cease from mourning,

and the pris'ner is set free ;   Fare you well, fare you well, fare you well, fare you well, fare you well, my friends.

Where the rich and the poor are both alike.

APPENDIX TO THE SACRED HARP:

CONTAINING A VARIETY OF

STANDARD AND FAVOURITE TUNES NOT COMPRISED IN THE BODY OF THE WORK.

COMPILED BY

A COMMITTEE APPOINTED BY "THE SOUTHERN MUSICAL CONVENTION."

―――――――――

THE Committee appointed by "The Southern Musical Convention," at its last session, to whom was referred the revision and enlargement of the Sacred Harp, beg leave to say to all whom it may concern, that we, according to appointment, have taken the work under consideration and inspection, and have corrected the rudimental errors in said work, and the typographical errors in the music, and have also added such pieces of composition as we 'think are calculated to enhance the value of the work, and are happily adapted to the use of the public generally, as an Appendix to the Sacred Harp, and have adopted the same.

All of which is respectfully submitted,

B. F. WHITE,	S. R. PENICK,
JOEL KING,	J. R. TURNER,
LEONARD P. BREEDLOVE,	R. F. M. MANN,
A. OGLETREE,	E. L. KING,

Committee.

Hamilton, Jan. 12, 1850

[Adopted.]

DUKE STREET.   L. M.

Great God! attend to my com-plaint, Nor let my drooping spirit faint; When foes in se - cret spread the snare, Let my sal - va - tion be thy care.

HEBRON.   L. M.

Thus far the Lord hath led me on, Thus far his power prolongs my days; And every evening shall make known Some fresh memorial of his grace.

RESTORATION.   L. M.   Baptist Hymn Book, p. 594.   *D. P. White.*

How many years has man been driv'n,
Far off from happiness and heav'n;

When wilt thou, gracious Lord, restore Thy wand'ring church to roam no more?

GRAVITY.   L. M.

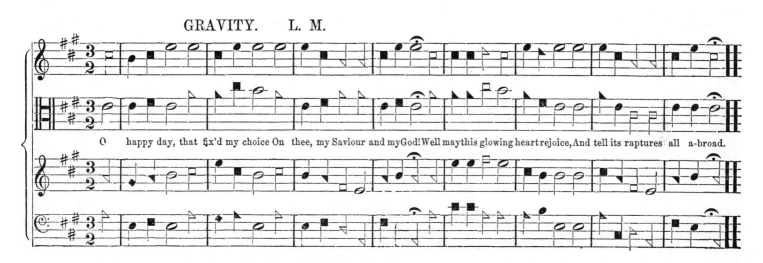

O happy day, that fix'd my choice On thee, my Saviour and my God! Well may this glowing heart rejoice, And tell its raptures all a-broad.

UXBRIDGE. L. M.

Thanks to the hand that set us free, E - ter-nal Spirit, thanks to thee, Whose pow'r resistless, un-confined, Subdues the passion of the mind.

LEBANON, NEW. L. M.

Rev. Jas. P. Carrell.

Come, sinners, to the gospel feast, Let ev'ry soul be Jesus' guest, Ye need not one be left behind, For God hath bid-den all.mankind.

DAY OF WORSHIP. L. M. D.

B. F. & E. K. Davis

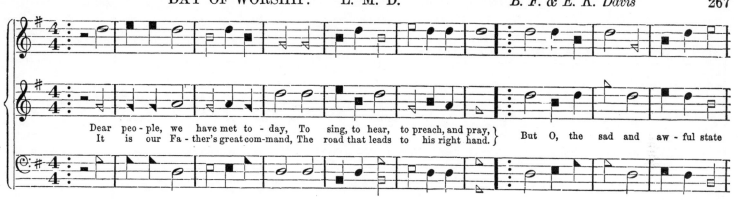

Dear peo-ple, we have met to-day, To sing, to hear, to preach, and pray,
It is our Fa-ther's great com-mand, The road that leads to his right hand.
But O, the sad and aw-ful state

Of those that stand and come too late! The fool-ish vir-gins did be-gin To knock, but could not en-ter in.

ALL SAINTS, NEW. L. M D.

Hall.

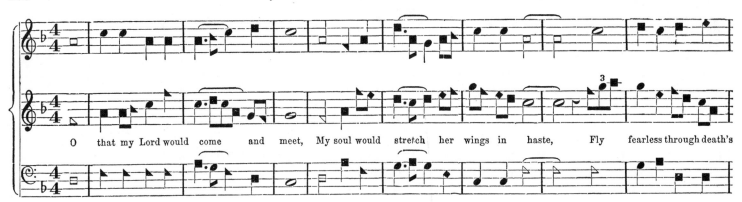

O that my Lord would come and meet, My soul would stretch her wings in haste, Fly fearless through death's

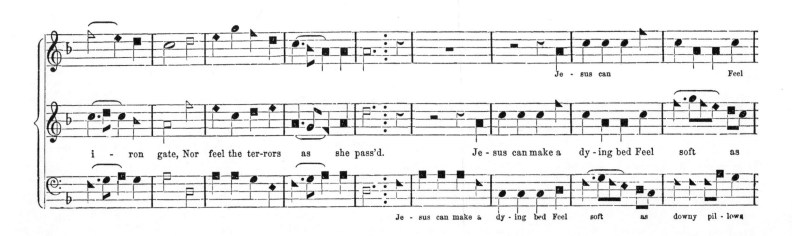

i - ron gate, Nor feel the ter-rors as she pass'd. Je - sus can make a dy - ing bed Feel soft as

Je - sus can make a dy - ing bed Feel soft as downy pil - lows

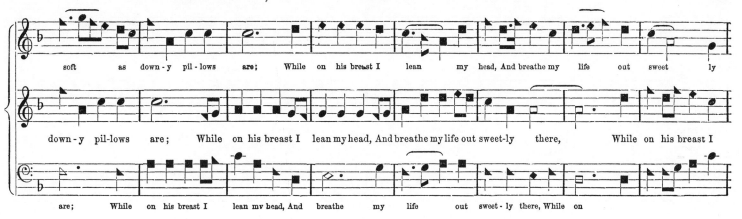

soft as down-y pil-lows are; While on his breast I lean my head, And breathe my life out sweet ly

down-y pil-lows are; While on his breast I lean my head, And breathe my life out sweet-ly there, While on his breast I

are; While on his breast I lean my head, And breathe my life out sweet-ly there, While on

there, While on And breathe, And breathe, And breathe my life

lean my head, And breathe, And breathe, And breathe, And breathe my life out sweetly there.

head, And breathe, And breathe, And breathe, And breathe, And breathe my life, &c.

CONFIDENCE.   L. M. D.   *By J. R. Turner.*

A - way, my   un - be - liev - ing fear;   Fear shall in me no more have place. }
My Saviour doth not yet ap - pear,   He hides the brightness of his face; } But shall I   there - fore   let him   go,

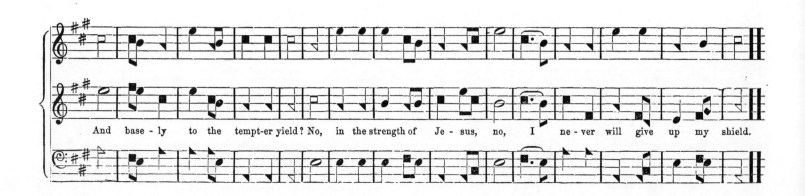

And base - ly   to the tempt-er yield? No, in the strength of   Je - sus, no,   I   ne - ver will give up my shield.

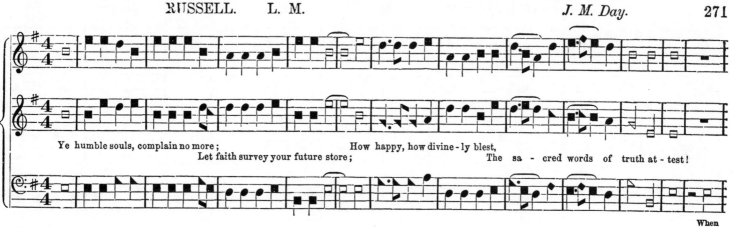

Ye humble souls, complain no more ; How happy, how divine - ly blest,
Let faith survey your future store ; The sa - cred words of truth at - test!

When

When conscious And pours Hope points, &c.

When conscious grief laments sincere, Hope points to your dejected eyes,
And pours the penitential tear, The bright reversion in the skies.

conscious grief la - ments sin - cere, And pours Hope points, &c.

Now, in the heat of youth - ful blood, Re - mem - ber your Cre - a - tor, God!   Be-

Be - hold the months come

Be - hold the months come hast'ning on, When

Be - hold the   When you   When you, &c.

hold the months come hast'ning on, When you shall say, My joys are gone,   When you shall say, My joys are gone.

hast'ning on, When you   Be - hold the   When you, &c.

you shall say, My joys are gone,   Be - hold the   When you, &c.

My waken'd soul, extend thy wings,   Be-yond the verge of mortal things,

And then we'll sing Ho - san - nah: And then we'll sing Ho-san-nah.

See this vain world in smoke decay,   And rocks and mountains melt away, And then we'll sing Ho-san-nah.

And then we'll sing Ho - san - nah,

We have but the one more river to cross,   We have, &c.

And then we'll sing Ho - san - nah,

We have, &c.   And then, &c.   We have, &c.   And then, &c

1. My spi-rit looks to God a-lone; My rock and re-fuge is his throne;   In all my fears, in

In all my fears, in all my straits, My

In all my fears, in all my straits, My soul on his sal-

all my fears, In all my straits, My soul, &c.

all my straits, My soul on his sal-va-tion waits.

soul on his sal-va-tion waits, My soul, &c.

va- - - tion waits, My soul, &c.

2. Trust him, ye saints, in all your ways,
Pour out your hearts before his face :
When helpers fail and foes invade,
God is our all-sufficient aid.

3. False are the men of high degree,
The baser sort are vanity;
Laid in the balance, both appear
Light as a puff of empty air.

4. Make not increasing gold your trust,
Nor set your hearts on glitt'ring dust;
Why will you grasp the fleeting smoke,
And not believe what God has spoke?

5. Once hath his awful voice declared,
Once and again my ears have heard,
All power is his eternal due;
He must be fear'd and trusted too.

6. For sovereign power reigns not alone,
Grace is a partner of the throne;
Thy grace and justice, mighty Lord,
Shall well divide our last reward.

LOVING-KINDNESS. L. M.

By J. L. P. & S. R. Penick.

Awake, my soul, to joyful lays, Halle, Hallelujah!
And sing the great Redeemer's praise, Halle, Hallelujah!

He justly claims a song from me,
Hal-le, Hal-le - lu-jah,

His loving-kindness, O how free!
Halle, Halle-lu-jah,

ROLL ON. L. M.

Miss Cynthia Bass.

Why should we start, and fear to die? What tim'rous worms we mortals are!
Death is the gate of endless joy, And yet we dread to enter there.
Roll on, roll on, sweet moments roll on,
And let the poor pilgrim go home, go home.

BRIDGEWATER. L. M.

Edson.

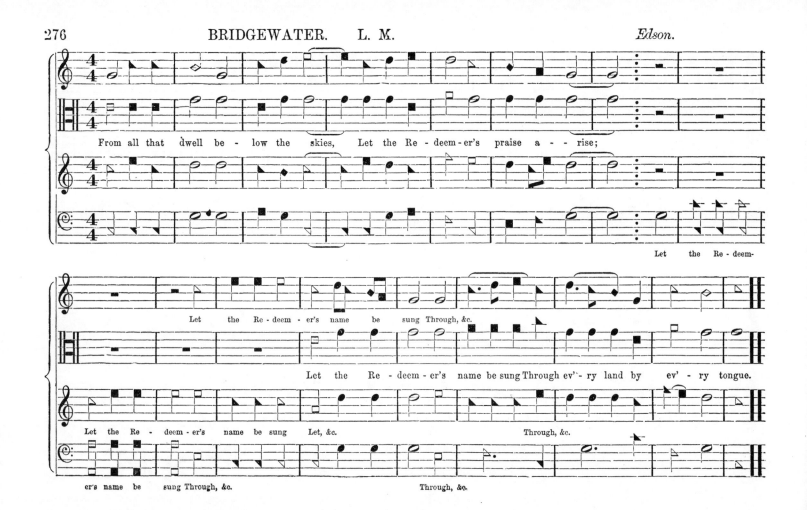

From all that dwell be - low the skies, Let the Re - deem - er's praise a - - rise;

Let the Re - deem-

Let the Re - deem - er's name be sung Through, &c.

Let the Re - deem - er's name be sung Through ev' - ry land by ev' - ry tongue.

Let the Re - deem - er's name be sung Let, &c. Through, &c.

er's name be sung Through, &c. Through, &c.

I know that my Re - deem - er lives, Glo - ry, hal - le - lu - jah!
What com - fort this sweet sen - tence gives, Glo - ry, hal - le - lu - jah!

Shout on, pray on, we're

gain - ing ground, Glo - ry, hal - le - lu - jah! The dead's a - live, and the lost is found, Glo - ry, hal - le - lu - jah!

SWEET HEAVEN. L. M.

Z. L. King.

The Lord, who built the earth and sky, In mercy stoops to hear thy cry; } Oh, heaven, sweet heaven, when shall I see?
His promise all may freely claim, Ask, and receive in Jesus' name. }

Oh, when shall I get there?

TRAVELLING PILGRIM. L. M.

CHORUS.

S. H. Rees.

1. Farewell! vain world, I'm going home,   stormy clouds to rise;
        Where there's no more
   My Saviour smiles, and bids me come,   stormy clouds to rise; }
        Where there's no more

To the land,   To the land I am bound,   stormy clouds to rise.
   To the land,   Where there's no more

2. Sweet angels beckon me a-way,   stormy clouds to rise;
        Where there's no more
   To sing God's praise in endless day,   stormy clouds to rise; }
        Where there's no more

To the land,   To the land I am bound,   stormy clouds to rise.
   To the land,   Where there's no more

THE BIRMAN HYMN. L. M.

W. W. Parks.

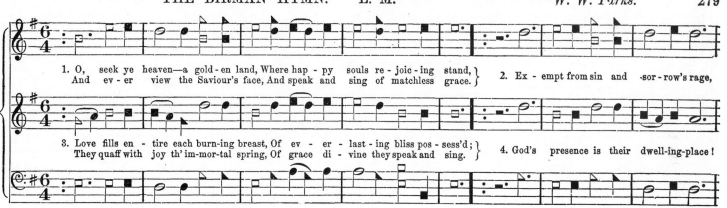

1. O, seek ye heaven—a gold-en land, Where hap-py souls re-joic-ing stand,
And ev-er view the Saviour's face, And speak and sing of matchless grace. } 2. Ex-empt from sin and -sor-row's rage,

3. Love fills en-tire each burn-ing breast, Of ev-er-last-ing bliss pos-sess'd; } 4. God's presence is their dwell-ing-place!

From sick-ness, death, and wast-ing age; All suff'ring ban-ish'd from the place, They speak, and sing of matchless grace!

The glo-rious and ef-ful-gent rays From Je-sus' face a-round them shine,—They speak, and sing of grace di-vine!

WESTFORD. L. M.

By Read.

I wait a

Fain would my eyes my Sa-viour see,

Let my re - li - gious hours a - lone,

Far from my thoughts, vain world, be - gone, Let, &c. Fain, &c. I wait a

vis - it, Lord, from thee, Fain, &c. I wait, &c.

Fain, &c. I wait a vis - it, Lord, from thee. My heart grows warm with

Fain, &c. I wait, &c.

vis - it, Lord, from thee, Fain, &c. wait, &c.

ho - ly fire, And kin-dles with a pure de - sire. Come, my dear Je-sus, from a - bove, And feed my soul with heav'nly love; Blest

Je-sus, what de - li-cious fare! How sweet thine en-ter-tain-ments are! Ne-ver did an-gels taste a - bove Re-deem-ing grace and dy - ing love.

I'M GOING HOME. L. M.

Leonard P. Breedlove.

Fare - well! vain world! I'm go - ing home! My Sa - viour smiles and bids me come, And I don't care to stay here long!
Sweet an - gels beck - on me a - way, To sing God's praise in end - less day, And I don't care to stay here long!

Right up yon - der, Christians, a - way up yon - der; O, yes, my Lord, for I don't care to stay here long.

BALLERMA. C. M.   Arranged by *B. F. White.*

There is a land of pure de-light, Where saints im-mor-tal reign; In - fi - nite day ex-cludes the night, And pleasures ban - ish pain.

ORTONVILLE. C. M.   Arranged by *B. F. White.*

How sweet the name of Je-sus sounds   It soothes his sorrows, heals his wounds,   And drives away his fear.
In a be - liev-er's ear!   And drives away his fear,

ROCKINGHAM. C. M.

B. F. White.

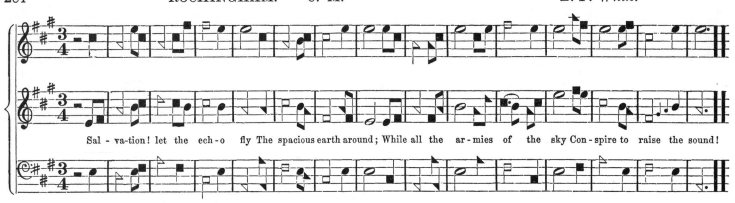

Sal - va-tion! let the ech-o fly The spacious earth around; While all the ar-mies of the sky Con-spire to raise the sound!

PIETY. C. M.

B. F. White.

O for a clo-ser walk with God, A calm and heavenly frame; } That leads me to the Lamb!
A light to shine up-on the road That leads me to the Lamb!

That leads me to the Lamb!

A light to shine up-on the road That leads me to the Lamb!

ARNOLD. C. M.

L. P. Breedlove.

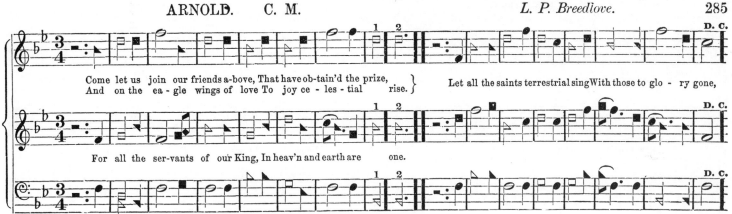

Come let us join our friends a-bove, That have ob-tain'd the prize,
And on the ea - gle wings of love To joy ce - les - tial rise.
Let all the saints terrestrial sing With those to glo - ry gone,

For all the ser-vants of our King, In heav'n and earth are one.

LAND OF REST. C. M.

By H. S. Rees.

O land of rest, for thee I sigh, When will the moments come, When I shall lay my ar - mour by, And dwell with Christ at home?

EMANUEL.   C. M. *J. M. Day.*

1. Dear Sovereign of my soul's desires, Thy love is bliss di - vine,   Accept the wish that love inspires,   And bid me call thee mine.
                                                                                                          And bid me call thee mine,

2. I would be thine, thou know'st I would,   Thee, O my all-sufficient good, I want, and thee a - lone, I want, and thee a-lone.
   And have thee all my own,

MELODY.   C. M. *B. F. White.*

And must I   be to judgment brought, And answer in that   day   For ev' - ry vain and i - dle thought, And   ev' - ry word I   say?

1. The Lord will hap-pi-ness di - vine On con-trite hearts be - stow; Then tell me, gra-cious God! is mine A contrite

heart, or no? A con-trite heart, or no, A con-trite heart, or no?

2. I hear, but seem to hear in vain,
   Insensible as steel;
   If aught is felt, 'tis only pain
   To find I cannot feel.

3. I sometimes think myself inclined
   To love thee, if I could;
   But often feel another mind
   Averse to all that's good.

4. My best desires are faint and few,
   I fain would strive for more;
   But, when I cry—"My strength renew,"
   Seem weaker than before.

5. Thy saints are comforted, I know,
   And love thy house of prayer;
   I sometimes go where others go,
   But find no comfort there.

SHEPHERDS REJOICE. C. M. D. *L. P. Breedlove.*

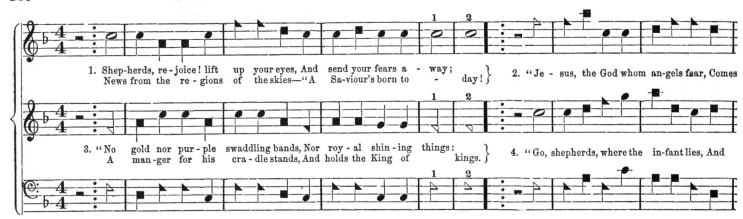

1. Shep-herds, re-joice! lift up your eyes, And send your fears a - way;
News from the re - gions of the skies—"A Sa-viour's born to - day! }

2. "Je - sus, the God whom an-gels fear, Comes

3. "No gold nor pur - ple swaddling bands, Nor roy - al shin-ing things:
A man-ger for his cra - dle stands, And holds the King of kings. }

4. "Go, shepherds, where the in-fant lies, And

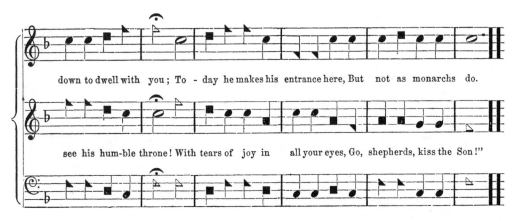

down to dwell with you; To - day he makes his entrance here, But not as monarchs do.

see his hum-ble throne! With tears of joy in all your eyes, Go, shepherds, kiss the Son!"

5. Thus Gabriel sang, and straight around
   The heavenly armies throng;
   They tune their harps to lofty sound,
   And thus conclude the song:

6. "Glory to God that reigns above!
   Let peace surround the earth;
   Mortals shall know their Maker's love,
   At their Redeemer's birth."

7. Lord! and shall angels have their songs,
   And men no tunes to raise?
   O may we lose our useless tongues,
   When they forget to praise!

8. Glory to God that reigns above,
   That pitied us forlorn!
   We join to sing our Maker's love,
   For there's a Saviour born

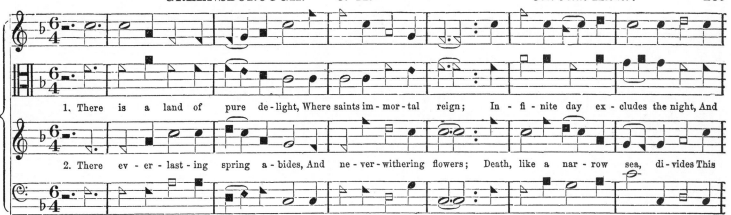

1. There is a land of pure de-light, Where saints im-mor-tal reign; In-fi-nite day ex-cludes the night, And

2. There ev-er-last-ing spring a-bides, And ne-ver-withering flowers; Death, like a nar-row sea, di-vides This

plea-sures ban-ish pain, And plea-sures ban-ish pain.

heaven-ly land from ours, This heaven-ly land from ours.

3. [Sweet fields, beyond the swelling flood,
   Stand dress'd in living green:
So to the Jews old Canaan stood,
   While Jordan roll'd between.

4. But timorous mortals start, and shrink
   To cross this narrow sea,
And linger, shivering on the brink,
   And fear to launch away.]

5. O! could we make our doubts remove,—
   Those gloomy doubts that rise,
And see the Canaan that we love,
   With unbeclouded eyes;

6. Could we but climb where Moses stood,
   And view the landscape o'er;
Not Jordan's stream, nor death's cold **flood**
   Should fright us from the shore.

VICTORIA. C. M.

Leonard P. Breedlove.

A - las! and did my Saviour bleed?   A - las! and did my Saviour bleed?

A - las! and did   my Saviour bleed?   And did my Sov'reign die?   1

Would he devote his   sa-cred head,   Would he de-vote his   sa-cred head

Would he de - vote   his sa-cred head,   For such a worm as   I?   I

have but one more   ri-ver to   cross,   I   have but one more ri-ver to cross,

I   have but   one   more ri-ver to   cross,   And then I'll be   at   rest.

have but one more   ri-ver to   cross,   I   have but one more   ri-ver to cross,

I   have but   one   more ri-ver to   cross,   And then I'll be at   rest.

1   2

The pro - mise of my Fa - - - - - ther's love Shall stand for ev - - - - - er good,

He

He said and gave his

He said, &c. And

said, and gave his soul to death, And, &c. He And, &c.

He said, and gave his soul to death, And seal'd the grace with blood . He blood. . . And seal'd the grace with blood.

soul to death, And, &c. He And, &c.

seal'd the grace with blood . . . He blood. . . . . And, &c.

THE SINNER'S RESOLVE. C. M.

By E. L. King.

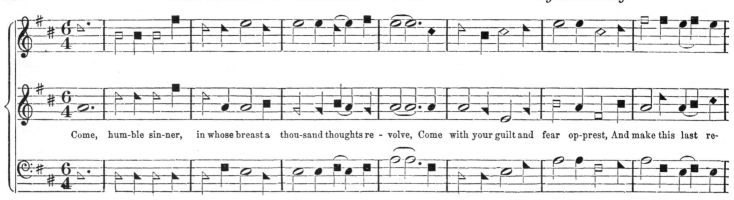

Come, hum-ble sin-ner, in whose breast a thou-sand thoughts re - volve, Come with your guilt and fear op-prest, And make this last re-

solve: I'll go to Je - sus, though my sin Hath like a moun-tain rose, I know his courts, I'll en - ter in What-ev - er may op-

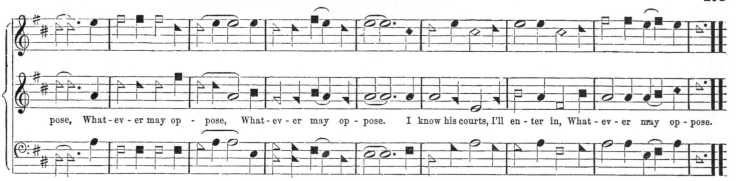

pose, What - ev - er may op - pose, What - ev - er may op - pose. I know his courts, I'll en - ter in, What - ev - er may op - pose.

ST. THOMAS. S. M.

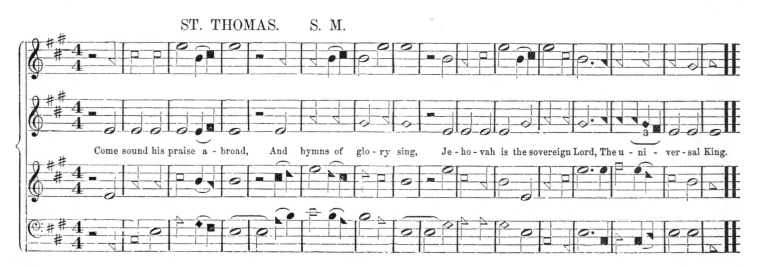

Come sound his praise a - broad, And hymns of glo - ry sing, Je - ho - vah is the sovereign Lord, The u - ni - ver - sal King.

NEVER PART. C. M. *Jno. Carwell.*

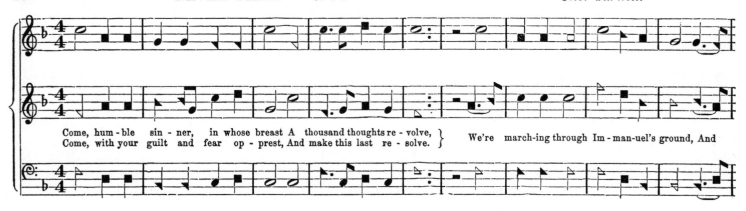

Come, hum-ble sin-ner, in whose breast A thousand thoughts re-volve,
Come, with your guilt and fear op-prest, And make this last re-solve. } We're march-ing through Im-man-uel's ground, And

soon shall hear the trum-pet sound, And then all shall with Je-sus reign, And ne-ver, ne-ver part a-gain. What? ne-ver part a-gain,

What, &c.   No, nev-er, &c.   And soon, &c.   And nev-er, nev-er, &c.

No, nev-er part a - gain. What, &c.   No nev-er, &c.   And soon, &c.   And never, never part a - gain.

No, nev - er, &c.   No, nev - er, &c.   And soon, &c.   And nev - er, nev - er, &c.

ZION'S JOY.   S. M.   *By Dr. W. J. Thomas.*

How beauteous are their feet, Who stand on Zi-on's hill! Who bring salvation on their tongue, Who, &c.   And words of truth reveal!

SARDINIA. C. M. D.

Castle.

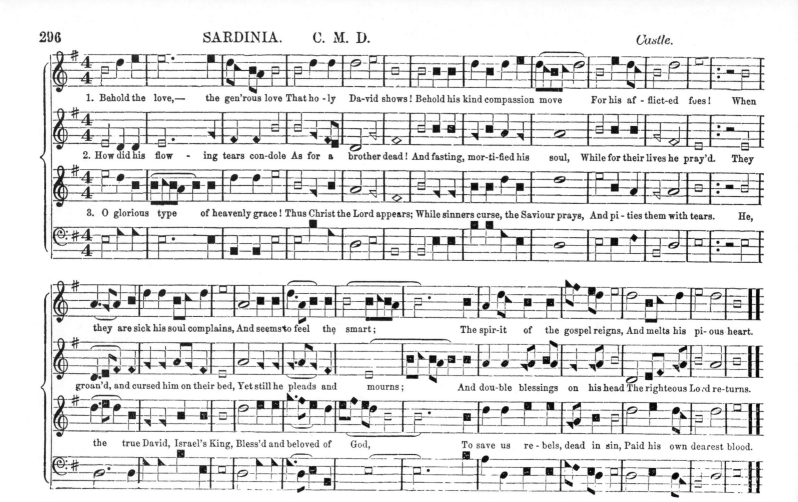

1. Behold the love,— the gen'rous love That ho-ly Da-vid shows! Behold his kind compassion move For his af-flict-ed foes! When

2. How did his flow - ing tears con-dole As for a brother dead! And fasting, mor-ti-fied his soul, While for their lives he pray'd. They

3. O glorious type of heavenly grace! Thus Christ the Lord appears; While sinners curse, the Saviour prays, And pi-ties them with tears. He,

they are sick his soul complains, And seems to feel the smart; The spir-it of the gospel reigns, And melts his pi-ous heart.

groan'd, and cursed him on their bed, Yet still he pleads and mourns; And dou-ble blessings on his head The righteous Lord re-turns.

the true David, Israel's King, Bless'd and beloved of God, To save us re-bels, dead in sin, Paid his own dearest blood.

My   rap - ture seem'd a

When   God re - veal'd his   gra - cious   name, And changed my mourn - ful   state,

My

pleas - ing dream, My   rap - ture   The   grace ap - pear'd so great, The grace, &c.

My   rap - ture seem'd a   pleas - ing   dream,   The grace ap - pear'd so   great!

rap - ture seem'd a   pleas - ing dream, My   rap - ture   The grace, &c.

My   rap - ture seem'd a   pleas - ing dream. The   grace   ʼd so   great,   The grace, &c.

My feet shall vis-it thine a-bode, My songs, &c.

What shall.. I ren - - der to my God For all his kind-ness shown? My songs address thy

My feet shall vis - it thine a - bode, My songs, &c.

throne. My feet shall vis - it thine a - bode, My songs, &c. My feet, &c. My songs, &c.

The for-mer   And   the - - -

Lo! what a glo-rious sight ap-pears To our be-liev-ing eyes;

The former seas have

The for-mer   And   the - - - - -   old

The for-mer seas have pass'd a-way, And   the - - - - -   old roll-ing skies!

- - - - -   old roll-ing skies,   The for-mer   And the   And the, &c.   1   2

pass'd away, And   the   old roll-ing skies,   And the old roll-ing skies, And the   old roll-ing skies!   1   2

roll-ing skies,   The for-mer   And the   And the, &c.

The for-mer   And   skies,   And the   1   2

CALVARY. C. M. *Reed.*

1. To our Re-deem-er's glorious name, A - wake the sa - cred song! O may his love (im - mor - tal flame!) Tune

2. His love, what mor-tal thought can reach! What mor - tal tongue dis - play! Im - a - gi - na-tion's ut - most stretch In

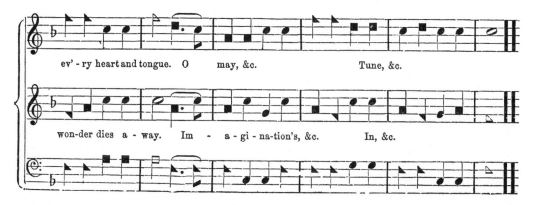

ev' - ry heart and tongue. O may, &c.   Tune, &c.

won-der dies a - way. Im - a - gi - na-tion's, &c.   In, &c.

3.

He left his radiant throne on high,
   Left the bright realms of bliss,
And came to earth to bleed and die!—
   Was ever love like this?

4.

Dear Lord, while we adoring pay
   Our humble thanks to thee,
May every heart with rapture say,
   "The Saviour died for me."

5.

O may the sweet, the blissful theme,
   Fill every heart and tongue:
Till strangers love thy charming **name**,
   And join the sacred song.

NEW JORDAN. C. M. D.

Thumwaz.

On Jordan's stormy banks I stand, And cast a wish - ful eye, To Ca-naan's fair and hap - py land, Where my possessions lie.

Oh

Oh, &c.   Oh, &c.   That ri - ses, &c.

Oh the transporting, rapturous scenes, That ri - ses to my sight,

Oh, &c.   That ri - ses, &c.

the transport - ing, rapturous scenes, That ri - ses to my sight, ...

NEW JORDAN. *Concluded.*

Sweet fields, &c. And, &c. Sweet fields, &c. And, &c.

Sweet fields ar - ray'd in living green, And riv - ers of de - light. Sweet, &c. And, &c.

Sweet fields, &c. And, &c. Sweet fields, &c. And, &c.

LITTLE MARLBOROUGH. S. M.

Wel - come, sweet day of rest, That saw the Lord a - rise; Wel - come to this re - viv-ing breast, And these re - joic - ing eyes.

304   MORGAN.   C. M.

With songs and hon - ours sound - ing loud, Ad - dress the Lord on high! O - ver the heavens he

spreads his cloud, And wa - ters veil the sky.

He sends his showers of bless-ings down, To

He sends his showers of

He sends his showers of bless-ings down, To

He sends his showers of bless-ings down, - - - T

MORGAN. C. M. *Concluded.*

He makes the grass the moun ...... tains crown, And corn in val - leys grow, And corn, &c.

He makes the grass the moun .... tains crown, And corn in val - leys grow.

grass the mountains crown, And corn in val - leys grow, ... And corn, &c.

mountains crown, And corn in val - leys grow, ... And corn, &c.

OXFORD. C. M. D. Meth. Hymn Book, p. 425. *John Massengale.*

Shepherds, re-joice! lift up your eyes, And send your fears a - way: News from the re-gions of the skies.—A

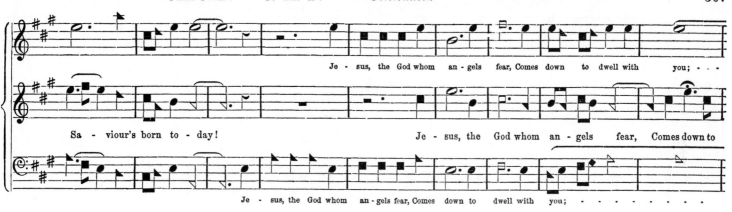

Je - sus, the God whom an - gels fear, Comes down to dwell with you; - - -

Sa - viour's born to - day! Je - sus, the God whom an - gels fear, Comes down to

Je - sus, the God whom an - gels fear, Comes down to dwell with you; - - - - - -

· · · · · · To - day, &c.

dwell with you; To - day he makes his en - trance here,—But not as mon - archs do!

· · · · · · To - day, &c.

PARTING FRIENDS. C. M.

E. L. King.

What is there here to court my stay, And keep me back from home,
When an - gels beck - on me a - way, And Je - sus bids me come? } Shall I re - gret my

part-ing friends Here in this vale con - fined? Nay, but where'-er my soul as - cends, They will not stay be - hind.

Am I a soldier of the cross, A follower of the Lamb? And shall I fear to own his cause, Or blush to speak his name?

CHORUS.

Oh the Lamb, the liv-ing Lamb, The Lamb on Cal-va-ry, The Lamb that was slain, But lives a-gain, To in-ter-cede for me.

THIS WORLD IS NOT MY HOME. C. M.

John Massengale.

On Jor - dan's stor - my banks I stand, And cast a wish - ful eye,

To Ca - naan's fair and hap - py land, Where my pos - ses - sions lie.} This world is not my

home, This world is not my home, This world's a wil - der - ness be - low, This world is not my home.

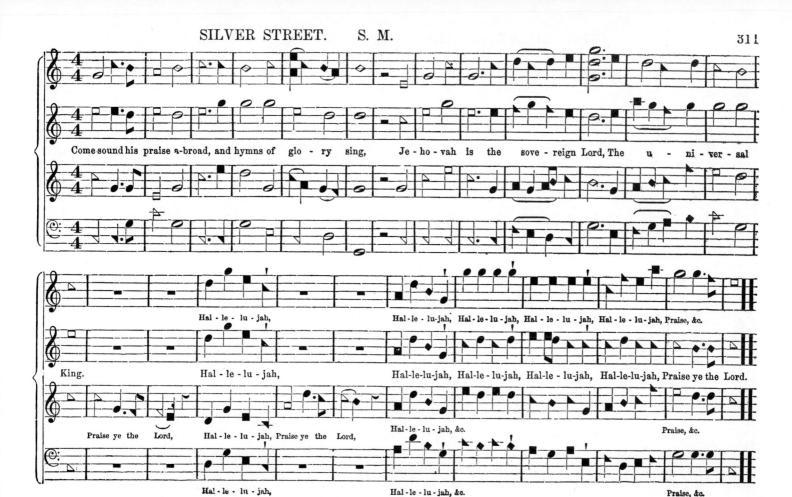

Come sound his praise a-broad, and hymns of glo - ry sing,   Je - ho - vah is the   sove - reign Lord, The   u   -   ni - ver - sal

King.   Hal - le - lu - jah,   Hal-le-lu-jah, Hal-le-lu-jah, Hal-le - lu - jah, Hal-le-lu-jah, Praise, &c.

Hal - le - lu - jah,   Hal-le-lu-jah, Hal-le-lu-jah, Hal-le - lu - jah,   Hal-le-lu-jah, Praise ye the Lord.

Praise ye the   Lord,   Hal - le - lu - jah, Praise ye the   Lord,   Hal - le - lu - jah, &c.   Praise, &c.

Hal - le - lu - jah,   Hal - le - lu - jah, &c.   Praise, &c.

SING TO ME OF HEAVEN.   S. M.   *John Massengale.*

1. O, sing to me of heaven, When I am call'd to die, Sing songs of ho - ly

2. When cold and slug - gish drops Roll off my mar - ble brow, Burst forth in strains of

ec - sta - sy, To waft my soul on high!

joy - ful - ness, Let heaven be - gin be - low!

3. When the last moment comes,
   O watch my dying face,
   And catch the bright, seraphic gleam
   Which on each feature plays.

4. Then to my ravish'd ear
   Let one sweet song begin;
   Let music charm me last on earth,
   And greet me first in heaven.

5. Then close my sightless eyes,
   And lay me down to rest,
   And clasp my cold and icy hands
   Across my peaceful breast.

6. Then round my senseless clay
   Assemble those I love,
   And sing of heaven, delightful heaven,
   My glorious home above.

1. The men of grace have found Glo - ry be - gun be - low; Ce - les - tial fruits, on earth - ly ground, Ce-

Ce - les - tial fruits, on earth - ly ground, Ce-

Ce - les - tial fruits, on earth - ly ground, Ce-

Ce - les - tial fruits, on earth - ly ground, . . . Ce-

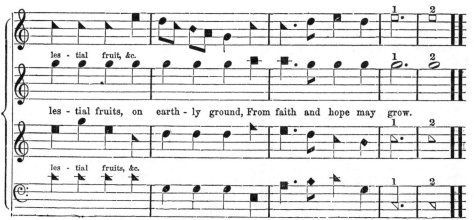

les - tial fruit, &c.

les - tial fruits, on earth - ly ground, From faith and hope may grow.

les - tial fruits, &c.

les - tial fruits, &c.

2.

The hill of Zion yields
A thousand sacred sweets,
Before we reach the heavenly fields,
Or walk the golden streets.

3.

Then let our songs abound,
And every tear be dry;
We're marching through Immanuel's ground,
To fairer worlds on high.

AMHERST. H. M.

Billings.

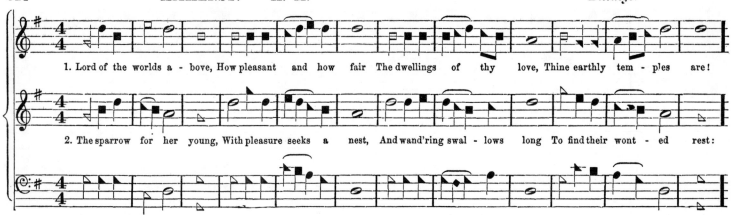

1. Lord of the worlds a - bove, How pleasant and how fair The dwellings of thy love, Thine earthly tem - ples are!

2. The sparrow for her young, With pleasure seeks a nest, And wand'ring swal - lows long To find their wont - ed rest:

To thine a - bode My heart a - spires, with warm de - sires To see my God.

My spi-rit faints With e - qual zeal To rise and dwell Among thy saints.

3.

O happy souls that pray
   Where God appoints to hear!
O happy men that pay
   Their constant service there!
    They praise thee still;
    And happy they
    That love the way,
    To Zion's hill.

1. Lord of the worlds a - bove, How plea - sant and how fair The dwell-ings of thy love, Thine earth - ly tem - ples are!

To thine a - bode My heart a - spires, With warm de - sires To see my God.

2.

To spend one sacred day
  Where God and saints abide,
Affords diviner joy
  Than thousand days beside:
    Where God resorts,
    I love it more
    To keep the door,
  Than shine in courts.

Re - joice! the Lord is King!—Your Lord and King a - dore; }
Mor - tals, give thanks and sing, And tri - umph ev - er - more; } Lift up your hearts, Lift

up your voice, Re - joice! a - gain, I say, re - joice! Re - joice! a - gain, I say, re - joice!

PLEYEL'S HYMN. 7s.

Pleyel.

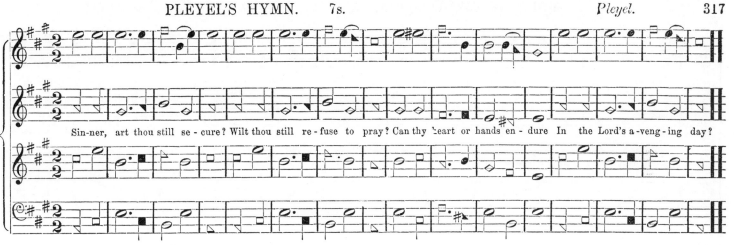

Sin-ner, art thou still se - cure? Wilt thou still re - fuse to pray? Can thy heart or hands en - dure In the Lord's a - veng - ing day?

AUBURN. 7s.

D. P. White.

Pilgrim, burden'd with thy sin, Haste to Zi - on's gate to - day; There, till mer-cy lets thee in, Knock, and weep, and watch, and pray.

Though the morn may be se - rene,—Not a threat'ning cloud be seen,
Who can un - der - take to say 'Twill be plea - sant all the day? }

Tem - pests sud - den - ly may

rise, Light'nings flash and thun - ders roar, Dark - ness o - ver - spread the skies Ere a short-lived day be o'er.

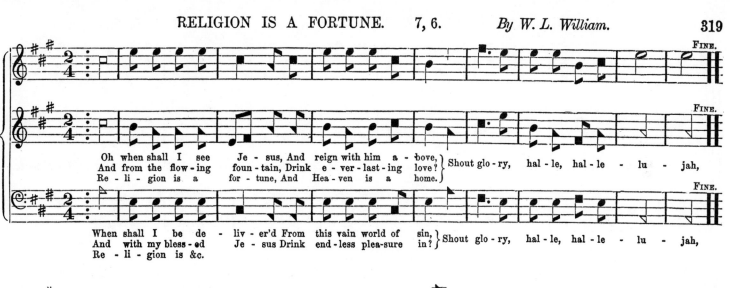

Oh when shall I see Je - sus, And reign with him a - bove,
And from the flow - ing foun - tain, Drink e - ver - last - ing love?
Re - li - gion is a for - tune, And Hea - ven is a home.
} Shout glo - ry, hal - le, hal - le - lu - jah,

When shall I be de - liv - er'd From this vain world of sin,
And with my bless - ed Je - sus Drink end - less plea - sure in?
Re - li - gion is &c.
} Shout glo - ry, hal - le, hal - le - lu - jah,

When we all get to Hea - ven We will shout a - loud and sing, Shout glo - ry, hal - le, hal - le - lu - jah.

THE LOST CITY. 7, 6.

By E. L. King.

O when shall I see Je - sus, And reign with him a - bove, And from the flow-ing foun - tain Drink e - ver-last-ing love, And to

glo - ry I will go, ... And to glo - ry I will go, will go, will go, And to glo - ry I will go.

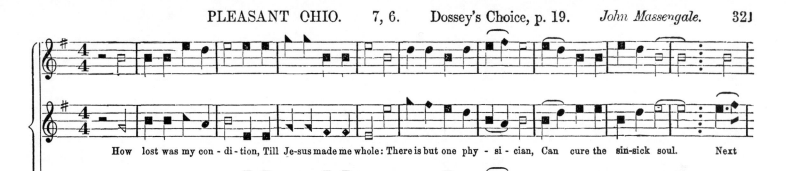

How lost was my con - di - tion, Till Je-sus made me whole: There is but one phy - si - cian, Can cure the sin-sick soul.   Next

door to death he found me, And snatch'd me from the grave, To tell to all a - round me, His wond'rous love to save.

V

AUTAUGA. 7, 6. *John Massengale.*

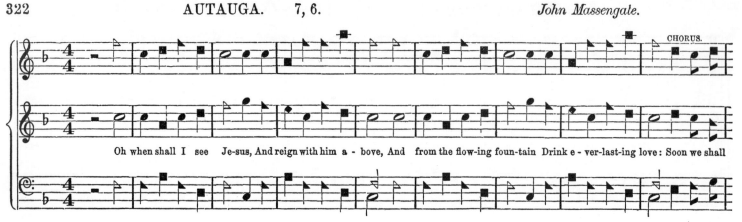

Oh when shall I see Je-sus, And reign with him a - bove, And from the flow-ing foun-tain Drink e - ver-last-ing love: Soon we shall

land on Canaan's shore, Soon we shall land on Canaan's shore, Soon we shall land on Canaan's shore, To live for e - ver-more.

GRIFFIN. 7, 6.

R. F. M. Mann.

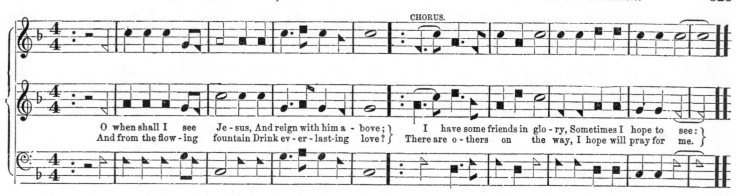

O when shall I see Je-sus, And reign with him a-bove; }
And from the flow-ing fountain Drink ev-er-last-ing love? }
I have some friends in glo-ry, Sometimes I hope to see:
There are o-thers on the way, I hope will pray for me. }

SOFT MUSIC. 7, 6, 7, 7.

B. F. White.

1. Soft, soft music is steal-ing,— Loud, :‖: now it is peal-ing, Yes, yes, yes, yes;
   Sweet, :‖: lingers the strain; Waking the echoes again! Waking the echoes a-gain!

2. Join, :‖: children of sad-ness, Now, :‖: changing to gladness, Yes, yes, yes, yes;
   Send, :‖: sorrow away; Warble this beautiful lay; Warble this beautiful lay.

3. Hope, :‖: fair and endur-ing, Love, :‖: heaven in-sur-ing, Yes, yes, yes, yes;
   Joy, joy, bright as the day; Sweetly invites you away; Sweetly invites you away.

NORTH PORT. L. M.

Dr. R. R. Osborne.—Bass by J. Smith.

Je - sus, my all, to heav'n is gone, Glo-ry Hal - le - lu - jah; He whom I fix my hopes up-on! Glory! Hal - le - lu - jah! I

want a seat in Pa - ra - dise, Glo-ry Hal - le - lu - jah! I love that un-ion nev-er dies, Glo-ry! Hal - le - lu - jah!

THE CAUSE OF CHRIST. 7, 7, 7, 5, 7, 7, 7, 5. *E. L. King.*

Who the cause of Christ would yield? Who would leave the bat - tle field? Who would cast a - way his lot? Let him base - ly go!

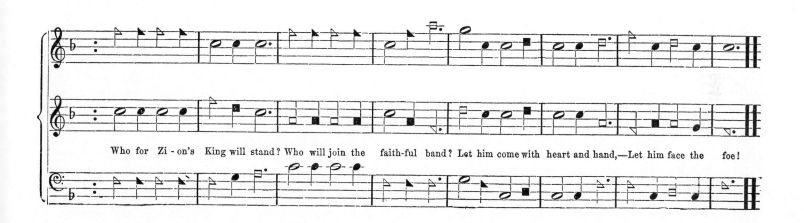

Who for Zi - on's King will stand? Who will join the faith-ful band? Let him come with heart and hand,—Let him face the foe!

WEARY PILGRIM. 7. 9. *Leonard P. Breedlove.*

Come and taste, a - long with me, The wea - ry pilgrim's con - so - la - tion; } Joy and peace in Christ I find,
Boundless mer - cy, running free, The earnest of complete sal - va - tion. }
My heart to him is all resign'd;

The ful - ness of his power I prove,
The sweetness of re - deem - ing love!
Je - sus is the pilgrim's por - tion,
Love as boundless as the o - cean.

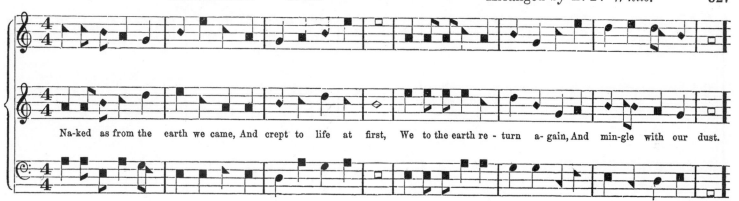

Na-ked as from the earth we came, And crept to life at first, We to the earth re - turn a- gain, And min-gle with our dust.

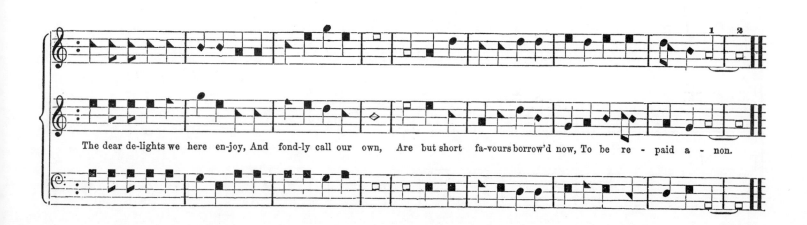

The dear de-lights we here en-joy, And fond-ly call our own, Are but short fa-vours borrow'd now, To be re - paid a - non.

Lo! on a nar - row neck of land, 'Twixt two un - bound - ed seas I stand, Yet how in - sen - si - ble!

A point of time, a mo - ment's space, Re - moves me to that hea - venly place, Or shuts me up in hell.

1. In the dark wood no In-dian nigh, Then me look heav'n and send up cry, Up-on my knee so low. That God on high

in shi-ning place, See me at night with tear-y face, The priest did tell me so.

2.
God send he angel, take me care,
He come himself, he hear my prayer,
 If inside heart do pray.
Now me love God with inside heart,
He fight for me, he take my part,
 He with me night and day.

3.
God love poor Indian in the wood,
So me love God, and that be good,
 He saved my life before.
He see me now, he know my tear,
He say, poor Indian, never fear,
 Me with you all time more.

O   hear - ken, sin ners, we have come To warn you of your dan - ger,
We   pray be re - con-ciled to him Who once lay in a man - ger. Ho! ev - ry one that thirst-

eth, Come ye to the wa - ters, Free - ly drink and quench your thirst, Like Zi - on's sons and daugh - ters.

COLUMBIANA. 8, 7. Buck's Hymn-book, H. 530. By D. P. White.

May the grace of Christ our Saviour, And the Fa-ther's bound-less love, With the Ho-ly Spi-rit's fa-vour, Rest upon us from a - bove.

VILLULIA. 8, 7. By J. M. Day.

Mer - cy, O thou Son of Da - vid, Thus poor blind Bartimeus pray'd, Oth-ers by thy grace are sa - ved, Now to me af-ford thine aid.

SONS OF SORROW 8, 7,

Treble by Wm. Houser.

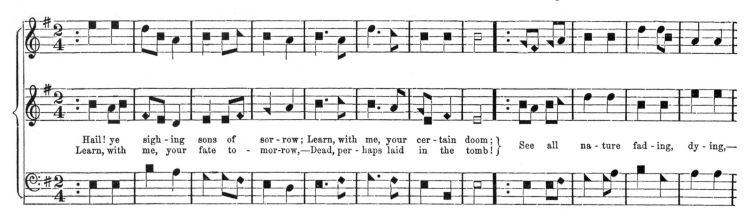

Hail! ye sigh-ing sons of sor-row; Learn, with me, your cer-tain doom; }
Learn, with me, your fate to - mor-row,—Dead, per - haps laid in the tomb! }
See all na - ture fad -ing, dy - ing,—

Si - lent, all things seem to mourn; Life from ve - ge - ta - tion fly - ing, Calls to mind the mould'r-ing urn.

FAMILY CIRCLE.   8, 7.

Rev. R. E. Brown & B. F. White.

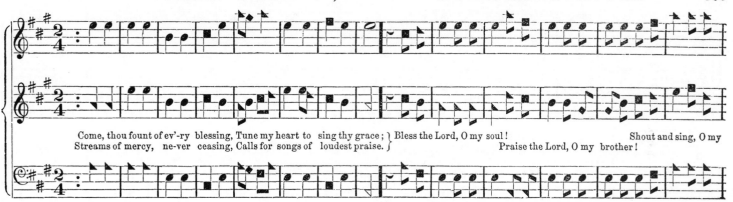

Come, thou fount of ev'-ry blessing, Tune my heart to sing thy grace; ⎱ Bless the Lord, O my soul!   Shout and sing, O my
Streams of mercy, ne-ver ceasing, Calls for songs of loudest praise. ⎰ Praise the Lord, O my brother!

sis-ter!   And re - joice, O my mother!   And we'll join heart and hands for Ca-naan.
    Give Him glo - ry, O my   father!   And we'll tra - vel on to - gether,

1. O come, come a-way, From la-bour now re-posing, Our ju-bi-lee has set us free,—O come, come a-way! Come, hail the day that

2. We welcome you here! With heart and hand wide open, Ye gallant sons of tem-perance, We wel-come you here! Heaven's blessings on your

3. We welcome you here! Ye who with taste per-vert-ed Have seized the cup, and drank it up,—We welcome you here! Come, join us in our

celebrates The ran-som of th' in-e-bri-ates From all that intox-i-cates, O come, come a-way!

plans we pray! Ye come our sinking friends to save, And rescue from a drunkard's grave, We welcome you here!

holy aim, The poor be-sot-ted to reclaim, The broken heart to cheer again,—O come, sign the pledge!

4.　　　We welcome you here!
　　Ye who your vows have broken,
　　Falling before the tempter's power,—
　　　We welcome you here!
　　Ye who have sold yourselves for naught,
　　Take back the priceless boon you bought,
　　O take a sober, second thought,
　　　　And try, try again!

5.　　　We welcome you here!
　　Ye maids and matrons lovely,
　　Whose charms, we yield, must win the field,—
　　　We welcome you here!
　　Ye who have hearts to feel for wo,
　　Wide as the streams of sorrow flow,
　　O frown on the deadly foe,
　　　　But smile on the sons!

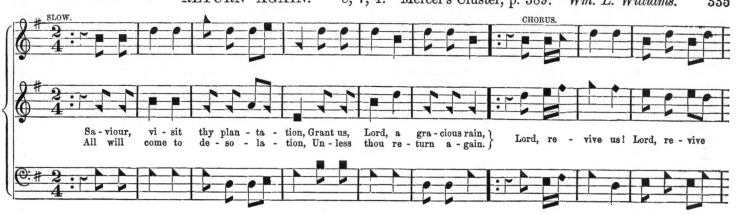

Sa - viour,   vi - sit   thy plan - ta - tion, Grant us,   Lord, a   gra - cious rain, }
All will   come to   de - so - la - tion, Un - less   thou re - turn a - gain. }
Lord, re - vive us! Lord, re - vive

us! All   our   help must come from thee, Lord, re - vive   us! Oh re - vive   us! All   our help must come from   thee.

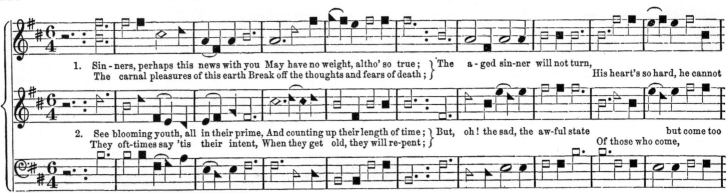

1. Sin-ners, perhaps this news with you May have no weight, altho' so true; } The a-ged sin-ner will not turn,
The carnal pleasures of this earth Break off the thoughts and fears of death; }   His heart's so hard, he cannot

2. See blooming youth, all in their prime, And counting up their length of time; } But, oh! the sad, the aw-ful state   but come too
They oft-times say 'tis their intent, When they get old, they will re-pent; } Of those who come,

3. When Christ the Lord shall come to reign, In solemn pomp and burning flame, } Oh! how will parents tremble there   without
See Gabriel go pro-claim the sound, A-wake, ye nations under ground! } Who've raised their children

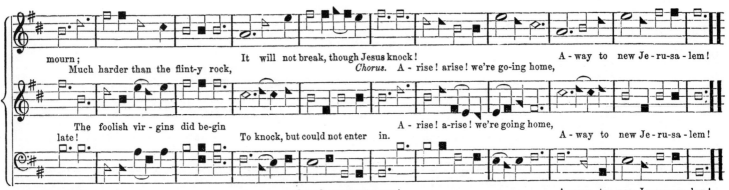

mourn;   It will not break, though Jesus knock!   A-way to new Je-ru-sa-lem!
Much harder than the flint-y rock,   *Chorus.* A-rise! arise! we're go-ing home,

The foolish vir-gins did be-gin   A-rise! a-rise! we're going home,
late!   To knock, but could not enter in.   A-way to new Je-ru-sa-lem!

prayer?   I ne-ver heard my parents pray!   A-way to new Je-ru-sa-lem!
Methinks you'll hear some children say—   A-rise! a-rise! we're going home,

1. What's this that in my soul is ris-ing? Is it grace? Is it grace?
Which makes me keep for mer-cy cry-ing, Is it grace? Is it grace? } This work that's in my soul be-gun, It makes me strive all

2. Great God of love I can but won-der, Mer-cy's free! Mer-cy's free!
Though I've no price at all to ten-der, Mer-cy's free! Mer-cy's free! } Though mer-cy's free, our God is just, And if a soul should

sin to shun, It plants my soul be-neath the sun, Mer-cy's free! Mer-cy's free!

ere be lost, This will tor-ment the sin-ner most, Mer-cy's free! Mer-cy's free!

W

3. Swell, O swell the heavenly chorus,
　　Mercy's free! Mercy's free!
The devil's kingdom falls before us,
　　Mercy's free! Mercy's free!
Sinners, repent, inquire the road
That leads to glory and to God,
Come wash in Christ's atoning blood,
　　Mercy's free! Mercy's free!

4. This truth through all our life shall cheer us,
　　Mercy's free! Mercy's free!
And through the vale of death shall bear us,
　　Mercy's free! Mercy's free!
And when to Jordan's banks we come,
And cross the raging billow's foam,
We'll sing, when safely landed home,
　　Mercy's free! Mercy's free!

SAWYER'S EXIT. 9, 8.

John Massengale.

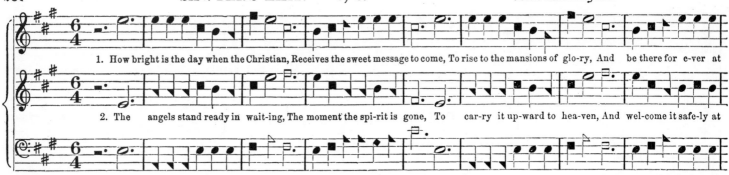

1. How bright is the day when the Christian, Receives the sweet message to come, To rise to the mansions of glo-ry, And be there for e-ver at

2. The angels stand ready in wait-ing, The moment the spi-rit is gone, To car-ry it up-ward to hea-ven, And wel-come it safe-ly at

3. The saints that have gone up before us, All raise a new shout as we come, And sing hal-le-lu-jah the lou-der, To welcome the tra-vel-lers

home, And be there for e-ver at home, And be there for e-ver at home, To rise to the mansions of glo-ry, And be there for e-ver at home.

home, And welcome it safe-ly at home, And welcome it safe-ly at home, To car-ry it upward to hea-ven, And welcome it safe-ly at home.

home, To welcome the travellers home, To welcome the travellers home, And sing hal-le - lu-jah the lou-der, To welcome the travellers home.

4. And there are our friends and companions,
Escaped from the evil to come,
And crowding the gates of fair Zion,
To wait our arrival at home.

5. And there is the blessed Redeemer,
So mild on his merciful throne,
With heart and hands widely extended,
To welcome his ransom'd ones home.

6. Then let us go onward rejoicing,
Till Jesus invites us to come,
To share in his glorious kingdom,
And rest in his bosom at home. *

* These words were composed by Rev. S. B. Sawyer on the day of his death, with request that this tune should be set to them

1. Shed not a tear o'er your friend's early bier,   When   I am gone, when I am gone : ⎫
Smile when the slow tolling bell you shall hear,   When   I am gone, when I am gone. ⎬ Weep not for me as you stand round my grave, Think who has

died his be - lov-ed to   save,   When   I am gone, I am gone.
Think of the crown all the ransom'd shall wear,

2. Shed not a tear as you all kneel in prayer,
    When I am gone, when I am gone :
Sing a sweet song when my grave you shall **see**,
    When I am gone, when I am gone,
Sing to the Lamb who on earth once was slain,
Sing to the Lamb who in heaven doth reign,
Sing till the earth shall be fill'd with his name,
    When I am gone, I am gone.

3. Plant you a rose that shall bloom o'er my grave,
    When I am gone, when I am gone :
Sing a sweet song, such as angels may have,
    When I am gone, when I am gone.
Praise ye the Lord that I'm freed from all **care**,
Pray ye the Lord that my joys you shall **share**,
Look up on high and believe that I'm there,
    When I am gone, I am gone.

MEDITATION. 11s. Dover Selection, p. 176. *L. P. Breedlove.*

From gloom - y de - jec - tion my thoughts mount the sky, And realms ev - er peace - ful, trans - port - ed, de - scry;
There joys, ev - er bloom-ing, en - rap - ture the soul, And riv - ers of plea - sure in - ces - sant - ly roll.

Oh! my soul is full of love! How I long to be at home, To range The new Je - ru - sa - lem!

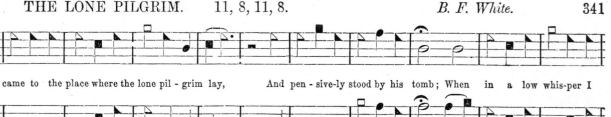

1. I came to the place where the lone pil-grim lay, And pen-sive-ly stood by his tomb; When in a low whis-per I

2. The tempest may howl, and the loud thunders roar, And gath-er-ing storms may a-rise, Yet calm are his feelings, at

heard something say, How sweet-ly he sleeps here a-lone.

rest is his soul, The tears are all wiped from his eyes.

3.

The cause of his Master propell'd him from home;
  He bade his companion farewell;
He bless'd his dear children who for him now mourn,
  In far distant regions they dwell.

4.

He wander'd an exile and stranger from home,
  No kindred or relative nigh;
He met the contagion and sank to the tomb,
  His soul flew to mansions on high.

5

O tell his companion and children most dear,
  To weep not for him now he's gone;
The same hand that led him through scenes most severe
  Has kindly assisted him home.

THE OLD-FASHIONED BIBLE.   12, 11.   *L. P. Breedlove.*

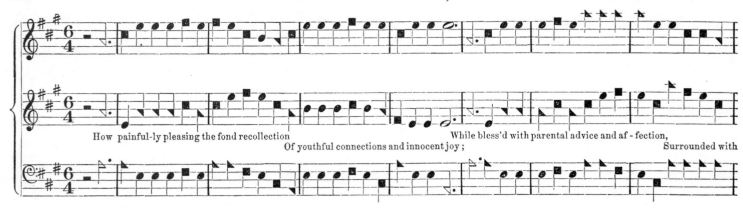

How painful-ly pleasing the fond recollection

Of youthful connections and innocent joy ;

While bless'd with parental advice and af - fection,

Surrounded with

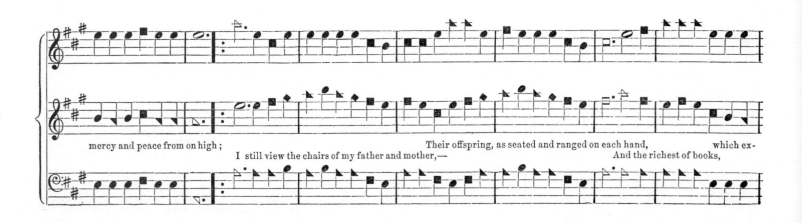

mercy and peace from on high ;

I still view the chairs of my father and mother,—

Their offspring, as seated and ranged on each hand,

And the richest of books,

which ex-

cels ev'ry o-ther,— The old-fashion'd Bible, the dear, blessed Bible!
The fam - i - ly Bi-ble, that lay on the stand! The fam-i - ly Bi-ble, that lay on the stand!

LET US GO. *C. A. Davis.*

Lift up your heads, Immanuel's friends, Oh! come, and let us go, let us go! Oh! come, and let us go, never dies!
And taste the pleasure Jesus sends. let us go, Where pleasure

Hosanna   to Jesus! I'm fill'd with his praises!   No theme is so charming, no love is so warming,   and comfort with-
          Come, O my dear brethren, and help me to sing!   It gives joy and gladness,

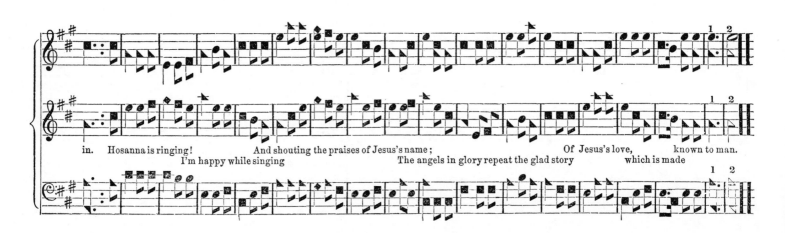

in.   Hosanna is ringing!   And shouting the praises of Jesus's name;   Of Jesus's love,   known to man.
       I'm happy while singing   The angels in glory repeat the glad story   which is made

C. A. Davis.

Our bu - gles sang truce, for the night-cloud had lower'd, And the sen - ti - nel stars set their watch in the sky; And thousands had

sunk on the ground o-ver-power'd,   The wea - ry to   sleep, - - - The wea - ry to sleep, And the wounded to   die!

THE AMERICAN STAR.

D. P. White.

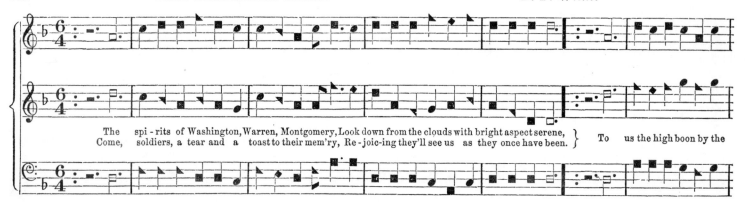

The   spi - rits of Washington, Warren, Montgomery, Look down from the clouds with bright aspect serene,
Come,   soldiers, a tear and a   toast to their mem'ry, Re - joic-ing they'll see us   as   they once have been.   } To   us the high boon by the

gods have been granted,

To spread the glad tidings of lib-er-ty far.

Let millions invade us, we'll meet them undaunted,

And conquer or die by the   American Star.

Wm. L. Williams.

SLOW.

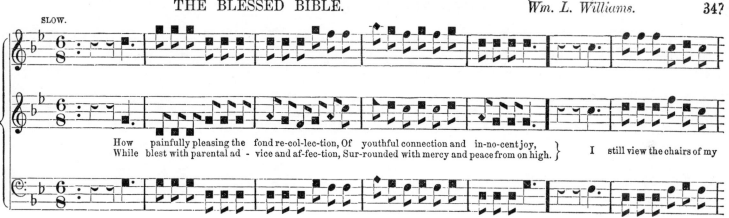

How   painfully pleasing the fond re-col-lec-tion, Of   youthful connection and   in-no-cent joy,
While   blest with parental ad - vice and af-fec-tion, Sur-rounded with mercy and peace from on high. }   I   still view the chairs of my

father and mother, The seats of their offspring as ranged on each hand, And the richest of books which excels ev'ry other,   The   fa-mi-ly Bi-ble that

THE BLESSED BIBLE. *Concluded.*

CHORUS.

lay on the stand. The old-fa-shion'd Bi-ble, the dear bless-ed Bible, The fa-mi-ly Bi-ble that lay on the stand.

TRANSPORTING NEWS. *J. H. Whaley.—Bass by C. A. Davis.*

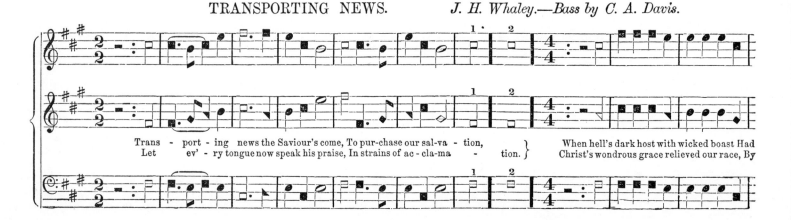

Trans - port - ing news the Saviour's come, To pur-chase our sal-va - tion,
Let ev' - ry tongue now speak his praise, In strains of ac-cla-ma - tion.
When hell's dark host with wicked boast Had
Christ's wondrous grace relieved our race, By

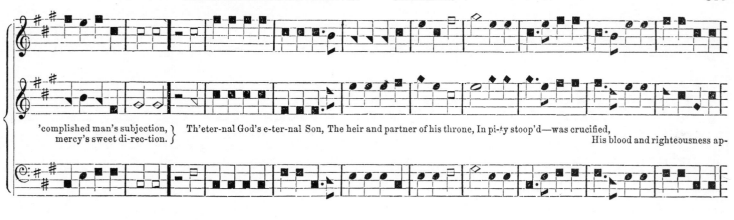

'complished man's subjection, }
mercy's sweet di-rec-tion. }

Th'eter-nal God's e-ter-nal Son, The heir and partner of his throne, In pi-ty stoop'd—was crucified,

His blood and righteousness ap-

plied, And thus our souls at freedom set,
By pay-ing off the dreadful debt: }

We there-fore are from guilt set free, Will joy-ful-ly a - dore him.

THE RED SEA ANTHEM. *Original.* B. F. White.

The Lord spoke unto Moses, say-ing, Sanc-ti-fy un - to me all the first born. And Moses said un-to the peo - ple, Re-mem-ber this day in

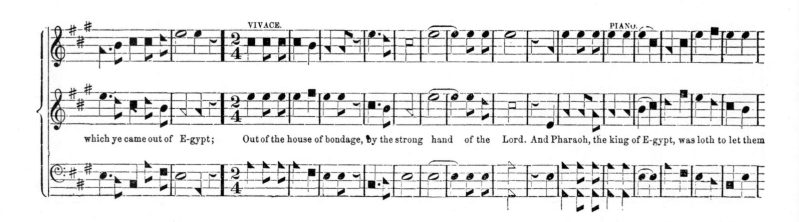

which ye came out of E-gypt; Out of the house of bondage, by the strong hand of the Lord. And Pharaoh, the king of E-gypt, was loth to let them

Led them to-wards the Red Sea, Through the wil-der-ness; And Pha-raoh, &c.

God, by his servant Moses led them towards the Red Sea, Through the wilderness; And Pharaoh the king pur-

go. And when he had let them go, God, by his ser-vant Moses, led them to-wards the Red Sea, Through the wil-der-ness; And Pha-raoh, &c.

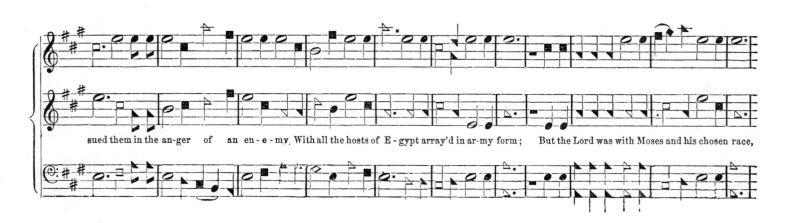

sued them in the an-ger of an en-e-my, With all the hosts of E-gypt array'd in ar-my form; But the Lord was with Moses and his chosen race,

And led them safe-ly on   and en - a-bled them to make their es-cape   from the hands of the king.   And when they arrived at the Red   Sea the

Lord commanded Moses to stretch out his hand over the sea.   And Moses obey'd the Lord, and the waters were roll'd back, and became a wall on either side,

and the children of Is-rael passed through on dry land, with all his ar-my; And when they enter'd

And Pha-raoh the king at-tempt-ed to pur-sue, &c.

in - to the deep, the waters return'd, and buried them all in the depth of the sea, Then Moses and his people stood on the banks of the sea and

shout-ed,   Glo-ry to God in the high-est!   Glo-ry and hon-our, pow-er and bless-ing be un-to his name for e-ver and e - ver.

HAPPY LAND.   6, 4, 7, 4.   *Leonard P. Breedlove.*

1. There is a happy land, Far, far a - way, ⎱
   Where saints in glory stand, Bright, bright as day, ⎰   Oh how they sweetly sing, Worthy is our Saviour king,
                                         Loud let his praises ring, Praise, praise for aye,

2. Come to the happy land, Come, come a - way, ⎱
   Why will you doubting stand, Why yet de-lay, ⎰   Oh we shall happy be, When from sin and sorrow free,
                                           Lord, we shall live with thee, Blest, blest for aye.

3. Bright in that happy land, Beams every eye, ⎱
   Kept by a father's hand, Love cannot die, ⎰   Then shall his kingdom come, Saints shall share a glorious home,
                                           And bright above the sun, We reign for aye.

My friends come listen awhileAnd I will tell you a sto-ry A-bout our loving Saviour; He came of low es-tate, Was re-ject-ed by his own, Was

born of the Virgin Ma-ry, And was cradled in a manger. The next we hear of this blessed Saviour, He was going about do-ing good, And

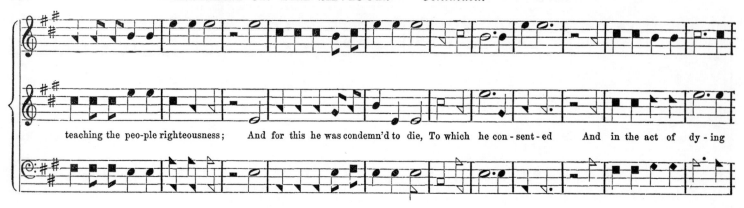

teaching the peo-ple righteousness; And for this he was condemn'd to die, To which he con-sent-ed And in the act of dy-ing

He rose from the grave A tri-

gave up the ghost, And said, It is finish'd! Then he was buried, He rose from the grave, He rose, &c. A tri-
And the third day,

He rose from the grave, He rose, &c. He rose, &c. A tri-

umph-ant con-quer - or, And as - cend-ed to mansions on high, And is now ex - alt - ed a Prince and a Saviour, And grants repentance un - to men.

Then, &c.   Mag - ni - fy, &c.   World, &c.

Then let us praise him, Then, &c.   Mag-ni - fy and a-dore, World without end,   A - men.

Then let us praise him   Then, &c.   Then, &c.   Mag-ni - fy, &c.   World, &c.

MURILLO'S LESSON. 11s. *Unknown.*

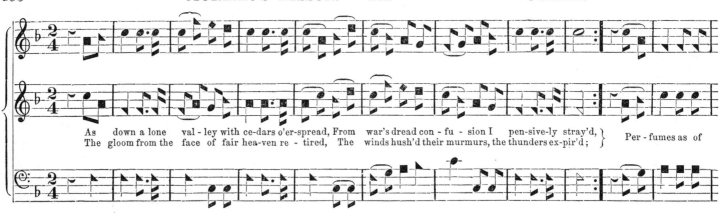

As   down a lone   val-ley with ce-dars o'er-spread, From   war's dread con - fu - sion I   pen-sive-ly stray'd, }
The   gloom from the   face of fair hea-ven re - tired,   The   winds hush'd their murmurs, the thunders ex-pir'd; }   Per - fumes as of

E - den flow'd sweetly a-long,   A   voice as of   an - gels en - chant-ing-ly   sung,   A   voice as of   an - gels en-chant-ing-ly

sung, Co - lum - bia, Co - lum - bia, to glo - ry a - rise, The queen of the world and the child of the skies.

PROSPERITY. 8s.

L. P. Breedlove.

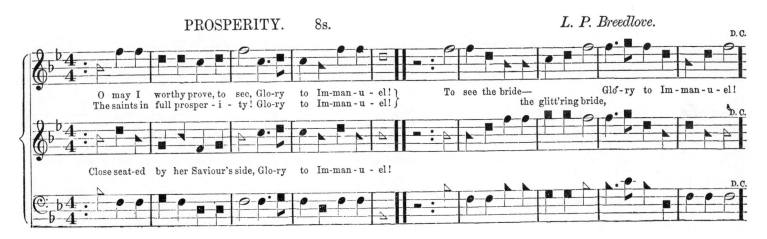

O may I worthy prove, to see, Glo-ry to Im-man-u-el!
The saints in full prosper - i - ty! Glo-ry to Im-man-u-el!

To see the bride— Glo-ry to Im-man-u-el!
the glitt'ring bride,

Close seat-ed by her Saviour's side, Glo-ry to Im-man-u-el!

THE ROYAL BAND.   12s & 11s.

W. T. Power.

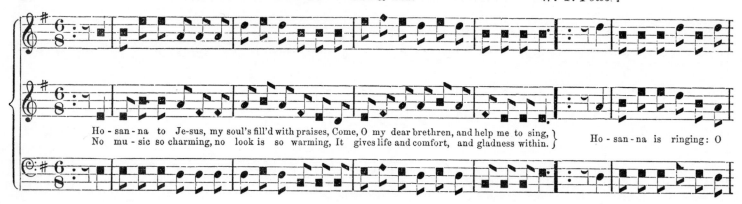

Ho - san - na to Je-sus, my soul's fill'd with praises, Come, O my dear brethren, and help me to sing, }
No mu - sic so charming, no look is so warming, It gives life and comfort, and gladness within. }

Ho - san - na is ringing: O

how I love singing,

There's nothing so sweet as the sound of his name.

The angels in glory repeat the glad story, Of love which in Jesus is made known to man.

Here's my heart, my lov-ing Je-sus, Here's my heart, my loving Je-sus, Here's my heart, my loving Je-sus,—Thou who did'st from sin re-lieve us,

Lov-ing Je-sus,   Lov-ing Je-sus,

Take the purchase of thy blood, Take the purchase of thy blood! Lov-ing Je-sus,   Lov-ing Je-sus,

Thou hast bought a ran-som!   Thou hast bought a ran-som!

LOVING JESUS. *Concluded.*

Glo-ry, glo-ry, hon-our, praise and pow·-er, Glo-ry, glo-ry to the Lord! Glo-ry, glo-ry to the Lord!

Glo-ry, hon-our, praise, and pow-er Be un-to the Lamb for-ev-er! Glo-ry, glo-ry to the Lord! Glo-ry, &c.

NORWICH. D. P. White.

Where Je-sus sheds the bright-est beams, Where Je-sus sheds the

Oh the de-lights, the heavenly joys, The glo-ries of the place Where

Where Je-sus sheds the bright-est beams, Where

Where Je-sus sheds the

brow, And all the glorious, all the glorious ranks a-bove At

brow, And

brow, And all the glorious ranks a-bove, And, &c. At hum-ble dis-tance

brow, And all the glorious ranks a-bove At hum-ble dis-tance bow. . .

hum-ble dis-.tance bow. And, &c. At hum - - ble dis-tance bow.

all the glo-rious ranks a-bove At hum-ble dis-tance bow, At hum - ble dis-tance bow.

bow. . . . And, &c. At, &c.

. . . . And, &c. At, &c.

'Tis fin-ish'd, 'tis fin-ish'd, 'tis fin-ish'd, 'tis fin-ish'd, The Redeemer said, And meek-ly bow'd his dy-ing

head. While we the sentence scan, Come, sinners, and observe the word, Behold the conquest of the Lord, Complete for sinful man, Com - plete,

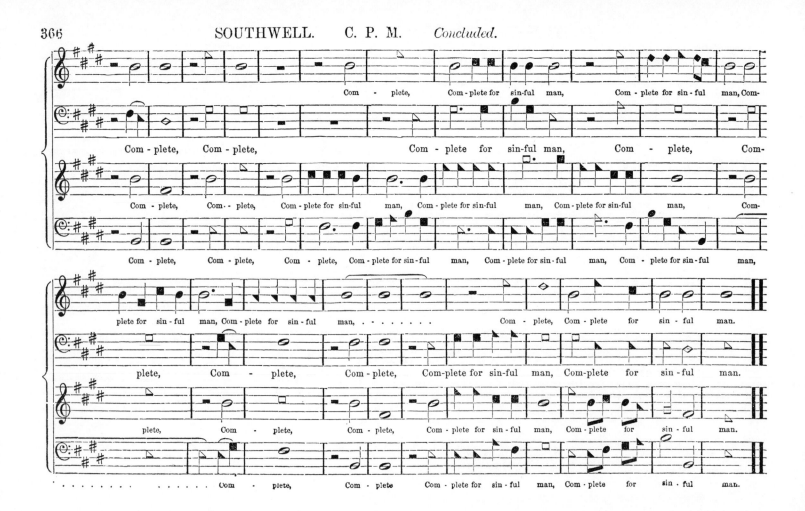

NEW APPENDIX.

———————

The Committee appointed by the Musical Convention to enlarge "The Sacred Harp," met according to appointment, and have adopted about one hundred pieces, being new compositions never before published, for a second Appendix to "The Sacred Harp."

All of which is respectfully submitted,

B. F. WHITE,   A. OGLETREE,

E. T. POUND,   T. WALLER,

J. P. REES,   J. T. EDMUNDS,

R. F. BALL,   A. S. WEBSTER,

Committee.

January 18, 1859.

REMEMBER ME.   C. M.

B. F. White. & L. L. Leadbeater.

NEWMAN.   C. M.

Music original, by *J. P. Rees.*

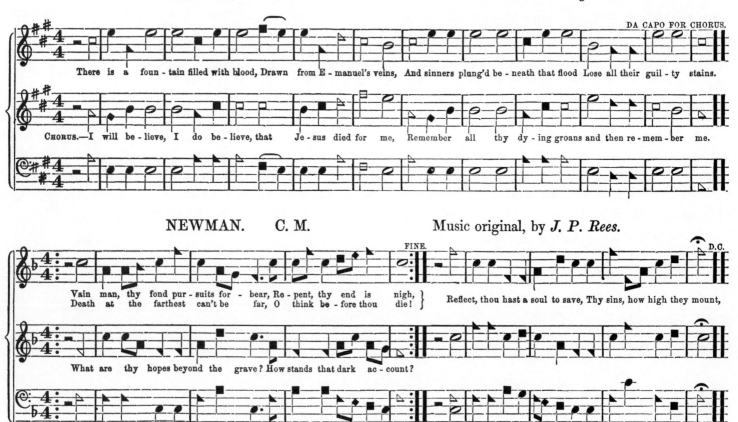

1. O, tell me no more   of this world's vain store,   The time for such tri - fles with   me   now is   o'er.
2. A coun - try I've found,   where true joys a - bound,   To dwell I'm de - ter - mined on   that   hap - py   ground. } Send a

blessing, Send a   blessing, Send a   blessing, Send a   blessing, Send a   blessing, just   now,   just now, just   now, Send a   blessing just   now.

Y

MONROE. 8, 7. *(Original.)* *W. S. Turner.*

Je - sus, I my cross have ta - ken, All to leave and fol - low thee;
Na - ked, poor, de - spised, for - sa - ken, Thou, from hence, my all shall be. } Per - ish, ev' - ry fond am - bi - tion,

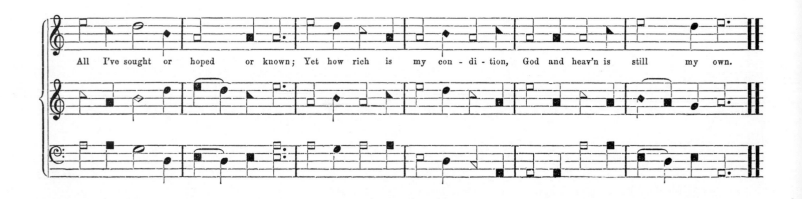

All I've sought or hoped or known; Yet how rich is my con - di - tion, God and heav'n is still my own.

A. Ogletree.

Kin - dle a flame of

Kin - dle a flame of   sacred love   In

Come Holy Spir - it, heavenly dove, With all thy quick'ning powers,   Kin - dle a flame   of sacred love, Kin - dle   a flame of

Kin - dle a flame of   sacred love,   Kindle a flame of   sacred love   In

sa - cred love   In   these cold hearts of   ours. Kin - dle   a   flame of   sa - cred love   In   these   cold   hearts of   ours.

these cold hearts of   ours.   - - - - -   Kin - dle   a   flame of   sa - cred love   In   these   cold   hearts of   ours.

sa - cred love   In these cold hearts of   ours. Kin - dle   a   flame of   sa - cred   love   In these - - -   cold   hearts of   ours.

these cold hearts of   ours.   - - - - -   Kin - dle   a   flame of   sa - cred   love   In these   cold   hearts of   ours.

ENDLESS DISTRESS. 8s, 11s. (Original.) By *Rev. Edmund Dumas.*

Floyd's Primitive Hymn Book, No. 382.

While sor-rows en-com-pass me round, And end-less dis-tress-es I see, As-ton-ish'd, I cry, can a

mor-tal be found, Sur-round-ed with troub-les like me, Sur-round-ed with troub-les like me.

Je - sus, let thy pity-ing eye Call back a wand'ring sheep, False to thee like Pe - ter, I Would fain like Pe - ter weep;

Let me be by grace re-stored, On me be all long suff'ring shown, Turn and look up - on me Lord, And break my heart of stone.

OH, SING WITH ME!

By *Miss P. R. Lancaster.*

Oh! sing with me of social spheres, Where breathes in kind - ness mu - tual love,
Where no un - gen - tle look appears, Though faith - ful - ness should ev'n re - prove.
Come sing of all that's

bright and fair In a - zure sky and beauteous earth, Oh! sing of heav'n, our hopes are there, With treasures of im - mor - tal worth.

A - las and did my Sa - viour bleed, And did my sovereign die,
Would he de - vote his sa - cred head For such a worm as I.

O who is like Je - sus,

hal - le - lu - jah, Praise ye the Lord, There's none like Je - sus, hal - le - lu - jah, Love and serve the Lord.

HELP ME TO SING. P. M.

B. F. White.

Ye souls who are bound unto Canaan, Come join in and help me to sing The praises of my lov-ing Je-sus, My prophet, my priest, and my king.

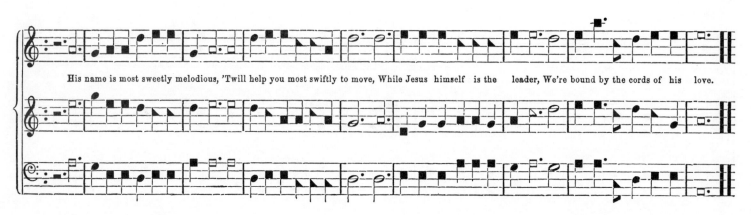

His name is most sweetly melodious, 'Twill help you most swiftly to move, While Jesus himself is the leader, We're bound by the cords of his love.

HAPPY HOME. L. M.

J. P. Rees.

O yes; my Saviour I will trust,
And though my body turns to dust,
} Oh what a happy time, when the Christians all get home, And we'll shout and praise the Lamb in Glory.

My spirit shall fly ont and sing,
E - ternal prises to my king,
}

PARTING FRIENDS. C. M.

Arranged by *J. C. Graham.*

The time must come when we must part, When we must say Fare - well? When I am gone and far a - way, I still will think of thee.

To part with you gives to my heart, A sting no one can tell,

I'll think of thee both night and day, O then re - mem - ber me.

THE HEAVENLY PORT. C. M.

By *Eld. Edmund Dumas.* Aug. 8, 1859.

On Jordan's stormy banks I stand, And cast a wish-ful eye - - - - To Canaan's fair and happy land, Where my possessions lie.

CHORUS.—We'll stem the storm, it won't be long, The heav'nly port is nigh,- - - - We'll stem the storm, it won't be long, We'll anchor by and by.

VALLEY GROVE. L. M.

By *R. F. Ball.*

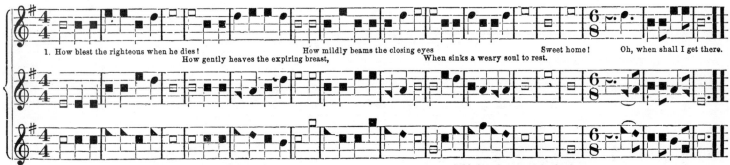

1. How blest the righteous when he dies!
How gently heaves the expiring breast,
How mildly beams the closing eyes
When sinks a weary soul to rest.
Sweet home! Oh, when shall I get there.

2. So fades a summer cloud away;
So sinks the gale when storms are o'er;
So gently shuts the eye of day;
So dies a wave along the shore.

3. Life's duty done, as sinks the clay,
Light from its load the spirit flies,
While heaven and earth combine to say,
How blest the righteous when he dies!

Blow ye the trumpet, blow Tho glad - ly solemn sound, Let all the nations know To earth's re - motest bounds, The year of Ju - bi -

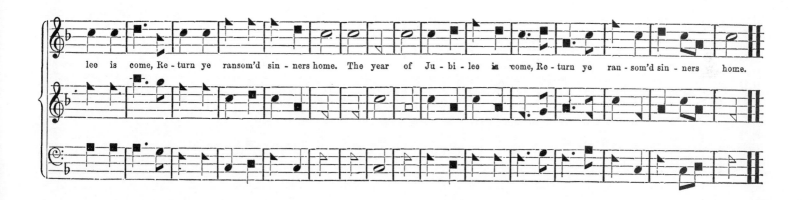

lee is come, Re - turn ye ransom'd sin - ners home. The year of Ju - bi - lee is come, Re - turn ye ran - som'd sin - ners home.

THE HILL OF ZION. S. M. (*Original.*) *B. F. White.*

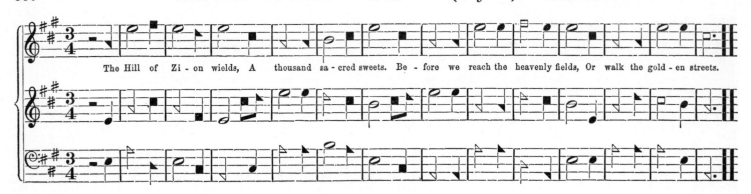

The Hill of Zi - on wields, A thousand sa - cred sweets. Be - fore we reach the heavenly fields, Or walk the gold - en streets.

PARADISE PLAINS. L. M. D. *J. L. Hinton* and *H. S. Rees.*

The busy scene of life is clos'd, And ac - tive useful - ness is o'er; }
The body's laid in calm repose, And sin shall ne'er distress it more. }
The happy soul is gone to rest, Where cares no more shall spoil its peace:

Re - clining on its Saviour's breast, It shall enjoy e - ternal bliss.

Christ was born in Beth - le - hem, Christ was born in Beth - le - hem, Christ was born in Beth - le - hem, And in a man - ger lay.

And in a man - ger lay, And in a man - ger lay. Christ was born in Beth - le - hem, And in a man - ger lay.

SWEET COMMUNION. 8s & 7s. H. S. Rees & J. H. Jenkins.

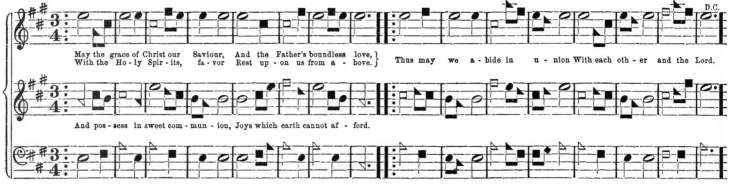

May the grace of Christ our Saviour, And the Father's boundless love, }
With the Ho - ly Spir - its, fa - vor Rest up - on us from a - bove. }
Thus may we a - bide in u - nion With each oth - er and the Lord.

And pos - sess in sweet com - mun - ion, Joys which earth cannot af - ford.

JESUS WEPT. S. M. (*Original.*) By *John P. Rees.* 1855.

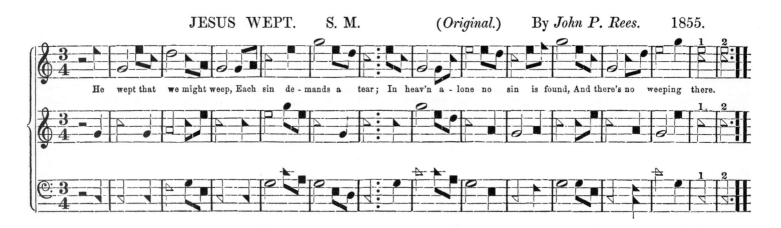

He wept that we might weep, Each sin de - mands a tear; In heav'n a - lone no sin is found, And there's no weeping there.

With that, etc.

O what of all my sufferings here, If, Lord, thou count me meet   With that enraptured host t'ap - pear - - - And   worship at thy feet.

With that, etc.   Give,

Give, etc.   But, etc.   a - -gain - - - - - In that eternal   day.

Give joy or grief, give ease or   pain,   Take   life or friends away,   But let me find them all a - gain - - In that eternal   day.

joy or grief, etc.   pain - - - -   But, etc.

JESUS ROSE.

H. S. Rees.

Go and tell his dis - ciples, Go and tell his dis - ciples, Go and tell his dis - ciples, He has risen from the dead.

CHORUS.

Je - sus rose, Brethren, Je - sus rose, Brethren, Je - sus rose, Brethren, he has ris - en from the dead, Through the earth And through the sky.

FIGHT ON. S. M. (*Original.*) *J. P. Rees.*

Fight on my soul 'till death, Shall bring thee to thy God, He'll take thee at thy part - ing breath Up to his blest a - bode.

ASLEEP IN JESUS. L. M. (*Original.*) *J. P. Rees.*

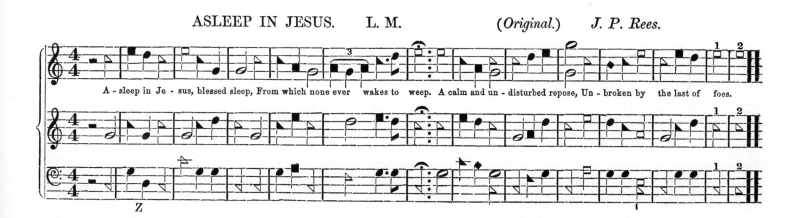

A - sleep in Je - sus, blessed sleep, From which none ever wakes to weep. A calm and un - disturbed repose, Un - broken by the last of foes.

THE GREAT DAY. (As sung by Judge Falkerner of Al'a.) *John P. Rees.*

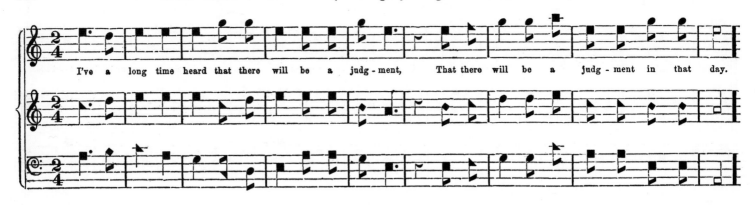

I've a long time heard that there will be a judg-ment, That there will be a Judg-ment in that day.

O, there will be a judgment in that day, O, sin-ner, where will you stand in that day?

2. I've a long time heard that the sun will be darken'd,
That the sun will be darken'd in that day.
O the sun will be darken'd in that day—
Oh! sinner, where will you stand in that day

3. I've a long time heard that the moon will be bleeding,
That the moon will be bleeding in that day.
O the moon will be bleeding in that day,
Oh! sinner, where will you stand in that day?

4. I've a long time heard that the stars will be falling,
That the stars will be falling in that day.
O the stars will be falling in that day,
Oh! sinner, where will you stand in that day?

5. I've a long time heard that the earth will be burning,
That the earth will be burning in that day.
O the earth will be burning in that day,
Oh! sinner, where will you stand in that day?

1. While traveling through the world be - low Where sore af - flictions come, My soul abounds with joy to know That I will rest at home.

CHORUS.

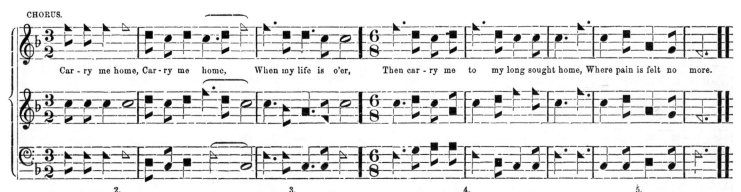

Car - ry me home, Car - ry me home, When my life is o'er, Then car - ry me to my long sought home, Where pain is felt no more.

2.
My soul's delight has been to sing
  Of glorious days to come,
When I shall, with my God and King
  Forever rest at home.

3.
Yes, when my eyes are closed in death,
  My body cease to roam,
I'll bid farewell to all below
  And meet my friends at home.

4.
My ceaseless pleasure then shall be,
  Through endless days to come,
To sing that Jesus died for me
  And range my peaceful home.

5.
And then I want these lines to be
  Inscribed upon my tomb,
Here lies the dust of S. R. P.
  His spirit sings at home.

THE HAPPY SAILOR.

B. F. White.

Come tell of your ship and what is her name, Oh, tell me, hap - py Sail - or! }
Come tell of your captain, and what is his fame, Oh, tell me, hap - py Sail - or! }

She's the

old ship of Zi - on, hal - le - lu! hal - le - lu! And her cap - tain, Ju - dah's Li - on, hal - le - lu - jah.

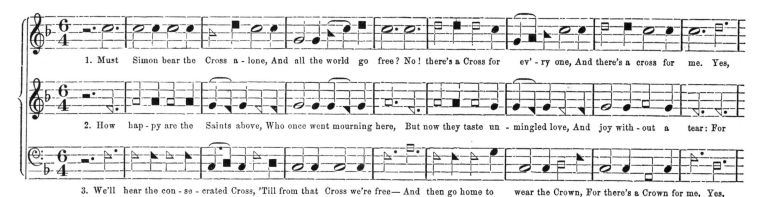

1. Must Simon bear the Cross a - lone, And all the world go free? No! there's a Cross for ev' - ry one, And there's a cross for me. Yes,

2. How hap - py are the Saints above, Who once went mourning here, But now they taste un - mingled love, And joy with - out a tear: For

3. We'll hear the con - se - crated Cross, 'Till from that Cross we're free— And then go home to wear the Crown, For there's a Crown for me, Yes,

4. The Saints shall hear the midnight cry: The Lord will then ap - pear— And virgins wise with burning lamps Will meet him in the air; For

there's a Cross on Calvary, Thro' which by faith the Crown I see, To me 'tis pardon bringing: Oh, that's the Cross for me, Oh, that's the Cross for me.

per - fect love will dry the tear, And cast out all tormenting fear— Which round my heart is clinging: Oh, that's the love for me, Oh, that's the love for me.

there's a Crown in Heaven above, The purchase of my Saviour's love, For me at his appearing; Oh! that's the Crown for me, Oh, that's the Crown for me.

there's a home in Heaven prepared, A house by Saints and Angels shared, Where Christ is interceding, Oh, that's the home for me, Oh, that's the home for me.

NEW PROSPECT. C. M. *W. S. Turner.*

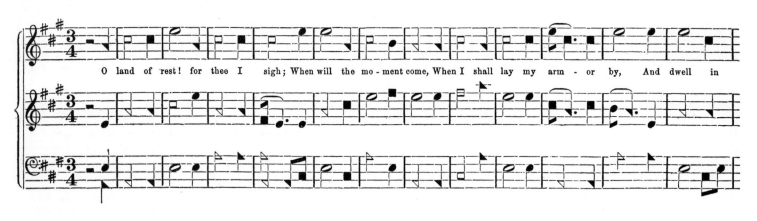

O land of rest! for thee I sigh; When will the mo-ment come, When I shall lay my arm-or by, And dwell in

peace at home? --- And dwell in peace at home. When I shall lay my arm-or by, And dwell in peace at home?

1. Be - hold the   morn - ing sun, Be - gins   his glorious way,
2. But when the   gos - pel comes It spreads   di - vi - ner light,
3. My gracious   God   how plain Are thy   di - rections given,

His beams through all the
It calls dead sinners
Oh, may I   nev - er

His beams through all the   na - tions run, And

His beams through all the na - tions run, And   life and light con -

na - tions run, And life and light   con - vey. His   beams through all the na - tions run And life and   light   con - vey.
from their tombs, And gives the blind   their   sight. It   calls dead sin - ners from the tomb And gives the   blind   their sight.
read in vain, But find the path   to heav'n. Oh,   may I   nev - er read in vain. But find the   path   to heav'n.

life and light con - vey. - - - - -   His beams, etc.

ver - - - -   His beams, etc.

CONVERTING GRACE. C. M. *R. E. Brown, Jr.*

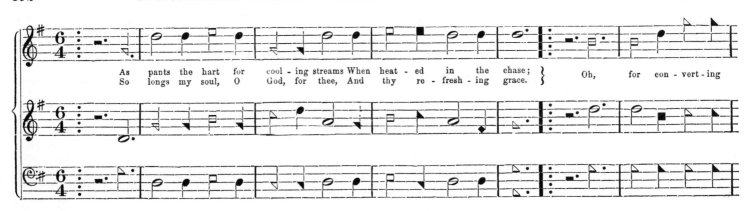

As pants the hart for cool - ing streams When heat - ed in the chase;
So longs my soul, O God, for thee, And thy re - fresh - ing grace.

Oh, for con - vert - ing

grace, and oh, For sanc - ti - fy - ing pow'r! Lord, we ask in Je - sus's name, A sweet, re - fresh - ing show'r.

NEW HUNDRED.   L. M.

Look from on high, great God, and see Thy saints lament - ing af - ter   thee, We sigh, we languish and complain, Revive thy gracious work again.

I'M ON MY JOURNEY HOME.   L. M.   (*Original.*)   *Miss S. Lancaster.*

O who will come and go with me,   I am on my journey home,
I'm bound fair Canaan's land to see,   I am on my journey home. } O come and go with me, O come and go with me, O come and go with me, For I'm on my journey home.

CHORUS.

REFLECTION. 6, 6, 6, 4. 6, 6, 6, 4. Composed by *E. Elmore.*

Come youth and mid - dle aged, That walks the earth - ly stage, And view this gra - ven age, I pray draw near.

And see the change of things Time with his fly - ing wings, The months and min - utes bring, As you shall hear.

CAN I LEAVE YOU?

Arranged by *John P. Rees.*

Yes, my native land, I love thee, All thy scenes I love them well,
Friends, connections, happy country, Can I bid you all farewell?

Can I leave you, Far in heathen lands to dwell?

Can I leave you, Far in, etc.

Can I leave you, Far in, etc.

I AM PASSING AWAY. L. M. (*Original.*) By *R. F. Ball.*

Pass a few swiftly fleeting years, And all that now in bodies are, Shall quit like me this vale of tears, Their righteous sentence to re - ceive.

HINGHAM. S. M.

Billings.

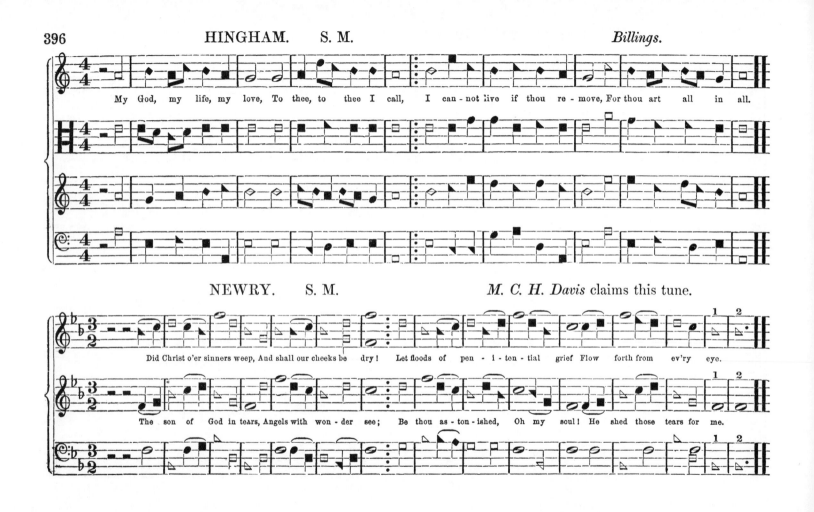

My God, my life, my love, To thee, to thee I call, I can-not live if thou re-move, For thou art all in all.

NEWRY. S. M.

M. C. H. Davis claims this tune.

Did Christ o'er sinners weep, And shall our cheeks be dry! Let floods of pen - i - ten - tial grief Flow forth from ev'ry eye.

The son of God in tears, Angels with won-der see; Be thou as - ton - ished, Oh my soul! He shed those tears for me.

WE'LL SOON BE THERE. L. M.

By *Oliver Bradfield.*

Alto by J. P. Rees.

Oh, who will come and go with me, We'll shout and sing Ho - sanna, I'm bound fair Canaan's land to see, We'll shout and sing Ho - san - na.

Go on, go on, we'll soon be there, We'll shout and sing Ho - sanna, Come on, come on, we'll soon be there, We'll shout and sing Ho - san - na.

FAREWELL TO ALL. L. M. (*Original.*) By *J. P. Rees.*

And now my friends, both old and young, I hope in Christ you'll still go on; }
And if on earth we meet no more, O, may we mest on Canaan's shoree.

I hope you'll all remember me, If you on earth no more I see.

An interest in your prayers I crave, That we may meet beyound the grave.

THE DYING BOY. C. M. D. Composed by *H. S. Rees.*

SOFTLY.

I'm dy-ing, moth-er, dy-ing now, Please raise my ach-ing head,
And fan my heat-ed, burn-ing brow, Your boy will soon be dead.

Turn o'er my pil-low once a-gain, And

Kis my fe - vered cheek, I'll soon be free'd from all the pain, For now I am so weak.

Now light the lamps, my mother dear,
 The sun has pass'd away;
I soon must go, but do not fear,
 I'll live in endless day.

I'm sinking fast, my mother dear
 I can no longer dwell;
Yet I'll be with you, do not fear,
 But now, oh now, farewell!

A band of angels beckon me,
 I can no longer stay;
Hark! how they sing, "We welcome thee:
 Dear brother, haste away."

The hour has come, my end is near,
 My soul is mounting higher;
What glorious strains salute my ear
 From heaven's angelic choir?

Their flowing robes in brightness shine,
 A crown is on each head;
Say, mother, will not such be mine
 When I am with the dead?

Then do not weep, sweet mother, now,
 'Twill break this body frail,
Those burning tears fall o'er my brow—
 Farewell, oh! fare thee well!

STRUGGLE ON.

H. S. Reese.

Our pray - ing time will soon be o'er, Hal - le - lu - jah, We'll join with those who 're gone be - fore, Hal - le - lu - jah.

To love and bless and praise the name, Hal - le - lu - jah, Of Je - sus Christ the bleed - ing Lamb, Hal - le - lu - jah.

Strug - gle on, strug - gle on, Hal - le - lu - jah, Struggle on for the work's most done, Hal - le lu - jah.

Strug - gle on, &c.

J. A. Bolen and **H. S. Reese.**

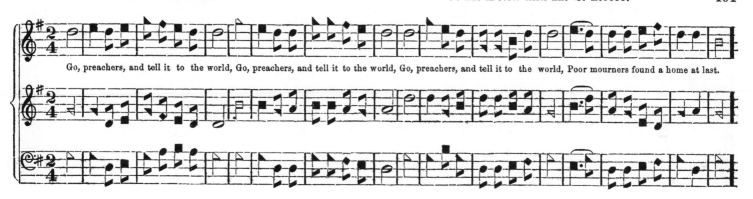

Go, preachers, and tell it to the world, Go, preachers, and tell it to the world, Go, preachers, and tell it to the world, Poor mourners found a home at last.

Through free grace and a dying Lamb, Through free grace and a dying Lamb, Through free grace and a dying Lamb, Poor mourners found a home at last.

2 A

FAME OF JESUS. L. M. (*Original.*) By *E. T. Pound.*

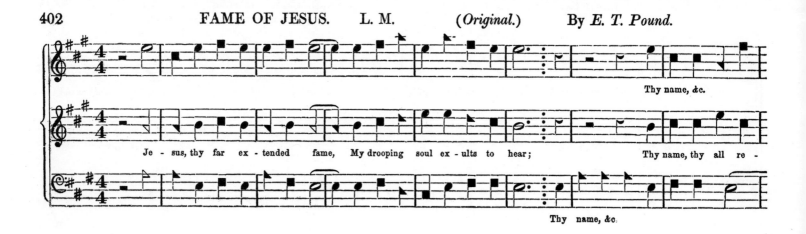

Thy name, &c.

Je - sus, thy far ex - tended fame, My drooping soul ex - ults to hear; Thy name, thy all re -

Thy name, &c.

storing name, Is mu - sic in a sin - ner's ear, Is mu - sic in a sin - ner's ear. - - -

PARADISE. C. M. D. (Original.) *Wm. H. B. Mosher.*

The pleasant fields of Par - a - dise, So glorious to be - hold,
The val - leys clad in liv - ing green, The mountains pav'd with ----- gold. The trees of life with

heavenly fruit, Be - hold how rich they stand! Blow, gen - tle gales, and waft my soul, A - way to Ca - naan's land.

YOUTH WILL SOON BE GONE L. M. D. (*Original.*) *J. P. Rees.*

Youth, like the spring, will soon be gone, By fleet - ing Time or conqu'ring Death, ⎫
Your morning sun may set at noon, And leave you ev - er in the dark. ⎭ Your spark - ling eyes and

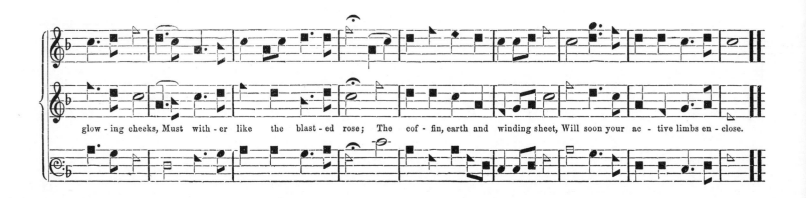

glow - ing cheeks, Must with - er like the blast - ed rose; The cof - fin, earth and winding sheet, Will soon your ac - tive limbs en - close.

THE MARCELLAS. 7s. (*Original.*) By *Rev. E. Dumas.*

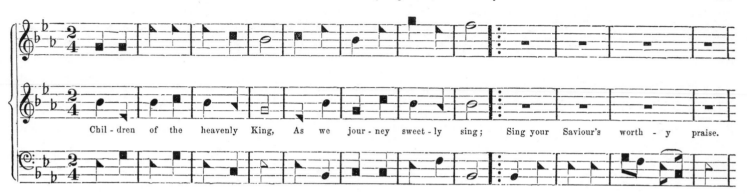

Chil - dren of the heavenly King, As we jour - ney sweet - ly sing; Sing your Saviour's worth - y praise.

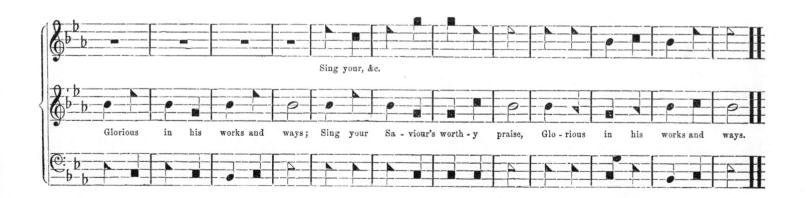

Sing your, &c.

Glorious in his works and ways; Sing your Sa - viour's worth - y praise, Glo - rious in his works and ways.

NEW HARMONY. 8, 7. Arranged by *Miss M. L. A. Lancaster.*

I want to live a Christian here, I want to die a shout-ing, I want to see bright An-gels
I want to feel my Sa-viour near, While soul and bod-y's part-ing,

stand And wait-ing to re-ceive me, To bear my soul to Ca-naan's land, Where Christ is gone be-fore me.

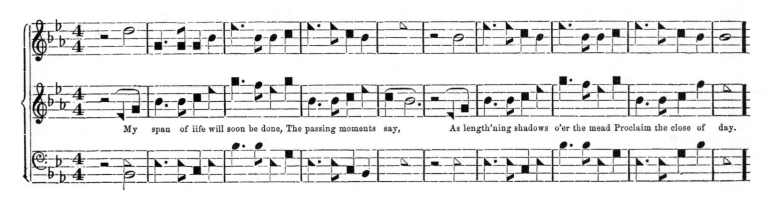

My span of iife will soon be done, The passing moments say, As length'ning shadows o'er the mead Proclaim the close of day.

O that my heart might dwell aloof From all cre-a-ted things, And learn that wisdom from above, Whence true contentment springs.

WEEPING MARY. By *J. P. Rees.*

They cru - ci - fied the Saviour, They cru - ci - fied the Saviour, They cru - ci - fied the Sa - viour, And

See Ma - ry come's a weep - ing, See Ma - ry come's a weep - ing, See Ma - ry come's a weep - ing To

nailed him to the Cross; He a - rose, He a - rose, -- He a - rose, And as - cend - ed in a cloud.

see where he was laid; He a - rose, He a - rose, -- He a - rose, And as - cend - ed in a cloud.

How long, dear Sa - viour oh, how long Shall this bright hour de - lay; Fly swift - ter round, ye wheels of time, And

bring the prom - ised day, And bring the prom - ised day. Fly swift - ter round, ye wheels of time, And bring the prom - ised day.

1. Lay up nearer, brother, nearer, For my limbs are growing cold; And thy presence seemeth nearer, When thine arms around me fold.

2. I am dy-ing, brother, dy-ing, Soon you'll miss me in your berth, For my form will soon be ly-ing 'Neath the ocean's bri-ny serf.

3. I am go-ing, surely go-ing, But my hope in God is strong; I am willing, brother, knowing That He doth nothing wrong.

4. Tell my father when you greet him,
That in death I prayed for him,
Prayed that I might only meet him
In a world that's free from sin.

5. Tell my mother,— God assist her,
Know that she is growing old,—
That her child would glad have kissed her
When his lips grew pale and cold.

6. Listen, brother, catch each whisper,
Tis my wife I'll speak of now;
Tell, O tell her, how I missed her,
When the fever burned my brow.

7. Tell her she must kiss my children,
Like the kiss I last impressed,
Hold them as when last I held them,
Folded closely to my breast.

8. Give them early to their Maker,
Putting all her trust in God,
And He never will forsake her,
For He's said so in his word.

9. Oh! my children, Heaven bless them;
They were all my life to me;
Would I could once more caress them,
Before I sink beneath the sea.

10. 'Twas for them I crossed the ocean,
What my hopes were I'd not tell,
But they gained an orphan's portion—
Yet He doeth all things well.

11. Listen, brother, closely listen,
Don't forget a single word,
That in death my eyes did glisten
With the tears her memory stored.

12. Tell them I never reached the haven,
Where I sought the precious dust,
But have gained a port called Heaven
Where the gold will never rust.

13. Tell my sisters, I remember
Every kind and parting word,
And my heart has been kept tender,
By the thoughts its memory stirred.

14. Urge them to secure an entrance
For they'll find a brother there;
Faith in Jesus and repentance
Will secure for them a share.

15. Hark! I hear my Saviour speaking,
'Tis—I know his voice so well,
When I am gone, O don't be weeping
Brother, hear my last farewell!

A HOME IN HEAVEN.

W. W. Parks & M. H. Thomas.

A home in Heaven! what a joy-ful thought, As the poor man toils in his wear-y lot; His heart oppressed, and with

A home in Heav'n! as the sufferer lies On his bed of pain, and up-lifts his eyes To that bright home, what a

anguish driv'n, From his home be-low to his home in Heav'n. In Heav'n— From his home be-low to his home in Heav'n.

joy is giv'n, From the blessed thought of his home in Heav'n. In Heav'n— From the blessed thought of his home in Heav'n.

A home in Heaven! When our pleasures fade,
And our wealth and fame in the dust are laid,
And strength decays, and our health is riven,
We are happy still with our home in Heaven.
    In Heaven—From the blessed thought of our
      home in Heaven.

A home in Heaven! When the faint heart bleeds
By the Spirit stroke, for its evil deeds,
Oh! then what bliss in that heart forgiven,
Does the hope inspire of its home in Heaven.
    In Heaven—From the blessed thought of its
      home in Heaven.

A home in Heaven! When our friends are fled
To the cheerless gloom of the mouldering dead,
We wait in hope on the promise given,
That we'll meet up there in our home in Heaven.
    In Heaven! That we'll meet up there in our
      home in Heaven.

NEW HOSANNA. L. M.

H. S. Rees.

CHORUS.

PIANO.

1. Wake, O my soul, and hail the morn For unto us a Saviour's born; } Glory, glo - ry, let us sing, While heaven and earth his praises ring, Hosanna,
See how the an - gels wing their way To usher in the glorious day.

2. Hark! what sweet music— what a song, Sounds from the bright celestial throng; } Glory, glory, etc.
Sweet song— whose melting sounds impart Joy to each raptured list'ning heart.

3. Come, join the Angels in the sky, Glory to God who reigns on high; } Glory, glory, etc.
Let peace and love on earth abound While time revolves and years roll round.

FORTE. CHORUS. PIANO. FORTE.

Hosanna, Hosanna to the Lamb of God. Glo - ry, glo - ry, let us sing, While heaven and earth his praises ring, Hosanna, Hosanna, Hosanna to the Lamb of God.

Be kind to thy father, for when thou wert young, Who loved thee so fond-ly as he? He caught the first

ac-cent that fell from thy tongue, And join'd in thy in-no-cent glee. Be kind to thy fath-er, for now he is

THE LOVED ONES. *Concluded.*

old, His locks in-ter-mingled with grey; His footsteps are fee-ble, Once fearless and bold, Thy fath-er is pass-ing a-way.

THE WANDERER'S GRAVE. C. M. *W. L. Williams.*

1. Away from home, away from friends, And all the heart holds dear,
A wear-y wanderer laid him down, Nor kindly aid was near.

2. And sickness prey'd upon his frame, And told its tale of woe,

While sorrow marked his pallid cheeks, And sank his spirit low.

3. Nor waiting friends stood round his couch
   A healing to impart,
   Nor human voice spoke sympathy,
   To soothe his aching heart.

4. The stars of night his watchers were,
   His fan the rude wind's breath,
   And while they sighed their hollow moans
   He closed his eyes in death.

5. No willing grave received the corpse
   Of this poor lonely one,
   His bones, alas, were left to bleach,
   And moulder 'neath the sun.

6. The night wolf howl'd his requiem,
   The rude winds danced his dirge,
   And e'er anon in mournful chime,
   Sigh'd forth the mellow surge.

1. O welcome, welcome festal day That marks our years, that cheers our way, We offer thanks and we would pray That God would bless us day by day. The

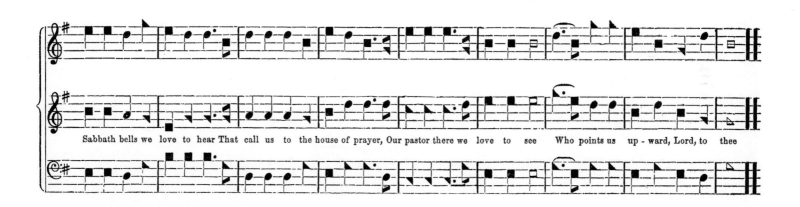

Sabbath bells we love to hear That call us to the house of prayer, Our pastor there we love to see   Who points us up - ward, Lord, to thee

THE CHRISTIAN'S NIGHTLY SONG. 6, 6, 10.　Cluster, pp. 382.　(*Original.*)　*E. T. Pound.*

I'll sing my Sa - vior's grace, And his sweet name I'll praise, While in this land of sor - row I re - main. My

sor - rows soon shall end, And then my soul as - cend, Where freed from trou - ble, sor - row, sin and pain.

MODERATE.

You may tell them fath-er when you see them—I'm a poor mourning Pil-grim, I'm bound for Canaan's land.
You may tell them moth-er when you see them—I'm a poor mourning Pil-grim, I'm bound for Canaan's land.

You may tell them brothers when you see them—I'm a poor mourning Pil-grim, I'm bound for Canaan's land.
You may tell them sisters when you see them—I'm a poor mourning Pil-grim, I'm bound for Canaan's land.

SLOW AND SOFT.

I weep, and I mourn, and I move slow-ly on,— I'm a poor mourning Pil-grim, I'm bound for Ca-naan's land.

I weep, and I mourn, &c.

2 B

REES. C. M.   (Original.)   *Edmund Dumas.*

There is a house not made with hands, E - ter - nal and on high;
And here my spir - it wait - ing stands, Till God shall bid it fly.

I long to see my friends a -

gain, And hear them sweet - ly say, Come, wea - ry dove, Here is thy home, Then fold thy wings and stay.

MELANCHOLY DAY. C. M. D. (Original.) H. S. Rees.

Death, 'tis a mel - an - chol - y day, To those who have no God, - - - - - When the poor soul is

forced a - way, To seek her last a - bode. In vain to heav'n she lifts her eye - -

In vain to heav'n, &c.

MELANCHOLY DAY. *Concluded.*

— — s, For guilt, a heav-y chain, Still drags her downward from the skies, To darkness, fire, and pain.

RELIGION IS SWEET. 7s.

W. R. Waldrup.

'Tis re - ligion that can give, Sweetest pleasures while we live. 'Tis re - ligion must sup - ply, Solid comforts when we die.

The hap - py day will soon ap - pear, And we'll all shout to - geth - er in that morn - ing.
When Ga - briel's trump - et you shall hear, And we'll all shout to - geth - er in that morn - ing.

Be - hold the right - eous march - ing home, And we'll all shout to - geth - er in that morn - ing.
And all the an - gels bid them come, And we'll all shout to - geth - er in that morn - ing.

CHORUS.

Sweet morn - ing, Sweet morn - ing, And we'll all shout to - geth - er in the morn - ing.

Sweet morn - ing, &c.

A SONG OF TEXAS. 11, 8.

S. W. Palmer & H. S. R.

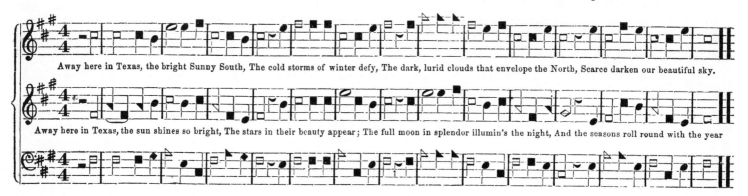

Away here in Texas, the bright Sunny South, The cold storms of winter defy, The dark, lurid clouds that envelope the North, Scarce darken our beautiful sky.

Away here in Texas, the sun shines so bright, The stars in their beauty appear; The full moon in splendor illumin's the night, And the seasons roll round with the year

THE GRIEVED SOUL. 7, 6.

Miss M. A. Hendon.

Come, my soul, and let us try For a lit - tle sea - son,}
Ev - 'ry bur - den to lay bye, Come and let us rea - son.}

What is this that casts thee down ? Who are those that grieve thee ?

Speak and let the worst be known ? Speaking may re - lieve thee.

GRANTVILLE. C. M.   *J. P. Rees.*   423

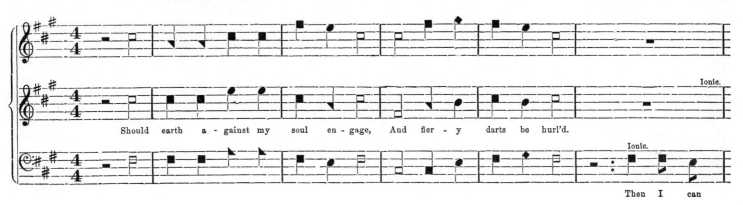

Should earth a-gainst my soul en-gage, And fier-y darts be hurl'd.

Then I can

Then I can smile at Sa-tan's rage, Then I can smile at Sa-tan's rage, --- And face a frown-ing world.

smile, &c

SWEET UNION. L. M. *J. P. Rees.*

A - wake my soul in joy - ful lays, Oh, Glo - ry Hal - le - lu - jah, And sing thy great Re - deemer's praise.

CHORUS.

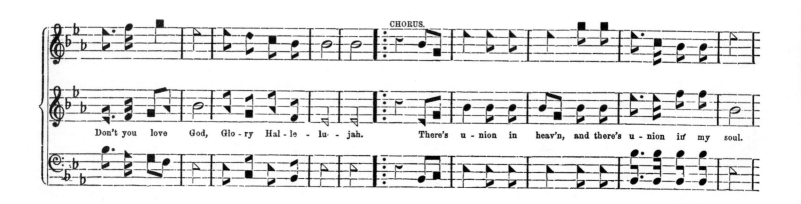

Don't you love God, Glo - ry Hal - le - lu - jah. There's u - nion in heav'n, and there's u - nion in my soul.

Oh, Glo - ry Hal - le - lu - jah, Sweet mu - sic in Zi - on's be - ginning to roll, Don't you love God, Glo - ry Hal - le - lu - jah.

GOLDEN STREETS.

J. L. Pickard.

I am on my journey home, I am on my journey home, I am on, - - - I am on - - my journey home.
To the New Jeru - sa - lem, To the New Jeru - sa - lem, To the New, - - To the New - Je - ru - sa - lem.

DUMAS.　C. M.　　　　(*Original.*)　*John P. Rees.*

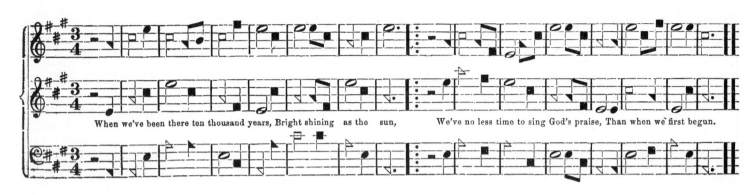

When we've been there ten thousand years, Bright shining as the sun,　We've no less time to sing God's praise, Than when we first begun.

SHILOAH.　C. M.　　　　*Thomas Waller.*

The time is swiftly rolling on, When I must faint and die, My body to the dust return, And there forgotten lie, And there forgotten lie.

Let persecutions rage around, And Anti-christ appear, My silent dust beneath the ground, There's no disturbance there, There's no disturbance there.

HOPE.   H. M.   *Oliver Bradfield.*

Young men and maidens raise Your tuneful voices high, }
Old men and children praise The Lord of earth and sky. }   Him three in one and one in three, Him three in one and one in three, Extol to all eternity.

WILLIAMS.   S. M.   *Oliver Bradfield.*

A charge to keep I have,   A God to glo - ri - fy—   A never dy - ing soul to save And fit it   for   the sky.

WORLD UNKNOWN. S. M. (Original.) H. S. Rees.

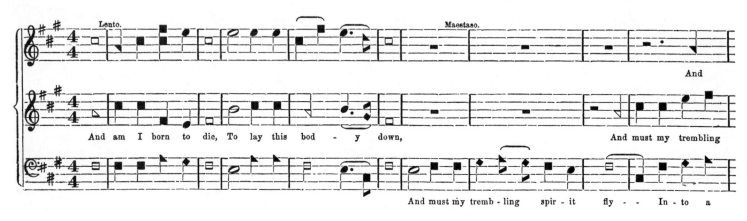

And am I born to die, To lay this bod - y down,

And must my trembling

And must my tremb - ling spir - it fly - - In - to a

must my trem - bling spir - it fly - -

spirit fly, - - - fly, fly, In - to a world un - known, - - - In - to a werld un - known.

world unknown. - - - - - - - - - In - to a world unknown, - - - - - Into, &c.

CHORUS.

Peace, trou - bled soul, thou need not fear, Je - sus says he will be with us to the end.
Thy great Pro - vi - der still is near. Je - sus says he will be with us to the end.

And he has been with us, And he yet is with us, And he's promised to be with us to the end.

GENERAL INDEX.

METRICAL INDEX.